ITALIAN PHYSICAL SOCIETY

TOPICS OF MODERN PHYSICS

VOL. I

Geometrodynamics

J. A. WHEELER

ACADEMIC PRESS • NEW YORK AND LONDON

SOCIETÀ ITALIANA DI FISICA

QUESTIONI DI FISICA MODERNA

VOL. I

Geometrodinamica

J. A. WHEELER

ACADEMIC PRESS • NEW YORK AND LONDON

ACADEMIC PRESS INC.
111 Fifth Avenue
New York 3, N. Y.

United Kingdom Edition
Published by
ACADEMIC PRESS INC. (London) Ltd.
Berkeley Square House, London W. 1

Library of Congress Catalog Card Number: 62-13645

PRINTED IN ITALY

PRESENTAZIONE

La Società Italiana di Fisica imprende una nuova attività: quella di curare la pubblicazione di una collana di volumi che trattino «Argomenti di Fisica Moderna». I volumi usciranno senza impegno di periodicità, cioè usciranno quando se ne veda la opportunità. Intanto, profittando dell'occasione dataci dal prof. John A. Wheeler, incominciamo la collana con questo volume da lui curato, e a lui porgiamo il ringraziamento più vivo e più cordiale. Come ringraziamo anche l'Academic Press per l'impegno editoriale assunto.

Alla nuova impresa della Società Italiana di Fisica auguro di cuore la miglior fortuna.

GIOVANNI POLVANI
Presidente della Società Italiana di Fisica

Milano, 22 Ottobre 1961

To the memory

of my brother

JOSEPH TOWNE WHEELER

Born Glendale, California, 10 August 1914

Killed in action

between Florence and Bologna,

25 October 1944

COURAGE - JUDGMENT - KINDLINESS

FOREWORD

This is a collection of papers dealing with geometrodynamics. Geometrodynamics is the study of the geometry of curved *empty* space and the evolution of this geometry with time according to the equations of Einstein's standard 1916 general relativity.

The sources of the curvature of space-time are conceived differently in geometrodynamics and in usual relativity theory. In the older analysis any warping of the Riemannian space-time manifold is due to masses and fields of non-geometric origin. In geometrodynamics — by contrast — only those masses and fields are considered which can be regarded as built out of the geometry itself.

This subject can be considered to date from the period 1955-1957 when it was discovered that mass and electricity can be fashioned out of curved empty space.

The three principal papers on geometrodynamics from the 1955-1957 period — long out of print — are gathered together here in chronological order in response to requests from several sides for an account of the basic ideas of the subject. I and II deal with geons; III, with the geometry of electromagnetism and the connection between electricity and topology. They are preceded by a more general summary (S) of the present state of the field, including its problems and prospects. This account evolved from lectures at Course XI, on Weak Interactions, at the Enrico Fermi International School of Physics at the Villa Monastero, Varenna, Italy, in the summer of 1959. These lectures were revised, augmented and published in 1960, and are reprinted here as a unit with the kind permission of the Italian Physical Society and its President, Professor G. POLVANI.

The central ideas of geometrodynamics can be easily summarized.

The past has seen many attempts to describe electrodynamics as one or another aspect of one or another kind of non-Riemannian geometry. Every such attempt at a unified field theory has foundered. Not a change in Einstein's experimentally tested and solidly founded 1916 theory, but a closer look at it by MISNER in 1956 (III), gave a way to think of electromagnetism as a property of curved empty space. Rainich already long before in an almost forgotten paper had shown under what conditions a curvature of space-time can be regarded as due to an electromagnetic field, and how in such cases to find the field from the geometry. Misner rediscovered the results of Rainich. He went on to point out that the electromagnetic field curves space in such a characteristic way — or makes such well defined « footprints » on space — that these footprints can *themselves* be considered as the full manifestation of the electromagnetic field. In other words one can say all that has to be said about electromagnetism in charge-free space without mentioning other than geometric quantities. In this sense Einstein's 1916 theory can be regarded as an « already unified » — and entirely geometrodynamical — theory of electromagnetism and gravitation. The dual language of electromagnetism plus geometry is usually more convenient than the language of already unified theory. This circumstance in no way removes electromagnetism out of the domain of pure geometrodynamics. Instead it is conceivable that this convenience of Maxwell's terminology may offer some help towards that day, perhaps far distant, when it will be understood why the space-time manifold is four-dimensional, and why this manifold is described by the special Rainich-Misner case of Riemannian geometry.

Already in 1955 it had been found (I) that out of electromagnetic radiation, or gravitational radiation, or any mixture of the two one can in principle construct a gravitational-electromagnetic entity, or « geon ». A geon (I, II) though built of curved empty space and completely free of any so-called « real mass », is nevertheless endowed — by reason of its radiation content — with mass of its own. This mass holds it together against leakage losses for a time very long in comparison with the natural time of travel of radiation through its interior. The geon moves through space as a unit. It responds to the gravitational fields of other masses. It also exerts forces on them. It provides a completely geometrical model for mass.

A completely geometrical model was found at the same time (I) for electricity, as lines of force trapped in the topology of a multiply connected manifold.

Due in great measure to the physical insight and mathematical knowledge of Charles Misner, it was possible two years later, in 1957, to trace out (III) the beautiful relations between this topological description of electricity and a central topic in modern mathematics, the theory of homology groups.

There is not the least direct connection (S) between the geons of classical geometrodynamics and the elementary particles of the real world of quantum physics. Also this theory in its classical version does not constrain the charges with which it deals either to be quantized or to be all of the same complexion — all electric, none magnetic — as observed in nature. These circumstances hardly deprive geometrodynamics of physical interest.

General relativity was already before 1955 a kind of master theory — the only description of physics to connect gravitation, geometry and the equivalence principle, and the only theory out of which the equation of motion of a mass can be derived as a consequence rather than being fed in as a postulate. Geometrodynamics retains these features and provides in addition a geon model for mass and a topological description for charge. Remote as are both pictures from anything of direct relevance to experiment, they indicate that curved empty space is a building material of previously unsuspected richness.

It is natural to turn from a physical theory of such scope to still deeper questions. Are all fields and particles constructed out of curved empty space? Does there exist some high and subtle and uniquely right theory of point sets out of which some day can be derived the quantum principle; the approximate validity of *four*-dimensional Riemannian geometry; the Rainich-Misner equations; neutrinos; and elementary particles? Advances since midcentury give new interest to these questions. Experiments at high energies have brought to light remarkable symmetries between the elementary particles. The discovery of parity non-conservation has revealed a connection between electricity and geometry — between the charge of a nucleon and the right or left handedness of the electron which it emits in a beta decay process.

Geometrodynamics is very far from being able to contribute to a discussion of these questions. It has nothing directly to say about meson theory or the origin of nuclear forces. Quantum geometrodynamics speaks if at all to a point closer to the foundations of physics. It advises that any multiple connectedness is a property, not of elementary particles, but of all space. Moreover, everywhere in space quantum fluctuations in geometry and in electromagnetic fields are calculated to have such high energy density that the extra energy density associated with the presence of an elementary particle is negligible by comparison. At the very smallest scale of distances the proper starting point for the description of physics would therefore seem to be, not the elementary particle, but the vacuum, complex in geometry and rich in dynamics.

This reasoning increases the motive to quantize geometrodynamics and to study the character of the resulting « model theory ». This theory may turn out to be only an academic exercise, or it can conceivably have direct relevance to the elementary particle problem. In either case it promises to pose issues at the frontier of physics, and to raise deep questions of principle. Some attempt is made in the survey paper (S; expanding a 1957 discussion of this topic) to assess the character of quantum electrodynamics. More important than any other evidence in deciding the distance between the « model theory » and the real physical world would seem to be its stance on the neutrino. Neutrinos are of course readily describable as foreign entities moving about in the arena of space and time. However, no way comes to light (S) to describe these simplest of physical entities with spin $\frac{1}{2}$ as related to any natural feature of quantum geometrodynamics. All the stronger then is the evidence for a gulf between the « model theory » and the electron and all heavier particles of half integral spin. Therefore quantum geometrodynamics is to be understood as very far removed from any treatment of elementary particles. It is a discipline to be studied in and for itself in the traditional modest spirit of theoretical physics with all openness to recognizing and formulating the new concepts which are hidden in it. Electricity viewed as lines of force trapped by topology is perhaps example enough of the kind of insight one would seek from the further study of this subject.

* * *

As preparation for the reading of these four papers little more is required than some knowledge of electromagnetic theory and introductory tensor analysis. Both topics are covered in more than enough detail, and with exceptional physical judgment, in the book of

L. LANDAU and E. LIFSHITZ, translated by H. HAMERMESH: *The Classical Theory of Fields* (Addison-Wesley Press, previously Cambridge, now Reading, Massachusetts, 1951);

which has excellent chapters on general relativity.

The reader who wants more on relativity will find it in several standard books:

A. EINSTEIN: *The Meaning of Relativity* (Princeton University Press, Princeton, New Jersey, 4th ed., 1953);
W. PAULI: *Theory of Relativity*, translated by W. FIELD (Pergamon Press, London, 1958);

and also in texts by A. S. EDDINGTON, P. BERGMANN, V. FOCK, A. LICHNEROWICZ, G. C. MC VITTIE, C. MØLLER, J. L. SYNGE, R. C. TOLMAN and H. WEYL. For more detail on tensor analysis and Riemannian geometry two sources are particularly appropriate:

É. CARTAN: *Leçons sur la géométrie des espaces de Riemann* (Gauthier-Villars, Paris, 1951);
L. P. EISENHART: *Riemannian Geometry* (Princeton University Press, Princeton, New Jersey, 1926).

An excellent and very brief introduction to topology is given by

P. ALEXANDROFF: *Elementary Concepts of Topology*, traslated by A. E. FARLEY (Dover Publications, New York, 1961).

Two of the longer standard texts are

S. LEFSCHETZ: *Introduction to Topology* (Princeton University Press, Princeton, New Jersey, 1949); and
H. SEIFERT and W. THRELFALL: *Lehrbuch der Topologie* (Photoreproduction by Chelsea Publishing Company, New York, 1947).

A brief survey of recent developments in topology has been given by

S. CHERN: *Geometrical Structures on Manifolds*; *Colloquium Lectures Delivered at the Summer Meeting of the American Mathematical Society, East Lansing, Michigan, August 30-September 2, 1960* (American Mathematical Society, Providence, Rhode Island, 1960).

More detail on the mathematics of the forms, exterior derivatives and harmonic vector fields used in paper III to analyse the electromagnetic field in a multiply connected space is given in

É. CARTAN: *Les systèmes différentiels et leurs applications géométriques* (Hermann, Paris, 1945);
G. DE RHAM: *Variétés différentiables: formes, courants, formes harmoniques* (Hermann, Paris, 1955);
W. V. D. HODGE: *The Theory and Application of Harmonic Integrals* (2nd ed., Cambridge University Press, 1952); and
H. K. NICKERSON, D. C. SPENCER and N. E. STEENROD: *Advanced Calculus* (D. Van Nostrand, Princeton, New Jersey, 1959).

A reference or two may be appropriate on a few other topics touched upon in the four collected papers:

C. S. WU: *The Neutrino*, a chapter in M. FIERZ and V. F. WEISSKOPF, editors, *Theoretical Physics in the Twentieth Century: A Memorial Volume to Wolfgang Pauli* (Interscience, New York, 1960);
J. WEBER: *General Relativity and Gravitational Waves* (Interscience, New York, 1961);
L. INFELD and J. PLEBANSKI: *Motion and Relativity* (Pergamon Press, New York, 1960);
J. A. WHEELER: *Geometrodynamics and the Problem of Motion* (Reviews of Modern Physics, **33**, 63 (1961));

and series of papers on how to express general relativity in Hamilton's canonical formalism by P. A. M. DIRAC, by R. ARNOWITT, S. DESER and C. W. MISNER, by P. BERGMANN, and by B. DEWITT.

For permission to reprint these articles appreciation is due first of all to co-authors of two of them, Dr. EDWIN A. POWER (II) and Professor CHARLES W. MISNER (III) without whose many contributions and valuable insights these papers could hardly have come into being. Thanks are also due to the publishers for their permission to reprint: The Italian Physical Society (S); The Physical Review and its editor, Dr. SAMUEL A. GOUDSMIT (I); Reviews of Modern Physics and its editor, Professor EDWARD U. CONDON (II); and Annals of Physics and Academic Press and its Vice-president, Mr. KURT JACOBY (III). Special appreciation goes to The Italian Physical Society and its president, Professor G. POLVANI, and to *Il Nuovo Cimento* and its editor, Ing. RENÉ CORBI, for their encouragement towards putting these papers together into a book. Much stimulus was also derived towards the preparation of the present collection by past occasions for reporting successive stages in the development of geometrodynamics: lectures on Fields and Particles given during tenure of the Lorentz Professorship at the University of Leiden in 1956; lectures at Edinburgh and London in 1958; the summer course at the Villa Monastero in 1959 (S); and the author's regular course in Relativity at Princeton University. Appreciation is expressed to the John Simon Guggenheim Memorial Fundation for keeping « on ice » until it could be used for this work in 1956 a fellowship which had been interrupted in 1950 by a three year call to urgent defense work; to the United States Air Force Office of Scientific Research for assistence in meeting publication charges and to The Friends of Elementary Particle Research (DALE BABCOCK, P. F. GAST, W. C. KAY, C. E. KIRCHER, DONALD NOTMAN, F. A. OTTO, JOHN B. PUTNAM, WALTER O. SIMON, H. C. VERNON, CHARLES WENDE, HOOD WORTHINGTON) for assistance in a variety of ways, especially towards the travel and summer expenses of student colleagues in research.

Finally deep appreciation is expressed to students and colleagues, at Princeton and elsewhere, for many treasured discussions.

JOHN A. WHEELER

Palmer Physical Laboratory
Princeton, New Jersey

8 May 1961.

TABLE OF CONTENTS

Neutrinos, Gravitation and Geometry

(by JOHN A. WHEELER)

(Reprinted from *Rendiconti della Scuola Internazionale di Fisica « Enrico Fermi »* XI Corso of July 1959, Zanichelli, Bologna, 1960.)

I. Geons

(by JOHN A. WHEELER)

(Reprinted from *Phys. Rev.*, **97**, 511-536 (1955))

II. Thermal Geons

(by EDWIN A. POWER and JOHN A. WHEELER)

(Reprinted from *Rev. Mod. Phys.*, **29**, 480-495 (1957))

III. Classical Physics as Geometry

Gravitation, Electromagnetism, Unquantized Charge, and Mass as Properties of Curved Empty Space

(by CHARLES W. MISNER and JOHN A. WHEELER)

(Reprinted from *Ann. of Phys.*, **2**, 525-660 (1957))

Neutrinos, Gravitation and Geometry.

J. A. WHEELER

Palmer Physical Laboratory, Princeton University - Princeton, N. J.

(Reprinted from *Rendiconti della Scuola Internazionale di Fisica* « Enrico Fermi », XI Corso, Zanichelli, Bologna, 1960)

Introduction: Resumé in Reverse.

7. – The central position of the neutrino in elementary particle physics.

The interest of neutrino physics is apparent not only from the very important parity investigations of the past two years, but also from the excellent and systematic accounts given at Varenna of weak interactions and elementary particle transformations. It is not possible today, as it was only a few years ago, to hear a comprehensive lecture on the theory of the β decay that makes not one reference to the neutrino. The impressive experiment of REINES, COWAN and collaborators [1] has given us double assurance that neutrinos carry energy across empty space.

The neutrino is recognized today to appear in the family tree of every elementary particle: in meson decay,

$$\begin{cases} \mu \rightarrow e + 2\nu \\ \pi \rightarrow \mu + \nu \\ K \rightarrow \mu + \nu \end{cases} \tag{1}$$

and therefore also in the lineage of the heavy particles, each of which absorbs or emits or can be induced to emit a π or K meson:

$$\text{baryon} \rightarrow (\pi \text{ or } K) \rightarrow \nu \,. \tag{2}$$

The neutrino is the only Fermi field which has no mass and no charge. It transmits energy from place to place with the speed of light. It is impossible

[1] F. REINES and C. L. COWAN jr.: *Phys. Rev.*, **90**, 492 (1953); C. L. COWAN, F. REINES, F. B. HARRISON, H. W. KRUSE and A. D. MCGUIRE: *Science*, **124**, 103 (1956); F. REINES and C. L. COWAN jr.: *Phys. Rev.*, **113**, 273 (1959); R. E. CARTER, F. REINES, J. J. WAGNER and M. E. WYMAN: *Phys. Rev.*, **113**, 280 (1959).

ever to catch up with a neutrino and transform it to rest. In this sense the neutrino has the character of a field, rather than the character of a particle, like the electron. It is therefore reasonable to think of the neutrino field as free of problems of internal structure in the same way that we think of the electromagnetic field as free of problems of internal structure. In this sense the neutrino is the only Fermi field we know that is pure and truly basic. It is the only field endowed with spin $\frac{1}{2}$ and antisymmetric statistics which can be supposed to be as fundamental in character as the electromagnetic field and the gravitational field. If we want to know why spin $\frac{1}{2}$ and Fermi-Dirac statistics occur among the elementary particles, it is natural to begin by asking about the why and how of neutrinos. Neutrino physics is central to elementary particle physics.

6. – The weakness of neutrino interactions.

Despite the newly stressed importance of the neutrino, its interactions have long been recognized as weak in comparison with all but gravitational interactions. The quantitative comparison of the two weak interactions depends

TABLE I. – *Effective energy of the Fermi interaction, g_B/L^3 and energy of the gravitational interaction between two protons, GM^2/L compared with each other and with energy of electrical interactions, e^2/L, and with energy of field fluctuations, $\hbar c/L$, the comparison being made for various assumptions about the distance L relevant for the energy in question.* (The collaboration of Dr. S. L. GLASHOW in the construction of this table is gratefully acknowledged.)

Distance	Compton $\lambda\!\!\!^{-}$ of electron	Classical electron radius	Compton $\lambda\!\!\!^{-}$ of nucleon	Characteristic L of metric fluctuations
L	$\hbar/mc$ $4\cdot 10^{-11}$ cm	e^2/mc^2 $3\cdot 10^{-13}$ cm	$\hbar/Mc$ $2\cdot 10^{-14}$ cm	$(\hbar G/c^3)^{\frac{1}{2}}$ $2\cdot 10^{-33}$ cm
Gravitational interaction of two nucleons	$2\cdot 10^{-33}$ eV	$3\cdot 10^{-31}$ eV	$4\cdot 10^{-30}$ eV	$4\cdot 10^{-11}$ eV
Effective strength of β coupling if concentrated in a region of dimension L	10^{-6} eV	3 eV	10^{4} eV	10^{61} eV
Electric interaction	$4\cdot 10^{3}$ eV	$5\cdot 10^{5}$ eV	$7\cdot 10^{6}$ eV	$7\cdot 10^{25}$ eV
Fluctuation energy	$5\cdot 10^{5}$ eV	$7\cdot 10^{7}$ eV	$9\cdot 10^{8}$ eV	10^{28} eV

upon some assumption about the scale of the lengths relevant for the β interactions, since the quantities

$$GM_p^2 = 6.67\cdot 10^{-8}\cdot(1.6\cdot 10^{-24})^2 = 1.7\cdot 10^{-55}\ \text{erg cm} \tag{3}$$

and

$$g_\beta = 1.3\cdot 10^{-49}\ \text{erg cm}^3$$

characteristic of the two couplings have different dimensions (Table I). The weakness of the β coupling of the neutrino field is a fundamental feature of nature for which no satisfactory explanation has ever been advanced.

5. – Conservation and equilibrium in neutrino physics.

Neutrino emission and absorption processes provide the means to approach equilibrium. What then is the nature of this ideal equilibrium state? Fermi's analysis of the thermal equilibrium of particles endowed with antisymmetrical statistics tells us that the temperature alone is not enough to characterize the equilibrium. The existence of temperature is associated with the fact that the total energy is conserved in a system of interacting particles. However, we know that there exists for a Fermi system another first integral of the equations of motion: the difference between the number of particles and antiparticles, or in our case, the lepton number. In consequence as is well known not only the temperature $T = kT_{\text{degrees}}$ but also the Fermi energy μ_ν are required to specify (Fig. 1) the average occupation number of a neutrino state of energy E:

$$\bar{n} = \frac{1}{\exp\left[(E-\mu_\nu)/T\right]+1}\,. \tag{4}$$

When the Fermi energy is positive and larger or at least comparable to the thermal energy T as illustrated in the diagram, then in equilibrium the number of neutrinos exceeds the number of antineutrinos. When the Fermi energy is zero, then particles and holes are equally numerous. In this case the typical energy of each is of the order of T, the number of occupied ν or $\bar{\nu}$ states per unit volume is of the order

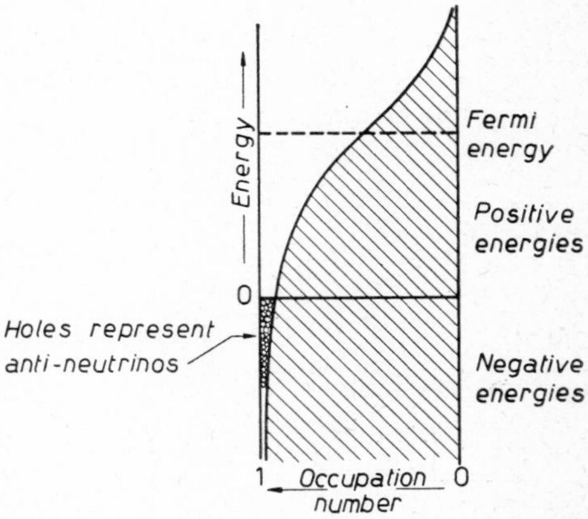

Fig. 1. – The equilibrium distribution of neutrinos follows the kind of law familiar from the electron theory of metals. Under the conditions illustrated, the number of antineutrinos present is a small fraction of the number of neutrinos.

$(T/\hbar c^3)$ and the total energy density is [2]

$$\varepsilon_\nu = \frac{7\pi^2}{120}\frac{T^4}{(\hbar c)^3}. \tag{5a}$$

In contrast electromagnetic blackbody radiation has a slightly higher energy density

$$\varepsilon_{\text{em}} = \frac{8\pi^2}{120}\frac{T^4}{(\hbar c)^3}, \tag{5b}$$

because occupation numbers in this case are not limited to 1 by the Pauli principle.

Just as a radiator of electromagnetic energy cannot be in thermal equilibrium unless the surrounding space is filled with black-body radiation at temperature T, so a system of elementary particles capable of emitting and absorbing neutrinos cannot be in equilibrium unless the temperature T *and* the Fermi energy μ_ν of the neutrino radiation agree with the T *and* the μ_ν of the system of elementary particles.

Unless matter in large amounts is squeezed to densities of the order of magnitude of nuclear densities, its opacity is of course very small [3]. Therefore it is normally impossible to maintain a density of neutrino radiation around matter sufficient to preserve the β decay equilibrium of that matter. Only when the temperature of the matter drops to absolute zero, and its Fermi energy μ_ν is also zero, is it in principle possible for the matter to be in β equilibrium without any neutrinos around.

GAMOW and SCHÖNBERG [4] long ago emphasized that normal stellar systems are unable to confine neutrinos. They pointed out the instability of hot condensed stellar matter against β decay, in the sense that the URCA process

$$\begin{cases} \text{p (hot)} + \text{e (hot)} \rightarrow \text{n (cool)} + \nu\ \text{(emitted)} \\ \text{n (hot)} \rightarrow \text{p (cool)} + \text{e (cool)} + \bar{\nu}\ \text{(emitted)} \end{cases} \tag{6}$$

will proceed more and more rapidly as the temperature and density of a star are increased in late phases of gravitational contraction (Fig. 2). We do not

---

(2) D. R. BRILL and J. A. WHEELER: *Rev. Mod. Phys.*, **29**, 465 (1957). In the derivation it is assumed that specification of the momentum of a neutrino — or anti-neutrino — uniquely determines the direction of its spin.

(3) R. N. EUWEMA has analyzed the opacity of matter with respect to neutrino as a function of temperature and density in his Ph. D. thesis, *Neutrinos and their Interactions with Matter* (Princeton, 1959), unpublished.

(4) G. GAMOW and M. SCHOENBERG: *Phys. Rev.*, **59**, 539 (1941).

know enough about the energy release in supernovae today to know whether the URCA process dominates in any of the observed events. As theory and observation of stellar evolution advance, increased possibilities to check the predictions of neutrino physics seem likely to develop.

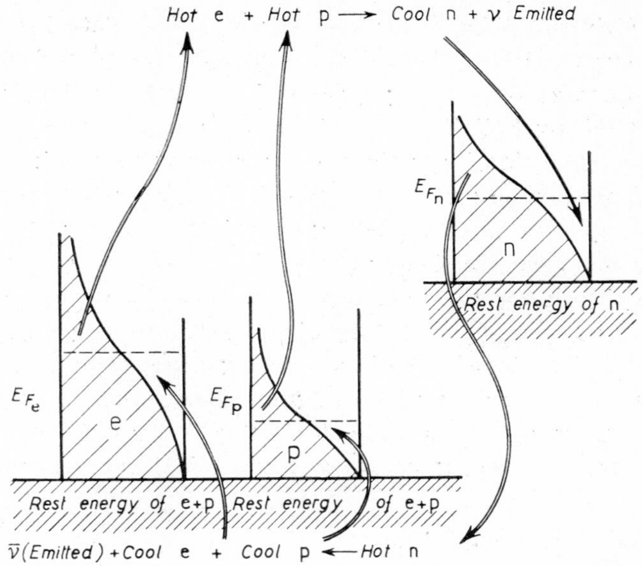

Fig. 2. – The URCA process can dissipate energy endlessly in the form of neutrinos and antineutrinos as long as the nuclear matter is kept under pressure and kept hot, and as long as there is no container that will allow the neutrinos and antineutrinos to build up to thermodynamic equilibrium with the nucleon matter. E_F in every case represents the relevant Fermi energy. If the temperature were zero, complete equilibrium and absence of reaction would be secured by the equality

$$(M_p c^2 + E_{F_p}) + (M_e c^2 + E_{F_e}) = (M_n c^2 + E_{F_n}) .$$

(Diagram adapted from EUWEMA).

Objects of stellar mass again come into consideration when one asks the question, what is the largest mass of *cold* matter, catalyzed to the end point of thermonuclear evolution, which can sustain itself against its own gravitational squeeze. Every kind of argument that one can give indicates that *there is no stable end point configuration for a collection of* more than $1.5 \cdot 10^{57}$ nucleons, about 20 percent more than the nucleonic content of the sun [5]. But nothing prevents one from adding as many nucleons as he pleases! The absence of any stable solution when more nucleons are added throws serious doubt

(5) Survey of literature and new calculations in B. K. HARRISON, M. WAKANO and J. A. WHEELER: Onzième Conseil de Physique Solvay, *La structure et l'évolution de l'univers* (Brussells, 1958).

on the law of conservation of nucleons under extreme conditions, at densities many times nuclear densities. Therefore doubt is raised whether even in *one* nucleus the number of nucleons is strictly conserved over long periods of time, particularly when the nucleus is subject to pressures that are high on a nuclear scale of pressure.

Not the slightest evidence has been discovered to date for any failure in the law of conservation of nucleons. Nucleons have been found to have a half life of 10^{24} years or more against any kind of decay that is accompanied by energetic ionizing radiation ([6]). If nucleons en masse *do* break down at high pressures, the dynamics of the process is completely unknown ([7]). However, it still appears reasonable to uphold three conservation laws: 1) the law of conservation of momentum-energy, 2) the law of conservation of electric charge, 3) some generalized version of the law of conservation of lepton number such that in thermal equilibrium the balance between breakdown and reconstitution is governed by the well defined Fermi energy μ_ν. In brief, the « law of conservation of nucleons » has to be regarded today, not as a theorem, but as a question; and the question will grow more intense the longer the difficulty of super-masses remains without solution. This difficulty stands at the unexplored frontier between gravitation physics and elementary particle physics.

4. – Elementary weak interactions.

The problem of scattering of photons by photons, and the closely associated problem of the coherent scattering of electromagnetic radiation by the Coulomb field of atomic nuclei, are well known to have been important issues in the evolution of modern quantum electrodynamics. Therefore it is not out of place to ask similar questions about the interaction of neutrino and gravitational fields with each other and with elementary particles. Topics of interest in this connection include the processes

$$\nu + \bar{\nu} \to \begin{pmatrix} & e^- + e^+ \text{ pair} \\ \text{or} & e^- + \mu^+ \\ \text{or} & \text{other intermediate states} \end{pmatrix} \to \nu' + \bar{\nu}' , \tag{7a}$$

(non-linearities in the neutrino field due to vacuum physics); also

$$\text{G (graviton)} + \text{G} \begin{matrix} \nearrow e^+ + e^- \\ \searrow \nu + \bar{\nu} \end{matrix} \tag{7b}$$

([6]) F. Reines, C. L. Cowan jr. and H. W. Kruse: *Phys. Rev.*, **109**, 609 (1958).

([7]) A. Brodsky and D. Ivanenko: *Nucl. Phys.*, **13**, 447 (1959) propose that the law of conservation of baryons is valid only modulo 4. See also G. Feinberg and M. Goldhaber: *Proc. U. S. Nat. Acad. Sci.*, **45**, 1301 (1959).

(non-classical effects in the gravitation field); also a reaction

$$\bar{\nu} + e^- \to (\bar{\nu})' + (e^-)' \tag{7c}$$

which may well prove measurable during the next decade and test the universality of the Fermi coupling.

Also of great interest is new theoretical evidence that the concept of gravitational radiation is well defined and that certain simple types of gravitational waves have positive definite energy. The possibilities to generate and detect gravitational waves have received extensive analysis, and serious experimental work is under way directed at ultimately observing, or setting an upper limit to, the density of cosmic gravitational radiation. In other words, gravitational radiation is beginning to come into its own today, as did neutrino radiation a few years ago.

3. – Spacelike description of the neutrino field.

Historically the electromagnetic field came into physics as a pair of vectors whose components can be specified at each point of space. Only later was it analysed into independent modes of oscillation. Still later came the quantum description of the electromagnetic field with yet another way of specification of the field, via a quantum number or occupation number associated with each of the independent modes. However, quantum mechanics obviously allows a wide latitude in choice of representation. Whatever the representation, the important fact is that the state specifies a probability amplitude for every conceivable configuration of the electromagnetic field. One can describe this configuration by giving the quantum number of each field oscillator,

$$n_1\,, \quad n_2\,, \quad \dots, \quad n_K\,, \quad \dots\,. \tag{8}$$

Equally well one can give the amplitude of each oscillator,

$$\xi_1\,, \quad \xi_2\,, \quad \dots, \quad \xi_K\,. \tag{9}$$

In this representation the ground state of the electromagnetic field, for example, takes the form of an infinite product of harmonic oscillator wave functions,

$$\psi = N \exp\left[-\xi_1^2 - \xi_2^2 - \dots - \xi_K^2 - \dots\right]. \tag{10}$$

Finally, one can give a completely space like description of the field, in terms of amplitudes not of field *oscillators*, but of the field *itself* at individual points, say the magnetic field:

$$\boldsymbol{H}(x_a)\,, \quad \boldsymbol{H}(x_b)\,, \quad \boldsymbol{H}(x_c)\,, \quad \dots \tag{11}$$

In this description the wave function for the ground state takes the form

$$\psi = N \exp\left[-\frac{1}{16\pi^3\hbar c}\int \frac{\boldsymbol{H}(1)\cdot\boldsymbol{H}(2)}{r_{12}^2}\,\mathrm{d}^3x_1\,\mathrm{d}^3x_2\right]. \tag{12}$$

Although the representations (8), (9), (11) are all equivalent, the first two of them depend for their usefulness on the possibility of making a Fourier analysis of the field. This approach is not a natural one to follow when one deals with curved space as one must in considering questions of gravitation, general relativity and geometry. Then it is natural to limit attention to a space like description of the quantum state of the electromagnetic field or gravitation field or both. Such a description makes a good sense and has been analysed in some detail, particularly by MISNER [8]. In order to complete the analysis one therefore has strong reason to seek likewise for a *spacelike description of the quantum state of the neutrino field.* Such a description is naturally sought for additional reasons: to gain increased insight into the nature of the simplest spinor field endowed with Fermi statistics, and to see in what way the properties of this field are related to those of the gravitational and electromagnetic fields.

2. – How is the neutrino field related to geometry?

Are fields and particles foreign objects that move about in the arena of space and time? Or are they in some way constructed out of space? Is the metric continuum a magic medium which bent up in one way here represents a gravitational field, rippled in another way there describes an electromagnetic field, and twisted up locally describes a long lived concentration of mass-energy? In other words, is physics at bottom a matter of pure geometry? Is geometry only an *arena*, or is it everything?

We are still very far today from being able to make a final judgment about the vision of physics which animated RIEMANN, CLIFFORD and EINSTEIN. However, the topic of « Neutrinos, Gravitation and Geometry » allows one to take a new look at this old question. We can review recent progress in securing a purely geometrical description of gravitation, electromagnetism, charge and mass. We can then look in turn at the questions which have been raised here in inverse numbering about the relation of the simplest Fermion field to geometry, about how to make a spacelike description of the neutrino field, about weak interactions, and about the law of conservation of nucleons.

---

(8) C. W. MISNER: *Rev. Mod. Phys.*, **29**, 497 (1957).

I. – Geometrodynamics: A purely Geometrical Description of Gravitation, Electromagnetism, Unquantized Charge and Long-Lived Entirely Classical Concentration of Mass-Energy.

That Einstein's theory of general relativity and Maxwell's equations of electromagnetism can be combined together in a purely geometrical form with no new postulates and no changes has become generally known only recently (9) although the basic equations of this « already unified field theory » were found long ago by RAINICH (10). Because the analysis deals entirely with geometry and its changes with time, it is appropriate to give it the name of « geometrodynamics » as perhaps better descriptive of its nature than « general relativity plus electromagnetism ».

1. – Measuring rods.

Measuring rods and clocks of atomic constitution appear prominently in treatises on general relativity. Yet reference to atoms, elasticity and rigidity should not be required. General relativity is a classical subject. Planck's constant is to be added to the theory in the process of quantizing it, not introduced at the start, at the classical level. Still less should it be necessary to say anything about atoms and their properties in order to define the quantities with which general relativity deals.

There is doubt, moreover, whether the customary standards of length supply a really well defined meter. The length of the Paris meter, for example, is a certain multiple of a metallic lattice dimension. Therefore, this meter is some dimensionless multiple of the basic unit $\hbar^2/me^2$ that characterizes all atomic dimensions:

$$L_1 = N_1(\hbar^2/me^2) \,. \tag{13}$$

More recently there has come into use the meter defined as a certain number of the wave lengths of a particular spectral line emitted by a particular isotope of mercury. The separation of the two energy levels involved in the transition is due very little to spin orbit coupling and other fine structure phenomena. The wave length of the Hg line is therefore basically fixed by the same combination of constants, $\hbar^3 c/me^4$, that determine the wave lengths of the characteristic lines of the hydrogen spectrum. Consequently the newer

(9) C. W. MISNER and J. A. WHEELER: *Ann. Phys.*, **2**, 525 (1957).

(10) G. Y. RAINICH: *Proc. Nat. Acad. Sci.*, **10**, 124 (1924); *Trans. Am. Math. Soc.*, **27**, 106 (1925).

meter is a fixed multiple of this alternate atomic unit:

$$L_2 = N_2(\hbar^3 c/me^4) \,. \tag{14}$$

In the two different definitions of the meter there appear atomic units that differ in size by the dimensionless factor

$$\hbar c/e^2 = 137.036\,6 \pm 0.000\,5 \,.$$

DIRAC, DICKE and others (11) have put forward arguments that $\hbar c/e^2$ and other dimensionless ratios in physics might be expected to change with time as the expansion of the universe proceeds. The best available determination of the relation between red shift and distance (12) leads to an inverse Hubble constant of $14 \cdot 10^9$ years. In other words, in the course of 14 years distances increase by 1 part in 10^9. During the same 14 years some of the dimensionless physical constants may undergo fractional changes—according to Dirac's hypothesis—not totally disparate in order of magnitude with 1 part in 10^9. In this event the two meters L_1 and L_2 will no longer agree with each other. Then both meters cannot continue to agree with the standard meter of general relativity, and it is impossible to be certain that *either* will serve for standard. For the time being rods and clocks of atomic constitution have to be judged as untrustworthy for measuring the space-time intervals so fundamental to general relativity.

For this reason it is important that general relativity in and by itself defines its own procedures for comparing an interval CD anywhere in space time with a standard interval AB, as first shown in detail by MARZKE (13). This comparison 1) makes no use of rods or clocks of atomic constitution and 2) makes no use of co-ordinates to designate the points of space-time. Instead, a point—whether A, B, C, D or any other point—is considered to be defined in accordance with Einstein by intersection of the world lines of two test particles, or of one test particle and a light cone, or of three light cones, etc. The measuring technique itself also makes use of light cones and the tracks of neutral test particles. These tools take the place of the ruler and compass of Euclidean geometry.

Two initially parallel world lines and the light scattered back and forth between them define in Marzke's analysis a « geodesic clock ». This clock propagates forward in time a very small time interval t (s) or corresponding interval of cotime τ (cm). When the curvature of space is negligible over the distances L that come into consideration, the clock remains true. Then AB and CD are compared as shown in Fig. 3. The interval $\mathscr{I}_{AB}$ is projected onto

(11) P. A. M. DIRAC: *Proc. Roy. Soc.*, A **165**, 199 (1938); R. H. DICKE: *Science*, **129**, 621 (1959) and *Am. Journ. Phys.*, **28**, 344 (1960).

(12) See for example the contribution of A. SANDAGE in the book cited in ref. (5).

(13) R. F. MARZKE: *The Theory of Measurement in General Relativity, A. B. Senior Thesis* (Princeton, 1959) unpublished.

the geodesic clock by way of two light rays. Let B have co-ordinates x, T relative to A as origin in a local Lorentz reference system in which the geodesic clock appears at rest; then

$$(15)\qquad \begin{cases} T_1 = T - x\,, \\ T_2 = T + x\,, \\ T_1 T_2 = T^2 - x^2 = \mathscr{I}^2_{AB}\,. \end{cases}$$

The cotimes T_1 and T_2 are directly expressible in terms of the repetition interval τ of the geodesic clock; for instance, in the diagram $T_1 = 5\tau$ and $T_2 = 21\tau$. Therefore the characteristic time of this clock is known in terms of the standard interval,

$$\tau = \mathscr{I}_{AB}/(5\cdot 21)^{\frac{1}{2}}$$

or more generally

$$(16)\qquad \tau = \mathscr{I}_{AB}(N_1 N_2)^{\frac{1}{2}}\,.$$

In a similar way the interval $\mathscr{I}_{CD}$ can be written in the form

$$(17)\qquad \mathscr{I}_{CD} = (T_3 T_4)^{\frac{1}{2}} = (N_3 N_4)^{\frac{1}{2}}\tau\,.$$

Thus finally *the unknown interval is expressed in terms of the geometrodynamical standard meter*:

$$(18)\qquad \mathscr{I}_{CD} = (N_3 N_4/N_1 N_2)^{\frac{1}{2}}\mathscr{I}_{AB}\,,$$

or in the example

$$\mathscr{I}_{CD} = (12\cdot 28/5\cdot 21)^{\frac{1}{2}} = 1.790\,\mathscr{I}_{AB}\,.$$

When the effective radius of curvature of space is no longer negligible, but of the order of magnitude R, then the geodesic clock makes a fractional error of the order $(L/R)^2$. In this case it is appropriate to impose the burden of continuig the repetition interval τ, not on a single clock, but on a sequence of N clocks. The two

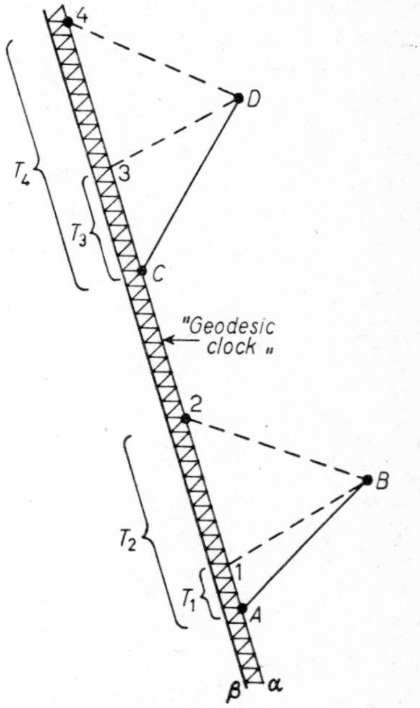

Fig. 3. – Arrangement for measuring an unknown interval in terms of the standard interval (geometrodynamical meter) AB in a flat region of space-time. Among different ideal test particles moving through space-time one is found, α, which passes through events A and C. A second test particle β moving on a parallel world line and alongside α defines, together with α, a geodesic clock. Light from α is scattered at β and comes back to α after a characteristic proper time τ. The zig-zags repeat this interval indefinitely into the past and future.

particles in each clock now have to remain nearly parallel only for the shorter distance L/N. The fractional error in each clock is of the order $(L/NR)^2$. The cumulative fractional error in the entire process of propagation from AB to CD is now

$$N(L/NR)^2\,, \tag{19}$$

a quantity that can be made as small as one pleases by making the number of clocks sufficiently great.

Marzke's analysis can be briefly summarized in the phrase « measuring rods without measuring rods ». Every interval $\mathscr{I}_{CD}$ can be expressed in terms of the interval $\mathscr{I}_{AB}$ between two chosen flashes of light which might well be fifty years in the past. No reference to any co-ordinates is required, as befits a purely geometrical theory.

	AZORES	BERLIN	BOMBAY	BUENOS AIRES	CAIRO	CAPETOWN	CHICAGO	GUAM	HONOLULU	LONDON	MELBOURNE	NEW YORK	PANAMA	RIO DE JANEIRO	SAN FRANCISCO	SANTIAGO	SHANGHAI	SINGAPORE	TOKYO	WELLINGTON
AZORES		2148	5930	5385	3325	5670	3305	8985	7421	1562	12190	2604	3918	4312	5114	5718	7324	8338	7370	11475
BERLIN	2148		3947	7411	1823	5949	4458	7158	7384	575	9992	4026	5902	6246	5744	7842	5323	6226	5623	11384
BOMBAY	5930	3947		9380	2698	5133	8144	4831	8172	4526	6140	7875	9832	8438	8523	10127	3219	2425	4247	7752
BUENOS AIRES	5385	7411	9380		7428	4332	5598	10516	7653	6919	7336	5295	3319	1230	6487	731	12295	9940	11601	6341
CAIRO	3325	1823	2698	7428		4476	6231	7175	8925	2218	8720	5701	7230	6242	7554	8100	5290	5152	6005	10360
CAPETOWN	5670	5949	5133	4332	4476		8551	8918	11655	5975	6510	7845	7090	3850	10340	5080	8179	6025	9234	7149
CHICAGO	3305	4458	8144	5598	6231	8551		7510	4315	4015	9837	711	2320	5320	1855	5325	7155	9475	6410	8465
GUAM	8985	7158	4831	10516	7175	8918	7510		3896	7605	3497	8115	9220	11710	5952	9946	1945	2990	1596	4206
HONOLULU	7421	7384	8172	7653	8925	11655	4315	3896		7320	5581	5051	5347	8400	2407	6935	5009	6874	3940	4676
LONDON	1562	575	4526	6919	2218	5975	4015	7605	7320		10590	3500	5310	5747	5440	7275	5841	6818	6050	11790
MELBOURNE	12190	9992	6140	7336	8720	6510	9837	3497	5581	10590		10541	9211	8340	7970	7130	4967	3768	5172	1655
NEW YORK	2604	4026	7875	5295	5701	7845	711	8115	5051	3500	10541		2211	4810	2568	5134	7460	9617	6846	9067
PANAMA	3918	5902	9832	3319	7230	7090	2320	9220	5347	5310	9211	2211		3311	3349	3000	9430	11800	8560	7580
RIO DE JANEIRO	4312	6246	8438	1230	6242	3850	5320	11710	8400	5747	8340	4810	3311		6655	1852	11510	9875	11600	7510
SAN FRANCISCO	5114	5744	8523	6487	7554	10340	1855	5952	2407	5440	7970	2568	3349	6655		5960	6245	8440	5250	6800
SANTIAGO	5718	7842	10127	731	8100	5080	5325	9946	6935	7275	7130	5134	3000	1852	5960		11850	10270	10850	5925
SHANGHAI	7324	5323	3219	12295	5290	8179	7155	1945	5009	5841	4967	7460	9430	11510	6245	11850		2395	1095	6080
SINGAPORE	8338	6226	2425	9940	5152	6025	9475	2990	6874	6818	3768	9617	11800	9875	8440	10270	2395		3350	5360
TOKYO	7370	5623	4247	11601	6005	9234	6410	1596	3940	6050	5172	6846	8560	11600	5250	10850	1095	3350		5730
WELLINGTON	11475	11384	7752	6341	10360	7149	8465	4206	4676	11790	1655	9067	7580	7510	6800	5925	6080	5360	5730	

Fig. 4. – The distances between the nearby points of space-time give all the information that is needed, according to RIEMANN and EINSTEIN, to determine the entire geometry of this 4-dimensional manifold, including all details of its curvature. No mention ever need be made of any coordinates. The information demanded in this description of nature is in one way less comprehensive and in another way more comprehensive than information of the kind included in the above table of air distances: the longer distances are not required, because they can all be deduced from the shorter distances. However the shorter distances have to be supplied in all detail. (Table of air distances reproduced from *The 1960 General Electric Diary* with the permission of the General Electric Co.)

To say that the ratio $\mathscr{I}_{CD}/\mathscr{I}_{AB}$ is independent of the route followed in the intercomparison is a statement of enormous content, and one that can in principle be tested with a thousand experiments (Fig. 4). That the physical world is in this sense a Riemannian manifold is a hypothesis fundamental to general relativity, but it is also a *testable* hypothesis. The most obvious test to date requires reference back to atomic physics: the identity, so far as one can tell, between atoms which have followed different routes through space-time to the same destination.

2. – Nothing but lengths.

It is easy to mock the use of feet to measure the width of a highway and the use of miles to measure its length. However, it is not a very different practice to measure intervals in one direction in seconds and intervals in other directions in centimeters. The factor of conversion from one metric unit of length to the other, $3\cdot 10^{10}$, is just as historical and accidental in character as the factor of conversion, 5 280, from one English unit to the other. To stop trying to « explain » $3\cdot 10^{10}$ it is enough to start trying to « explain » 5280.

Fig. 5. – Gravitational bending of light.

Time is really a length, not a new and independent concept, according to general relativity; and mass too is another way of speaking about length. For example, the mass m^* (cm) of the sun may be determined by measuring the deflection θ of light (Fig. 5) which passes by at the distance r:

$$m^* = r\theta/4 = (6.94\cdot 10^{10}\ \text{cm}/4)\cdot \begin{cases} 8.50\cdot 10^{-6}\ \text{radian predicted} \\ (9.8 \pm 1.3)\cdot 10^{-6}\ \text{observed 1947} \\ (8.2 \pm 0.5)\cdot 10^{-6}\ \text{observed 1952} \end{cases} = 1.5\cdot 10^{5}\ \text{cm}\,. \tag{20}$$

The expression for the mass m in grams is

$$\begin{cases} m = (c^2/G)m^* \\ \quad = (1.347\cdot 10^{28}\ \text{g/cm})(1.5\cdot 10^{5}\ \text{cm}) = 2.0\cdot 10^{33}\ \text{g} \end{cases} \tag{21}$$

but the conversion factor in this formula is as much a matter of convention as are c and 5 280. Mass, time and length are all equally matters of pure geometry. So are electromagnetic fields. In principle they can be measured by way of the curvature $R_{\mu\nu}$ they produce in space-time:

$$R_{\mu\nu}\ (\text{cm}^{-2})\ \text{proportional to (field)}^2\,. \tag{22}$$

The « geometrized » expressions $f_{\mu\nu}$ for the components of the electromagnetic field have the units cm^{-1}. They are connected with the familiar field components $F_{\mu\nu}$ ($g^{\frac{1}{2}}\, cm^{\frac{1}{2}}\, s^{-1}$ or gauss or es volt/cm) by the formula

$$
(23)\qquad \begin{cases} f_{\mu\nu} = (G^{\frac{1}{2}}/c^2)F_{\mu\nu}\,, \\ \qquad = (2.874\cdot 10^{-25}\ \text{cm}^{-1}/\text{gauss})F_{\mu\nu}\,. \end{cases}
$$

The same conversion factor connects the usual measure of charge q($g^{\frac{1}{2}}\, cm^{\frac{3}{2}}\, s^{-1}$ or esu) with the purely geometrical measure of charge q^*(cm):

$$
(24)\qquad \begin{cases} q^* = (G^{\frac{1}{2}}/c^2)q\,, \\ \qquad = (2.874\cdot 10^{-25}\ \text{cm/esu})q\,. \end{cases}
$$

In brief classical physics—gravitation plus electromagnetism—deals with *nothing but lengths*, however much historical terminology conceals this circumstance from view.

It is worthwhile to spell out the basic equations of classical physics in these purely geometrical units of length. Four of Maxwell's equations take the form

$$
(25)\qquad \begin{cases} \dfrac{\partial f_{23}}{\partial x^1} + \dfrac{\partial f_{31}}{\partial x^2} + \dfrac{\partial f_{12}}{\partial x^3} = 0\,, & (\text{div}\ \boldsymbol{h} = 0)\,, \\[2ex] \dfrac{\partial f_{32}}{\partial x^0} + \dfrac{\partial f_{03}}{\partial x^2} + \dfrac{\partial f_{20}}{\partial x^3} = 0\,, & \\[2ex] \cdot\ \cdot\ \cdot\ \cdot\ \cdot\ \cdot\ \cdot\ \cdot\ \cdot & (-\,\partial \boldsymbol{h}/\partial T) - \text{curl}\ \boldsymbol{e} = 0)\,, \\ \cdot\ \cdot\ \cdot\ \cdot\ \cdot\ \cdot\ \cdot\ \cdot\ \cdot & \end{cases}
$$

or more briefly,

$$
(26)\qquad [\alpha\beta\gamma\delta]\,\frac{\partial f_{\gamma\delta}}{\partial x^\beta} = 0\,. \qquad (\alpha = 0, 1, 2, 3)\,.
$$

Here repeated indices are understood to imply summation, and the symbol [0123] has the value 1, and $[\alpha\beta\gamma\delta]$ changes sign on interchange of any two indices. The other four of Maxwell's equations involve not only the field quantities

$$
(27)\qquad \left.\begin{matrix} e_x: & f_{01} \\ e_y: & f_{01} \\ e_z: & f_{03} \end{matrix}\right\}\ \begin{matrix}\text{geometrized}\\ \text{components}\\ \text{of electric}\\ \text{field}\end{matrix} \qquad \begin{matrix}\text{geometrized}\\ \text{components}\\ \text{of magnetic}\\ \text{field}\end{matrix}\ \left\{\begin{matrix} f_{23}: & h_x \\ f_{31}: & h_y \\ f_{12}: & h_z \end{matrix}\right.
$$

but also the components of the metric that tells the interval between two points with nearly equal co-ordinates:

$$\mathrm{d}s^2 = g_{\mu\nu}\,\mathrm{d}x^\mu\,\mathrm{d}x^\nu\,. \tag{28}$$

Let g denote the determinant of the metric tensor, and $g^{\mu\nu}$ designate the reciprocal of this tensor. Also let raised indices denote the result of applying this reciprocal matrix to any tensor, so that

$$\begin{cases} f^\alpha{}_\nu = g^{\alpha\mu} f_{\mu\nu}\,, \\ f^{\alpha\beta} = g^{\alpha\mu} g^{\beta\nu} f_{\mu\nu}\,. \end{cases} \tag{29}$$

Then the remaining four of Maxwell's equations read

$$\frac{1}{(-g)^{\frac{1}{2}}}\frac{\partial}{\partial x^\beta}(-g)^{\frac{1}{2}} g^{\alpha\mu} g^{\beta\nu} f_{\mu\nu} = 4\pi\varrho^\alpha, \tag{30}$$

or

$$\operatorname{div} \boldsymbol{e} = 4\pi\varrho^* \qquad (\alpha = 0)$$

and

$$\operatorname{curl} \boldsymbol{h} - \partial \boldsymbol{e}/\partial T = 4\pi \boldsymbol{j}^* \qquad (\alpha = 1, 2, 3)\,.$$

The density of field energy, $(E^2+H^2)/8\pi$, and the Poynting flux $c(\boldsymbol{E}\times\boldsymbol{H})/4\pi$, are four of the sixteen components of the Maxwell stress energy tensor which, upon multiplication by $8\pi G/c^4$, serves as source term in Einstein's equations for the metric which governs the geometry of space-time. The covariant generalization of the d'Alembert $\Box^2 g_{\mu\nu}$ in these equations is provided by a certain combination of first and second derivatives of the metric coefficients, or in other words, a combination of the Ricci curvature tensor $R_{\mu\nu}$ and the curvature invariant $R = g^{\mu\nu} R_{\mu\nu}$. When the field is expressed in the geometrized form $f_{\mu\nu}$ (cm^{-1}), these equations take the form

$$\underbrace{R_\mu{}^\nu - \tfrac{1}{2}\delta^\nu_\mu R}_{\text{Einstein curvature}} = \underbrace{2 f_\mu{}^\alpha f_\alpha{}^\nu - \tfrac{1}{2}\delta^\nu_\mu f^\tau_\sigma f^\sigma_\tau\,.}_{\text{Geometrized Maxwell tensor}} \tag{31}$$

The equation of motion of an infinitesimal test particle is

$$m^*\left(\frac{\mathrm{d}^2 x^\mu}{\mathrm{d}\mathscr{I}^2} + \Gamma^\mu_{\alpha\beta}\frac{\mathrm{d}x^\alpha}{\mathrm{d}\mathscr{I}}\cdot\frac{\mathrm{d}x^\beta}{\mathrm{d}\mathscr{I}}\right) = q^* f^\mu_\alpha \frac{\mathrm{d}x^\alpha}{\mathrm{d}\mathscr{I}}, \tag{32}$$

where $\Gamma^\mu_{\alpha\beta}$ is a certain combination of the metric and its first derivative.

3. – Deducing the electromagnetic field from measurements on the geometry of space.

3·1. *Footprints of the electromagnetic field on the metric.* – The field leaves foot prints on the curvature of space so specific that from them one can almost always read back to get all he needs to know about the electromagnetic field (Fig. 6). Even more, one can first check whether the curvature of space is actually due only to classical sources—to gravitational and electromagnetic causes alone. Not every conceivable geometry of 4-dimensional space-time, not every Einstein curvature tensor, can be identified with a Maxwell stress tensor. Certain conditions have to be satisfied by the curvature if there is to exist any electromagnetic field $f_{\mu\nu}$ (or $\boldsymbol{e}$ and $\boldsymbol{h}$) at all which will bring about that curvature. These conditions on the curvature —which hold in general—are most easily found by considering the situation where the curvature is produced by a « normal » electromagnetic field: a field for which the ratio of the Poynting flux to the energy density is less than the speed of light. This ratio is exactly equal to the speed of light for a plane wave, but it is less than c for the wave produced by a localized source, and it is less than c for a superposition of plane waves going in different directions. In other words, in the normal case the equation

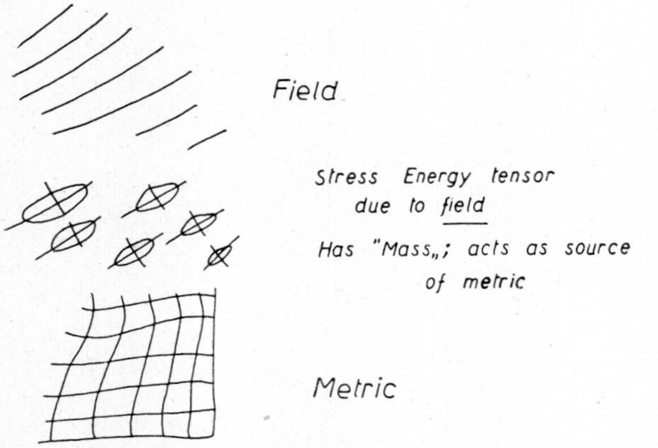

Fig. 6. – The footprints of the electromagnetic field on the metric.

(33) $$\boldsymbol{l}\,\text{tgh}\,2\theta = \frac{2\boldsymbol{e}\times\boldsymbol{h}}{\boldsymbol{e}^2+\boldsymbol{h}^2},$$

gives a well defined value for the direction of the unit vector $\boldsymbol{l}$, and a real value for the hyperbolic angle θ. Now let the same field be examined by a new observer whose local Lorentz frame moves at the rate

(34) $$\boldsymbol{v}/c = \boldsymbol{l}\,\text{tgh}\,\theta$$

with respect to the frame of reference previously used. In this frame the

Poynting flux will be zero ([14]). The electric and magnetic fields ($\boldsymbol{e}'$ and $\boldsymbol{h}'$ in units cm^{-1}) will therefore be parallel. Let the axis to which they are parallel be called the x' axis. Then in this frame of reference all components of the stress-energy tensor (right hand side of (31)) vanish except these (Table II):

TABLE II. – *The non-zero components of the Maxwell stress-energy tensor for a normal electromagnetic field as evaluated in a suitably selected Lorentz frame of reference.* The components actually listed — the right-hand side of (31) — have the dimensions cm^{-2} and are directly equal to the corresponding components of the Einstein curvature tensor. They have to be divided by $8\pi G/c^4$ to give energy density and stress in $\mathrm{erg/cm}^3$ or $\mathrm{dynes/cm}^2$.

Upper and lower labels of component	General value	Value in specially selected Lorentz frame	Interpretation of this results by Maxwell
$\binom{0}{0}$	$-e_x^2 - e_y^2 - e_z^2 - h_x^2 - h_y^2 - h_z^2$	$-e_x^2 - h_x^2$	negative of energy density
$\binom{1}{1}$	$-e_x^2 + e_y^2 + e_z^2 - h_x^2 + h_y^2 + h_z^2$	$-e_x^2 - h_x^2$	tension ∥ lines of force
$\binom{2}{2}$	$e_x^2 - e_y^2 + e_z^2 + h_x^2 - h_y^2 - h_z^2$	$e_x^2 + h_x^2$	pressure ⊥ lines of force
$\binom{3}{3}$	$e_x^2 + e_y^2 - e_z^2 + h_x^2 + h_y^2 - h_z^2$	$e_x^2 + h_x^2$	pressure ⊥ lines of force

In this frame of reference the stress energy tensor is diagonal, with components down the diagonal which can be written in the form $(-\xi^2, -\xi^2, \xi^2, \xi^2)$. In consequence the stress-energy tensor has two obvious properties (1) its trace—the sum of its diagonal elements—is zero, 2) its square is a multiple (ξ^4) of the unit matrix. Both of these properties, moreover, are *covariant* properties in this sense, that if they hold in one co-ordinate system, they hold in all co-ordinate systems. A special Lorentz frame helped to bring to light these properties of the stress-energy tensor ([15]) —and therefore the same properties for the Einstein curvature tensor—but now attention can return to the general frame of reference. Quite generally, if a curvature of space is to

(14) It might have seemed reasonable to identify $\boldsymbol{v}/c$ with the ratio $2(\boldsymbol{e}\times\boldsymbol{h})/(\boldsymbol{e}^2+\boldsymbol{h}^2)$ itself, as was erroneously done in Fig. 1 of C. W. MISNER and J. A. WHEELER: *Ann. Phys.*, **2**, 525 (1957). This would have been appropriate if $\boldsymbol{e}\times\boldsymbol{h}$ and $\frac{1}{2}(\boldsymbol{e}^2+\boldsymbol{h}^2)$ were the components of a 4-vector. However, they are actually 4 of the 16 components of a tensor — the Maxwell tensor. The transformation coefficients are therefore not $\sinh\theta$ and $\cosh\theta$, but products like $\sinh^2\theta$, $\sinh\theta\cdot\cosh\theta$ and $\cosh^2\theta$ — hence the double angle in [33].

(15) Professor V. BARGMANN kindly pointed out the properties (1) and (2) of the stress-energy tensor to C. W. MISNER and the writer in 1955, noting that they had been discovered independently by a number of investigators: G. Y. RAINICH, D. REICH, J. L. SYNGE, W. B. BONNOR and L. MARIOT.

be attributed to classical causes—that is, to an electromagnetic field—it is necessary first of all that the following trace shall vanish:

$$0 = R_{\alpha}^{\alpha} - \tfrac{1}{2}\delta_{\alpha}^{\alpha} R = R - 2R = - R\ ;$$

or more simply,

$$R_{\alpha}^{\alpha} = 0\ . \tag{35}$$

When this condition is satisfied, then the Einstein curvature tensor on the left hand side of eq. (31) reduces to the Ricci curvature tensor itself, $R_{\mu}^{\ \nu}$. Second, if the curvature of space is to be attributed to an electromagnetic field, it is also necessary that the square of the Einstein curvature tensor—or therefore the square of the Ricci curvature tensor—shall be a multiple of the unit matrix:

$$R_{\mu}^{\ \alpha} R_{\alpha}^{\ \nu} = \delta_{\mu}^{\ \nu} (R_{\sigma}^{\ \tau} R_{\tau}^{\ \sigma}/4)\ . \tag{36}$$

Third, it is necessary that the energy density shall be non-negative definite:

$$R_0^{\ 0} \leqslant 0\ . \tag{37}$$

3·2. *The complexion of the field.* – What is the situation when with test particles and light rays one has measured the Ricci curvature throughout an extended region of space time and found that it satisfies the conditions (35), (36), (37)? Consider the normal case, that is, the case where the quantity

$$\xi^4 = R_{\sigma}^{\ \tau} R_{\tau}^{\ \sigma}/4\ , \tag{38}$$

equivalent to

$$(e^2 + h^2)^2 - (2e \times h)^2\ ,$$

or to

$$(h^2 - e^2)^2 + (2e \cdot h)^2\ ,$$

does not vanish. Then there exists at each point P in the space-time region in question a suitable Lorentz reference system L_P, such that the Ricci and Einstein curvature tensors are diagonal at this point in this reference system, with diagonal elements $(-\xi^2,\ -\xi^2,\ \xi^2,\ \xi^2)$. In other words, the observed curvature can be interpreted as due to electric and magnetic fields which are parallel to each other and to the x-axis, of such magnitude that $e^2 + h^2 = \xi^2$. Unknown is the precise complexion of this electromagnetic field; one can only write in this particular frame of reference

$$(39) \qquad \begin{cases} e = (\xi,\ 0,\ 0) \cos \alpha\,, \\ h = (\xi,\ 0,\ 0) \sin \alpha\,, \end{cases}$$

where the angle α *defines* the complexion.

A few comments may be made about the complexion of an electromagnetic field. When $\alpha = 0$, the field $\{e = \xi, 0, 0;\ h = 0, 0, 0\}$ may be said to have a « purely electric complexion ». If regarded from a reference system other than the standard one, the electromagnetic field tensor in this case, $\xi_{\mu\nu}$, will of course generally have both magnetic and electric components; nevertheless, the *complexion* of the field is still said to be purely electric. When $\alpha = \pi/2$, the complexion of the field is termed « purely magnetic ». The field in this case is called the *dual* of the field encountered in the case $\alpha = 0$. Its components in the general frame of reference ([16]) are denoted by the symbol $^*\xi_{\mu\nu}$. Thus, in the general frame of reference *the most general electromagnetic field which will reproduce the observed curvature of space* (satisfying (35), (36), and (37)) *has the form*

$$(40) \qquad f_{\mu\nu} = \xi_{\mu\nu} \cos \alpha + {}^*\xi_{\mu\nu} \sin \alpha\,.$$

Here $\xi_{\mu\nu}$ and $^*\xi_{\mu\nu}$ are functions of position which are uniquely determined in the normal case as soon as the curvature is known.

3·3. *Finding the complexion from the curvature.* – The complexion α is still an unknown function of position. Does this circumstance mean that the foot-

---

([16]) These components can be calculated from the general formula

$$^*\xi_{\mu\nu} = \tfrac{1}{2}(-g)^{\frac{1}{2}}[\mu\nu\alpha\beta]\xi^{\alpha\beta}\,.$$

For example, in any local Lorentz frame of reference,

$$^*\xi_{23} = [2\ 3\ 0\ 1]\,\xi^{01} = \xi^{01} = -\xi_{01} = \xi_{10}\,,$$

or the x-component of the magnetic part of the dual electromagnetic field is equal to the x-component of the electric part of the original electromagnetic field. Similarly

$$^*\xi_{01} = [0\ 1\ 2\ 3]\xi^{23} = \xi_{23}\,,$$

or

$$^*\xi_{10} = -\xi_{23}\,,$$

or the x-component of the electric part of the dual electromagnetic field is equal to the negative of the x-component of the magnetic part of the original electromagnetic field. The dual of the dual of an electromagnetic field is the negative of that field.

prints of the electromagnetic field on the metric are not sharp enough to allow one to read back from purely geometrical measurements to a complete knowledge of the electromagnetic field?

Not all the available information has been put to use. It is still necessary to demand that the electromagnetic field of eq. (40) shall satisfy Maxwell's equations. It is understandable that this requirement should determine the variation of the complexion from one point to a neighboring point. By fixing the gradient of the complexion,

$$\alpha_\mu = \partial\alpha/\partial x^\mu , \tag{41}$$

Maxwell's equations should therefore permit one to determine through (40) the electromagnetic field in the entire region of space-time, up to a single additive constant of integration:

$$\alpha(x) = \int\limits_0 \alpha_\mu(x)\, \mathrm{d}x^\mu + \alpha_0 . \tag{42}$$

The appropriate formula for this purpose is the following, derived first by RAINICH [17] and then independently by MISNER [18]:

$$\alpha_\mu = \frac{(-g)^{\frac{1}{2}}[\mu\alpha\beta\nu]\, R^{\alpha\varrho;\beta} R_\varrho{}^\nu}{R_\xi{}^\eta R^\xi{}_\eta} , \tag{43}$$

(definition of α_μ). Only geometrical quantities appear here, so the goal has been fulfilled: *the electromagnetic field has been expressed in terms of purely geometrical quantities.*

3·4. *Already unified field theory and the structure law of space-time.* – The electromagnetic field determined by (40), (42) and (43) will not be *consistently* determined unless the value of α is independent of the path of integration. For this purpose it is necessary that the curl of the vector α_μ shall vanish:

$$\frac{\partial\alpha_\mu}{\partial x^\nu} - \frac{\partial\alpha_\nu}{\partial x_\mu} = 0 . \tag{44}$$

This is a requirement on the metric. The vector α_μ contains the first derivative of the curvature, and thus (44) involves second derivatives of the curvature. Consequently (44) contains derivatives up to the fourth order of

---

[17] G. Y. RAINICH: *Proc. U. S. Nat. Acad. Sci.*, **10**, 124 (1924); *Trans. Am. Math. Soc.*, **27**, 106 (1925).

[18] See C. W. MISNER and J. A. WHEELER: *Ann. Phys.*, **2**, 525 (1957). The semicolon followed by β in eq. (43) stands for the covariant derivative of $R^{\alpha\varrho}$ with respect to x^β.

the metric itself. This set of fourth order equations, plus the algebraic Rainich relations (35), (36) and (37), contain in the normal case ($R_\sigma^{\ \tau} R_\tau^{\ \sigma} > 0$) the entire content of Maxwell's equations for empty space plus Einstein's field equations with the Maxwell stress-energy tensor as source. One set of equations of the fourth order—purely geometrical in character—takes the place of two sets of equations of the second order. The resulting theoretical structure may be termed « *already* unified field theory. » It is a reformulation in other words of the standard theory of general relativity as put forward by EINSTEIN in 1916. In this respect it is very different from later so-called unified field theories, which give up the Riemann hypothesis that there exists an interval

$$ds^2 = g_{\mu\nu}\, dx^\mu\, dx^\nu\,.$$

No such modified theory has ever been put forward which is free of objection. In contrast, against Einstein's original theory no objection of logic or principle has ever been established, nor has any discrepancy of observation ever been sustained. No substitute theory has ever been put forward which approaches general relativity in simplicity and comprehensiveness.

It is appropriate to give the combined apparatus of gravitation theory and electromagnetism the name « geometrodynamics » as more indicative of its character than simply « general relativity. » In so far as geometrodynamics can be said to contain all the physics that is known today to be purely classical, it can be said that this physics is summarized in eqs. (35), (36), (37) and (44). *These equations state the structure law of space-time.* They select out of all conceivable Riemannian spaces those 4-dimensional geometries which are consistent with the classical laws of gravitation and electromagnetism.

3·5. *Geometrodynamics is free of coupling constants.* – When the laws of interaction of electromagnetic and gravitational fields are written in the usual form of Einstein's field equations, and in the usual units, there appears on the right hand side the factor

$$(45)\qquad \begin{cases} 8\pi G/c^4 = 8\pi(6.670\cdot 10^{-8}\ \text{cm}^3/\text{g s}^2)\big/(2.997\,9\cdot 10^{10}\ \text{cm/s})^4 \\ \qquad\quad = 2.07\cdot 10^{-48}\ (\text{gauss cm})^{-2}\,, \end{cases}$$

on which count it is often said that « the coupling constant of gravitational forces is very small. » However, such a statement within the framework of classical physics is devoid of any meaning, for there is no natural scale with respect to which to compare physical effects. Out of the two constants G and c alone no combination can be formed which has the dimensions of a length, or a mass, or a time. The equations of geometrodynamics in the « already unified » form contain no reference whatever to any coupling constant. Satisfyingly enough, no constant has to be brought in from outside, later to be explained by some more fundamental classical theory. What quantum theory has to add to the story is of course a separate question. At the classical theory geometrodynamics is a self-contained theory. In brief, it supplies *coupling without any coupling constants.*

3·6. *Assessment of already unified field theory.* – If by « classical physics » is understood all that physics which does not depend upon the quantum of action or upon particles of quantized charge and mass, then all of classical physics is summarized in the structure law of space-time of eqs. (35), (36), (37) and (44). How then can these equations be made to appear natural? Or if they cannot, what conclusion can be drawn from this circumstance?

SHARP [19] has suggested the possibility that the structure equations can be derived from the variational principle

$$\delta\int L(-g)^{\frac{1}{2}}\,\mathrm{d}^4x = 0\,,$$

based on the invariant Lagrangian density

$$L = R - \tfrac{1}{2}(R_{\mu\nu}R^{\mu\nu})^{\frac{1}{2}}\cos 2\int_0^x \alpha_\beta\,\mathrm{d}x^\beta\,,$$

where α_β is defined in terms of the curvature as in eq. (43). From this principle he has derived the curl eq. (44). It is not yet known whether the other—algebraic—structure equations can be derived from this variational principle.

Both the proposed variational principle and the original curl equation itself contain an invariant of the curvature in a denominator. Therefore the gradient of the complexion is an undefined quantity in a region of space where there is no electromagnetic field. PENROSE [20] has pointed out that this circumstance makes a difficulty of principle for already unified field theory in the following special type of situation. Electromagnetic fields exist in region A, and in B, but not between. Therefore it is not possible in this case to determine from the metric alone throughout *this particular* THREE-*space* the complexion of the field in region A *relative* to the field in region B (Table III). However, if configurations I and II are allowed to evolve in time, the fields will spread out from regions A and B, will meet, and will then overlap more and more. Very different outcomes will be observed in the region of overlap according as the original configuration is I or II or something intermediate.

---

(19) D. SHARP: *Phys. Rev. Lett.*, **3**, 108 (1959).

(20) Thanks are expressed here to Dr. R. PENROSE for communication of this unpublished result, and to him, D. SHARP and Professor C. MISNER for discussion of its implications. See also L. WITTEN: *Phys. Rev.*, **120**, 635 (1960).

Measurements of the curvature of space made at such a time are easily adequate to distinguish *outcomes* in cases I and II, although the « already unified » version of geometrodynamics was blind to the difference between the *initial value* data of I and II.

TABLE III. – *Two different field configurations, I and II, defined over a space like 3-surface can look identical from the exclusively geometric point of view.* They can have identical metric and curvature and stress-energy. Yet they can be very different in that alternative and more familiar way of speaking of Einstein's standard theory which keeps in evidence both metric *and* electromagnetic field quantities. For this situation to arise it is necessary that there exist regions of the 3-space which contain electromagnetic fields, completely surrounded by space which is free of electromagnetic fields.

	Field in region A	Field in region B	Field elsewhere
Configuration I	Pure E	Pure H	Zero
Configuration II	Pure E	Pure E	Zero

The Einstein-Maxwell version did not have this blind spot. The blindness arose only when the two sets of second order equations were combined into one purely geometrical set of fourth order equations. There is a truly physical distinction between the complexions in regions A and B even though there is no way to define the complexion in the *three*-space between. Limited to this three-space, the already unified formulation under certain circumstances cannot keep track of the difference in complexion between two or more regions.

The difficulty disappears when a complete history—rather than the state of affairs on an initial 3-surface—is to be described in purely geometrical terms. Either 1) the fields in the two regions, propagating in time, come into a region of overlap where relative complexion makes a difference. Then there exist routes in space-time connecting the two regions, proceeding along which one can determine their relative complexion by purely geometrical means. Or 2), the fields never come into a region of overlap. The relative complexion of the two regions can never make a difference and need not be defined. In brief, when relative complexion matters, it is fully defined by purely geometrical measurements provided that they are free to penetrate anywhere in space-time.

Restricted to certain 3-surfaces and certain circumstances, however, purely geometrical measurements cannot bring to light the difference in complexion between disparate regions. Yet Nature knows how to keep account of this difference in complexion. Hence, if Nature is purely geometrical, the complexion must be purely geometrical in character too. But complexion does not always clearly show this purely geometrical character in already unified field theory. Does this theory fall short because it always uses as its tool *differential* geometry—the geometry in the immediate neighborhood of a point? Is its flaw this, that it fails to recognize the community in character between well separated points? Are the usual geometrical tools inappropriate because, to speak loosely, they introduce far too many points, and take the distinguishability of points as a postulate beyond question? Is there no way to drop this odd foundation and still keep the relevant parts of the superstructure? Isn't one point enough? Can't it play its part over and over, much as the electron beam in a television set dancing about fast enough constructs a whole picture? With a much more intimate relation of this type between point and point, would not the relative complexion of two points much more readily have a part to play? There is no thought here of course of *changing* Einstein-Maxwell theory, but only of seeking another kind of language in which to *state* that theory. *The existence in the basic structure law of classical space-time of such a quantity as the relative complexion of two widely separated points compels anyone seeking a purely geometrical description of nature to conclude that the concept of complexion has not yet found its happiest geometrical means of expression.*

Relative complexion comes to the fore in another unsolved problem: why do all the charges in nature have the same complexion?

In conclusion, already unified field theory gives a basis for stating that all of classical physics can be put into geometrical terms, but it is not the most convenient way to describe that geometry. For that purpose the dual language of electromagnetic fields and metric is still the more useful.

4. – Equations of motion without equations of motion.

Long after general relativity was put forward in 1916 the theory was found to have an important new consequence. The equation for the motion of a test particle in a known geometrodynamical field (eq. (32)) was found not to be needed as a separate postulate, as it is in every other formulation of physics. Instead, the equation of motion of the object has been shown to follow as a *consequence* of the field equations ([21]). The historical situation brings

([21]) General idea in A. Einstein and J. Grommer: *Sitz. Ber. preuss. Akad. Wiss.*, 2 and 235 (1927). Treatment of case of slowly moving masses in a space which is asymptotically flat: A. Einstein, L. Infeld and B. Hoffmann: *Ann. Math.*, **39**, 65 (1938). Case of an infinitesimal neutral test particle moving at arbitrary speed in a specified background metric: L. Infeld and A. Schild: *Rev. Mod. Phys.*, **21**, 408 (1949). Case when the test particle is charged: D. M. Chase: *Phys. Rev.*, **95**, 243 (1954) and L. Infeld: *Acta Phys. Polon.*, **13**, 187 (1954). Application of the same method of analysis to the later « unified field theory » of Einstein (now generally abandoned) showing that in this theory a test particle would move as if uncharged, no matter how much charge is loaded upon it: J. Callaway: *Phys. Rev.*, **92**, 1567 (1953). (No cyclotron could operate!) General survey: L. Infeld and J. Plebanski: *Motion and Relativity* (New York, 1960).

to mind an imaginary parallel. Dark spots come drifting over the the surface of a lake into the area of vision of an observer on a high tower. He studies their motions carefully enough to deduce equations of motion and an effective law of force between these spots. He knows in addition from other investigations the laws of hydrodynamics for the fluid of the lake. One day a new glass of improved resolving power shows him that the « spots » are not foreign objects at all. They are vortices in the medium whose properties he already knows. He goes back to the equations of hydrodynamics and from them *derives* the laws of motion of vortices and their interactions. In this way he acquires a much deeper understanding of what he sees.

The equations of motion cannot be derived from the field equations if the field equations are linear. The equations of electrodynamics, for example, allow the field to be calculated from the motion of the charge just as well for an impossible motion as for the real motion. That the equation of motion of a test particle and the Lorentz law of force can be derived from general relativity or geometrodynamics means that this theory is in some sense a « master theory » of physics. No formulation of physical law of lesser scope possesses this power.

5. – The geon: mass without mass.

5·1. *Past models for mass.* – The derivation of the equations of motion from the field equations assumes that a massive object *exists*.

It is unhappy to have to introduce such an object from outside into a theory which is otherwise self-contained. This objection has been recognized in one treatment of the problem of motion. This analysis sticks to relativity as it is, but treats the object as a singularity in the metric. Many questions then arise: Should the singularity be assumed to be spherically symmetric? How can such symmetry be defined? Are any asymmetries allowed, and if so which? If one allows a singularity anywhere, is he not in principle opening the way to singularities everywhere? Does not a continuous distribution of singularities amount to an arbitrary source term in the equations? If such a term can be introduced at will, how can the structure of the theory possibly be well defined? Another approach seeks to avoid singularities by treating each object as a mass of fluid obeying one or another equation of state. The metric is then everywhere regular. In this model the mass evidently possesses internal degrees of freedom of its own which can be excited by the external forces to which it is subject. The properties of these degrees of freedom depend in a critical way upon what equation of state is assumed. Moreover, the equation of state is itself something foreign to pure geometrodynamics, a relation introduced from outside. Thus neither approach leads to a closed theory of motion.

5·2. *Equilibrium of radiation pressure and gravitational pull in a geon.* – Therefore it is interesting to find that there exists a third way to treat the concept of body in general relativity. An object can in principle be constructed

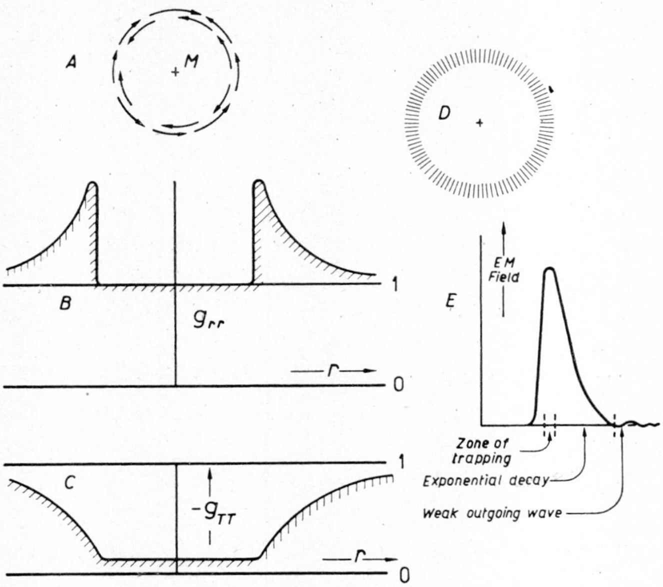

Fig. 7. – Conditions near and inside a geon. A: photons travelling in circular orbits under the influence of a sufficiently concentrated, and sufficiently great, mass M located at the center. When more and more electromagnetic energy is supplied and put into orbit, this radiation itself contributes an increasing share to the stabilizing gravitational force. The mass M can be decreased. Ultimately the mass M can be dispensed with altogether, and a geon is in existence — a standing electromagnetic wave which has enough mass-energy of its own to hold itself together. The gravitational field serves as a wave guide for this energy. This field is described in the case of a simple spherical geon by the metric

$$ds^2 = g_{TT}\,dT^2 + g_{rr}\,dr^2 + r^2(d\theta^2 + \sin^2\theta\, d\varphi^2)\,.$$

B: the radial factor in this metric can be written in the form

$$g_{rr} = [1 - 2r^{-1}m^*(r)]^{-1}\,.$$

Here the quantity $m^*(r)$ represents the mass (in cm) included within a sphere of radius r. This mass increases suddenly as a function of r in the « active region » where most of the radiation is concentrated. C: the time factor in the metric in the case of a simple spherical geon has the value $-g_{TT} = 1/9$ well inside and $1 - 2m^*(\infty)/r$ well outside the geon. The radius of the active part of the geon is $r_{\text{active}} = (9/4)m^*(\infty)$. A standard clock inside ticks at one third the rate of a standard clock far away. D: a schematic representation of the electromagnetic waves in the active region of the geon. E: a more detailed picture of the dependence of the electromagnetic field strength upon r, showing the analogy with α particle decay through a potential barrier — or here, the slow leakage of radiation through a refractive index barrier.

out of electromagnetic radiation which will hold itself together by its own gravitational attraction for a very long period of time. The gravitational acceleration *needed* to hold the radiation in a circular orbit of radius r is of the order of c^2/r. The acceleration *available* from the gravitational pull of a concentration of radiant energy of mass M is of the order GM/r^2, where $G = 6.670 \cdot 10^{-8}\ \text{cm}^3/\text{g s}^2$ is Newton's constant of gravitation. The two accelerations agree in order of magnitude when the radius r is of the order

$$r \sim GM/c^2 = (0.742 \cdot 10^{-28}\ \text{cm/g})M\,. \tag{46}$$

A collection of radiation held together in this way, a « gravitational electromagnetic entity » [22], or geon (Fig. 7), is a purely classical object. It has nothing whatsoever directly to do with the world of elementary particles. Its structure and stability can be treated entirely within the framework of classical geometrodynamics, provided that a size is adopted for it sufficiently great that quantum effects do not come into play. Studied from a distance, such an object presents the same kind of gravitational attraction as any other mass. Moreover, it moves through space as a unit, and undergoes deflection by slowly varying fields of force just as does any other mass. Yet nowhere inside the geon is there a place where one can put his finger and say « here is mass » in the conventional sense of mass. The geon owes its existence to a localized—but everywhere regular—curvature of space-time, and to nothing more. In brief, the geon describes *mass without mass*.

5·3. *Leakage of energy from a geon.* – For a geon to be completely stable is just as impossible as it is for a finite block of glass to confine radiation within it for all time by total internal reflection. The optical wave guide provided by the glass-air interface is analogous to the electromagnetic wave guide provided by the metric (Fig. 7). The glass is well known to be completely effective in confining radiation when the interface is planar: the electromagnetic disturbance in the « forbidden » zone falls off exponentially with a characteristic fall-off distance of the order $\lambda\!\!\!^{-} = \lambda/2\pi = c/\omega$. Not so well known is the fact that outside a spherical piece of glass of radius a the exponential decay proceeds only for a distance that is also of the order of a, thereafter to be followed by the oscillatory behavior of a weak outgoing wave train. The energy of the trapped radiation therefore leaks away from the glass sphere—and also from the geon—much as α particles leak out of radioactive nuclei. The barrier in the case of the glass and the geon may be said to be primarily « centrifugal » in origin, while that in the case of the α particle is of course ordinarily mainly coulombic in origin. The radioactive decay constant that is associated by the leakage mechanism with the geon contains an exponential of the

(22) J. A. WHEELER: *Phys. Rev.*, **97**, 511 (1955); F. ERNST: *Rev. Mod. Phys.*, **29**, 496 (1957); E. POWER and J. A. WHEELER: *Rev. Mod. Phys.*, **29**, 480 (1957).

Gamow type,

(47) $$\exp\,[-\,4.56 \text{ radius of active zone}/\lambda\!\!\!{}^{-}]\,.$$

Table IV shows calculated rates of leakage of energy from two illustrative geons.

TABLE IV. – *Leakage of radiation from two simple spherical geons.* The last column gives the factor of change of scale for any similarity transformation which leaves the geon a classical object (electric field in active region small compared to critical field required to produce electron pairs copiously out of the vacuum). For purpose of comparison note mass of sun is $1.987\cdot10^{33}$ g, radius is $6.94\cdot10^{10}$ cm, mean density is 1.42 g/cm^3, average distance from earth is $1.497\cdot10^{13}$ cm.

Property	Geon I	Geon II	Scale factor
Mass	10^{42} g	10^{42} g	$\times n$
Radius of active zone	$1.67\cdot10^{14}$ cm	$1.67\cdot10^{14}$ cm	$\times n$
Number of waves around circumference (see Fig. 7*D*)	10	$8.43\cdot10^{9}$	unchanged
Circular frequency of emergent radiation	$6.00\cdot10^{-4}$ rad/s	$5.06\cdot10^{5}$ rad/s	$\times(1/n)$
Wavelength outside	$3.14\cdot10^{14}$ cm	$3.72\cdot10^{5}$ cm	$\times n$
Thickness of active zone	$\sim 3.59\cdot10^{13}$ cm	$\sim 4.02\cdot10^{7}$ cm	$\times n$
Fractional loss of mass-energy in one radian of electromagnetic vibration	$2.5\cdot10^{-7}$	$10^{-5\,570\,000\,000}$	$\times 1$
Time to collapse assuming only leakage important and assuming classical behavior at all stages of decay	212 years	$\sim\infty$	$\times(1/n)$
Root mean square electric (and magnetic) fields in most active region	$4.66\cdot10^{10}$ esu/cm (G)	$4.41\cdot10^{13}$ esu/cm (G)	$\times(1/n)$
Critical constant or slowly varying electric field associated with mechanism of production of (e^+, e^-) pairs out of vacuum	$4.41\cdot10^{13}$ esu/cm	$4.41\cdot10^{13}$ esu/cm	a constant
Density of mass-energy in active region	0.192 g/cm^3	$1.72\cdot10^{5}$ g/cm^3	$\times(1/n^2)$

A second mechanism by which a geon can dissipate energy was kindly pointed out by Professor E. McMillan in a personal discussion. If the object travels through space even as thinly populated as intergalactic space, it will encounter protons and electrons to a number density of the order of 10^{-1} to 10 per m^3. Its slowly varying and very strong internal electric fields will accelerate these ions to very great energies at the expense of the geon. The rate of dissipation will be proportional to the cross-sectional area of the geon and to its velocity. If the velocity is comparable to the speed of light, the dissipation will be rapid. The most favorable case is that where the relative velocity is of the order of the random velocity of typical gas clouds, say 100 km/s:

$$-\frac{\mathrm{d}\,(\text{energy})}{\mathrm{d}t} \sim \begin{pmatrix}\text{particle}\\ \text{density}\end{pmatrix}\begin{pmatrix}\text{cloud}\\ \text{velocity}\end{pmatrix}\begin{pmatrix}\text{geon cross}\\ \text{section}\end{pmatrix}\begin{pmatrix}\text{ejection}\\ \text{energy}\end{pmatrix}.$$

For example, in the case of geon I (or II) of Table IV, this product might be of the order

$$(48)\qquad (10^{-6}\ \text{cm}^{-3})(10^{7}\ \text{cm/s})(10^{29}\ \text{cm}^2)\begin{Bmatrix} 20\ \text{dyn}\cdot 5\cdot 10^{13}\ \text{cm}\\ 2\cdot 10^{4}\ \text{dyn}\cdot 6\cdot 10^{4}\ \text{cm}\end{Bmatrix} \to$$

$$\to \begin{Bmatrix} 10^{45}\ \text{erg/s}\\ \text{or}\ 10^{39}\ \text{erg/s}\end{Bmatrix} \to \begin{Bmatrix} 10^{24}\ \text{g/s}\ \ \text{I}\\ 10^{18}\ \text{g/s}\ \ \text{II}\end{Bmatrix},$$

implying a life of the order

$$10^{18}\ \text{s} \quad \text{or} \quad 3\cdot 10^{10}\ \text{yr} \quad (\text{I})$$

$$10^{24}\ \text{s} \quad \text{or} \quad 3\cdot 10^{16}\ \text{yr} \quad (\text{II})$$

for a geon in the space between galaxies, and a life roughly a million times shorter *within* a galaxy, where the density of ionized matter is very roughly a million times greater. Thus there is no convincing reason to believe that geons could survive to this stage in the history of the universe. Neither is there any obvious reason to believe that they would have been created in the first place by the extreme conditions of those very early days. In other words, the geon is an object of interest, not because it might explain anything seen by observational science, but because it gives some impression of the *extraordinarily rich physics of curved empty space* predicted by standard general relativity.

5·4. *Place of geon in scheme of classical physics.* – To have the geon as a model for the masses or bodies that classical physics speaks about allows a deeper insight into some aspects of geometrodynamics. First, the geodesic equation of motion of a body shows itself clearly as an idealization. The position-dependent quantities that appear in this equations have to be regarded as the « background field »—the gravitational and electromagnetic magnitudes that would be present in the absence of the geon. It will only be possible to speak of such a background field in a reasonably well defined way when the total field—due to background plus geon—varies slowly over a distance comparable to the linear extension of the geon. In this case the object will accelerate coherently under the action of external forces. This behavior fits into the scheme of physics envisaged by Newton and Maxwell: preexisting bodies generating forces and being acted upon by forces. It does not violate this plan for the equation of motion to contain the corrections associated with special and general relativity.

Second, when the fields do not approach uniform values outside the geon, but instead are inhomogeneous, then the geon will not react as a unit. Its internal degrees of freedom are disturbed. When the external inhomogeneities are strong, the system will break into two or more parts.

A special instance of such a disruptive interaction is provided by the collision between two geons of similar size when the distance of closest approach is comparable with or small compared with the size of either object. Not only will there be strong departures from an effective inverse square law of force but also energy exchanges and energy losses. Where the refractive index barrier between the two system is thinnest, radiation will leak across from one body to the other. Some modes of oscillation of trapped electromagnetic radiation, previously excited weakly or not at all, will gain energy, and other important modes will lose energy. Thus the two bodies will part company with a ratio of masses different from what they had when they met. Their total mass will be diminished at the same time, both via momentary stimulation of the leakage of radiation to the outside, and by way of local perturbations of the gravitational field that deflect some light rays to the outside from orbits that previously were relatively stable.

When two geons collide still more directly, it will be rare for the two systems to emerge from the encounter without much loss of mass. Almost everything that can happen will happen. There will be a substantial loss of energy in the form of free radiation. Collective modes of motion will be excited. Individual electromagnetic modes will have quite new amplitudes. Forces will be at work to induce fission of the original geons into smaller fragments. In view of this richness of phenomenology, it is not appropriate to describe the close interaction of two classical geons in terms of an effective law of force, or potential curve. Instead, it is necessary to use the much more complicated language of transmutation physics, in which the center of attention is the distribution of the products of reaction in mass, in velocity and in direction. In brief, one has *transmutation physics without transmutations*.

The existence of geon transformation processes makes clear a third point about classical relativity physics, that there exists in principle no sharp distinction between geons as concentrations of electromagnetic energy, capable of break-up and assembly processes, and the «free» electromagnetic waves that pass through the space between the geons, and experience scattering, absorption or emission by geons. Legalistically speaking, the state of the universe of classical physics is described by the singularity-free electromagnetic and gravitational magnitude at every point, and by nothing more.

6. – The initial value problem: field equations without field equations.

6·1. *Initial data for electromagnetism.* – How much information has to be specified at one moment of time—that is, on one 3-space-like surface σ—in order to determine uniquely and consistently the entire future (and past) of the geometrodynamical field? Though the field equations of general relativity were put forward in 1916, this important issue about the initial value data was not solved until three decades later, through the important work of LICHNEROWICZ and FOURES-BRUHAT ([23]). The analogous problem in the theory of source-free electromagnetic fields is well known. It is enough to know the electric and magnetic fields on a single space-like 3-surface σ (co-ordinates u, v, w) in order to be able to predict the fields on a surface moved ahead by a proper time interval $\mathrm{d}\mathscr{T}(u, v, w)$ normal to σ. The equations required to predict the fields $\boldsymbol{e}+\mathrm{d}\boldsymbol{e}$ and $\boldsymbol{h}+\mathrm{d}\boldsymbol{h}$ on the new surface are best known in the case of flat space-time ([24]):

$$\left\{\begin{aligned} \mathrm{d}\boldsymbol{e}/\mathrm{d}T &= \quad \operatorname{curl} \boldsymbol{h}\,, \\ \mathrm{d}\boldsymbol{h}/\mathrm{d}T &= -\operatorname{curl} \boldsymbol{e}\,. \end{aligned}\right. \tag{49}$$

The initial value data in electromagnetism, the values of $\boldsymbol{e}$ and $\boldsymbol{h}$ on σ, cannot be freely selected, despite the absence of any obvious warning on this point

---

([23]) A. LICHNEROWICZ: *Problèmes globaux en méchanique relativiste* (Paris, 1939); *Journ. Math. Pure Appl.*, (9) **23**, 37 (1944); *Helv. Phys. Acta. Suppl.*, **4**, 176 (1956); Y. FOURÈS-BRUHAT: *Acta. Math.*, **88**, 141 (1952); *Journ. Rational Mech. Anal.*, **5**, 951 (1956); and especially Livre I of the book of A. LICHNEROWICZ: *Théories relativistes de la gravitation et de l'électromagnétisme* (Paris, 1955).

([24]) In curved space-time these equations retain their validity when the terms are understood in the appropriate covariant sense. Thus $\boldsymbol{e}$ and $\boldsymbol{h}$ are vectors or 1-forms on the space-like hypersurface σ. Their duals, *referred to the 3-space metric* ${}^{(3)}g_{mn}$ *on* σ, are $*e$ and $*h$, with the components $(*e)_{mn}=({}^{(3)}g^{\frac{1}{2}})[mnp]({}^{(3)}g^{pq})e_q$. These 2-forms, or antisymmetric tensors, are identified with the projections of the 4-dimensional 2-form or antisymmetrical field tensor $\boldsymbol{f}$, and its dual, onto σ:

$$*h = \text{projection of } \;\; f \text{ on } \sigma\,,$$
$$*e = \text{projection of } *f \text{ on } \sigma\,.$$

Define in addition the generalized curl or «exterior derivative» $\boldsymbol{da}$ of any vector

from eqs. (49). This data must satisfy the *initial value equations*,

$$\operatorname{div} \boldsymbol{e} = 0\,, \qquad \operatorname{div} \boldsymbol{h} = 0\,. \tag{50}$$

Then eq. (49) guarantees that the same divergence conditions are satisfied by the field on the new surface,

$$\begin{cases} \boldsymbol{e} + \mathrm{d}\boldsymbol{e} = \boldsymbol{e} + (\mathrm{d}T)\operatorname{curl}\boldsymbol{h}\,, \\ \boldsymbol{h} + \mathrm{d}\boldsymbol{h} = \boldsymbol{h} - (\mathrm{d}T)\operatorname{curl}\boldsymbol{e}\,. \end{cases} \tag{51}$$

In effect eqs. (50) cut the number of disposable quantities from 6 per space point (3 components of $\boldsymbol{e}$ and 3 components of $\boldsymbol{h}$) to 4. It is possible to connect this standard result with a still more familiar way of speaking when the space is flat. Go over from co-ordinate space to wave number space. For each point in wave number space there are known 4 disposable constants associated with the electromagnetic field: the co-ordinate and momentum (or amplitude and phase) of the two oscillators associated with the two independent states of polarization. Therefore it is not surprising to find 4 disposable constants per point also in co-ordinate space. This loose and tacit identification of the number of points in co-ordinate space with the number of points in wave number space provides a useful tool not only in electromagnetism but also in gravitation theory.

6·2. *Conditions on the initial value data of geometrodynamics.* – Weak gravitational waves were studied long ago by EINSTEIN and others. In the approximation where the deviations from flat space are small, the concept of wave number is well defined. There are two transverse states of polarization per wave number for these waves just as for electromagnetic waves. However,

---

or antisymmetrical tensor by the statement

$$(\boldsymbol{d}\boldsymbol{a}_{\alpha_1\alpha_2\ldots\alpha_{p+1}}) = \sum_{\text{permutations } P} (-1)^P \, \partial a_{\beta_2\ldots\beta_{p+1}}/\partial x^{\beta_1}\,.$$

Then Maxwell's equations have the form

$$\begin{aligned} \boldsymbol{d}{}^*\boldsymbol{h} &= 0; & \partial({}^*h)/\partial T &= -\boldsymbol{d}\boldsymbol{e}\,; \\ \boldsymbol{d}{}^*\boldsymbol{e} &= 0; & \partial({}^*e)/\partial T &= \boldsymbol{d}\boldsymbol{h}\,. \end{aligned}$$

For these equations and other aspects of geometrodynamics, reference is made to C. W MISNER and J. A. WHEELER: *Ann. Phys.*, **2**, 525 (1957).

the polarization is tensorial in character instead of vectorial (Fig. 8). Because gravitational waves demand for their specification (2 constants per state of polarization) $\times$ (2 states of polarization per wave number) $=$ 4 constants per point in wave number space when co-ordinate space is nearly flat, it is reasonable to expect 4 quantities to be needed per point in 3-space to specify the initial conditions for the gravitational field, over and above the 4 quantities per point needed to specify the initial conditions for the electromagnetic field. It is therefore satisfying to find these quantities showing up in the analysis of the initial value problem due to Lichnerowicz and Foures-Bruhat. They show that it is necessary and sufficient—in order to determine the future and past—to specify on a 3-space σ not only the electric and magnetic fields $\boldsymbol{e}$ and $\boldsymbol{h}$, but also the 3-dimensional metric of that space, ${}^{(3)}g_{mn}$, and its rate of change $\sim {}^{(3)}P_{mn}$, with respect to proper cotime measured in the normal direction off the 3-space σ. Just as the initial value data for the electromagnetic field are subject to the conditions of vanishing divergence —or, in the language of exterior differential forms, to the conditions

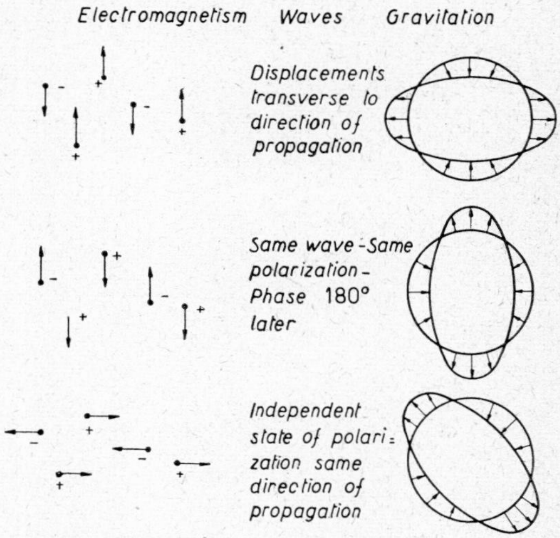

Fig. 8. – Polarization of electromagnetic waves and gravitational waves compared and contrasted. A gravitational wave travelling perpendicular to the plane of the paper and acting on a group of test particles spaced about the rim of a circle changes their separations as indicated by the ellipses. The two independent states of polarization are separated by 45 degrees, not by 90 degrees as for electromagnetic waves.

$$d*\boldsymbol{e} = 0\,, \qquad d*\boldsymbol{h} = 0\,, \tag{52}$$

—so the geometrical data ${}^{(3)}g_{mn}$ and ${}^{(3)}P_{mn}$ cannot be specified completely freely either; their values are subject to conditions in which there appear the Poynting flux and the Maxwell energy density:

$$(P_k^{\ m} - \delta_k^{\ m} P_s^{\ s})_{;m} = -2\,[\,*(\boldsymbol{e}\wedge\boldsymbol{h})]_k \tag{53}$$

and

$$(P_s^{\ s})^2 - P_s^{\ t} P_t^{\ s} + {}^{(3)}R = 2*(\boldsymbol{e}*\boldsymbol{e} + \boldsymbol{h}*\boldsymbol{h})\,. \tag{54}$$

Here ${}^{(3)}R$ is the curvature invariant for the 3-dimensional space σ. It refers only to the curvature that is intrinsic to this space (Fig. 9) whereas the quantities P_{mn} or $P_m{}^n$ describe the extrinsic curvature of this 3-space in the surrounding and still unknown 4-space. Thus (54) can be written more descriptively in this form:

$$(55)\qquad \begin{pmatrix}\text{intrinsic curvature}\\ \text{invariant of } \sigma\end{pmatrix} - \begin{pmatrix}\text{extrinsic curvature}\\ \text{invariant of } \sigma\end{pmatrix} = \begin{pmatrix}\text{density of electromagnetic}\\ \text{energy in suitable units}\end{pmatrix}.$$

The requirement that the electric and magnetic fields should be divergenceless quite obviously reduced 6 degrees of freedom per point down to the correct number of 4. However, the corresponding conditions on the initial

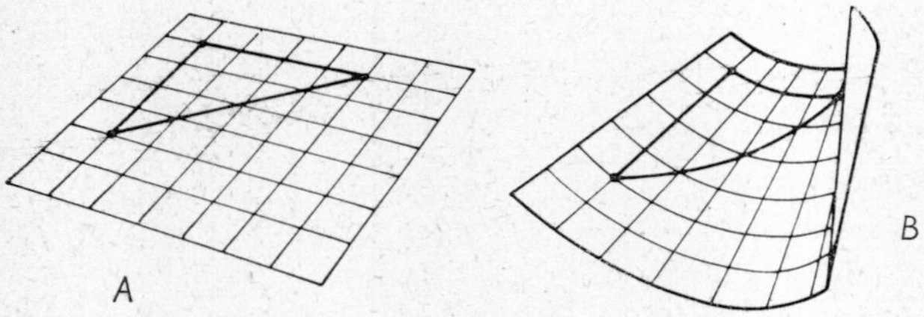

Fig. 9. – Elementary example of the distinction between intrinsic and extrinsic curvature. The sheet of paper in the example happens to be flat, so that the intrinsic curvature of the sheet is zero, ${}^{(2)}R=0$. The Pythagorean theorem therefore holds in this particular example for a triangle drawn on the surface. However, the Pythagorean theorem also holds within the surface when the paper is bent up as at B. Thus the geometry *intrinsic* to the 2-surface — a geometry that in the example happens to be Euclidean — is unaffected by the way this 2-surface is imbedded in the surrounding 3-space. The *extrinsic* curvature, on the other hand, depends upon the way in which this imbedding is carried out. The extrinsic curvature is zero in case A, non-zero in case B. Analogous concepts apply in general relativity, where the initial value problem deals with the geometry intrinsic to the original 3-space σ, and also with the extrinsic curvature of this 3-space in the surrounding 4-geometry — a geometry which is at the start entirely unknown except for the information provided by the intrinsic and extrinsic curvature of σ, but which can be worked out uniquely from this initial data plus Einstein's field equations.

value data of gravitation physics, the 4 equations (53) and (54), do not appear at first sight to be sufficient to reduce the apparent dozen pieces of information per point about the metric (6 components of ${}^{(3)}g_{mn}$ and 6 components of ${}^{(3)}P_{mn}$) down to the 4 that one is naturally led to expect: $12-4$ is not equal to 4! The discrepancy of 4 can be understood in the following way. Part of the information contained in the 6 components of the metric tensor ${}^{(3)}g_{mn}$ is not really information at all about the *geometry* of the 3-space σ, but only information about the *coordinate system* that happens to be used to describe it. There are less than 6 significant pieces of information per point carried in the ${}^{(3)}g_{mn}$.

It may not be out of place to picture the situation in everyday terms. Ford automobile fenders are stamped out of sheet metal and—although all identical—come out of the production plant on conveyor belts to a variety of line-painters, some of whom paint on fenders one type of co-ordinate system; others, other co-ordinate systems. The distances between points with co-ordinates (7, 11, 57) and (7.01, 11.01, 57.01) will therefore be very different from one fender to another, or in other words, the metric coefficients g_{mn} will be very different. The *intrinsic geometry*, however, is obviously identical from one fender to another. To recognize this point it is possible to use a standard piece of mathematical machinery for calculating *curvature invariants* from the metric coefficients. Equipped with this machinery, one can at once tell from the functions of position g_{mn}, without any additional data, that the fenders with such apparently different metrics are actually identical. The same machinery will also serve to distinguish Fiat fenders from Ford fenders. However, it is not necessary to go into the subject of curvature invariants to recognize in the case of the 3-space σ how many of the 6 pieces of data per point ${}^{(3)}g_{mn}$ are geometrically significant. It is enough to notice that the co-ordinates u, v, w in the 3-space are free up to any change of variable of the form

$$\left\{\begin{aligned} \bar{u} &= \bar{u}(u, v, w) \\ \bar{v} &= \bar{v}(u, v, w) \\ \bar{w} &= \bar{w}(u, v, w) \end{aligned}\right. \tag{56}$$

—three quantities per space point. Therefore the metric coefficients ${}^{(3)}g_{mn}$ carry only $6-3=3$ pieces of information per space point about the geometry. In other words, the $6+6=12$ numbers ${}^{(3)}P_{mn}$ and ${}^{(3)}g_{mn}$ together supply only $12-3=9$ significant numbers per point.

What is this geometrical information good for? A knowledge of the intrinsic and extrinsic geometry of the initial surface σ, together with Einstein's field equations, makes it possible to work ahead to the geometry in a near-lying 3-surface σ', and from there to the geometry in a further near-lying 3-surface σ'', and so on. Thus, step by step the previously unknown geometry of the 4-space can be discovered from the initial value data on σ plus the field equations. This procedure is the analogue in geometrodynamics of the procedure in electrodynamics by which one works out the whole history of the field from the values of $\boldsymbol{e}$ and $\boldsymbol{h}$ on σ. Here it is the whole geometry of 4-space wich is worked out.

Every set of initial value data leads to a unique 4-geometry; but a 4-geometry that satisfies Einstein's equations—the structure law of space-time—

does not uniquely determine a set of initial value data. The reason is simple. There is enormous freedom in choice of the 3-surface σ, which is in general curvilinear. Any given choice corresponds to an arbitrary way of slicing the 4-space apart with a curved and waving knife into a region before and a region after σ. On this surface the 9 pieces of geometrically significant information implied by ${}^{(3)}g_{mn}$ and ${}^{(3)}P_{mn}$ of course have well determined values. However, if the cut is made slightly differently, a varied 3-surface σ' will result, and the 9 pieces of data will have values that are a little changed.

The perpendicular distance from σ to σ' can be expressed as an interval of proper cotime that depends upon the three space co-ordinate within σ. In this sense it can be said that *one number is required per space point to specify the position of a 3-surface σ'*. There are many different ways to state this number. But however this number is *stated*, it is *derived* in the last analysis from the 9 pieces of geometrically significant information contained in ${}^{(3)}g_{mn}$ and ${}^{(3)}P_{mn}$ on σ'.

It is possible to be still more specific on how to derive the separation of σ and σ'. Given the data ${}^{(3)}g_{mn}$ and ${}^{(3)}P_{mn}$ on σ (plus $\boldsymbol{e}$ and $\boldsymbol{h}$), calculate from Einstein's field equations (plus Maxwell's equations in curved space-time) the whole geometrodynamical history (« 4-dimensional fender ») Given corresponding data on σ', repeat the calculation, and obtain a new geometrodynamical history, with all *its* history of geons, their collisions, electromagnetic and gravitational waves, and their scattering and interactions. Compare the two histories—the two 4-dimensional « fenders ». If they do not agree, the two alternate specifications of initial value data have to do with different physical problems and the discussion can stop. If they do agree, then the two 4-spaces can be identified with each other point by point. Moreover, in the absence of unusual symmetry this identification will be *unique*: the point in one 4-space where a particular curvature invariant has a maximum value can be identified with the point in the other space where the same curvature invariant has a maximum value, and so on. Thus the relative locations of σ and σ' in the 4-space are well defined, and so is the separation between them.

It follows that of the 9 pieces of geometrical information in ${}^{(3)}g_{mn}$ and ${}^{(3)}P_{mn}$, one merely tells *where* the surface is, and only eight serve to distinguish one physical situation from another. Moreover, the four initial value equations (53) and (54) impose 4 conditions per space point on this information. Therefore there are only $8-4=4$ disposable magnitudes per space point that are really free to describe gravitational degrees of freedom, just as there are four electromagnetic degrees of freedom per space point, as was to be shown (25).

---

(25) Appreciation is expressed here for discussions with C. MISNER and D. SHARP which were of great assistance in arriving at this way of speaking about the initial value problem.

6.3. *The number of distinct histories.* – If Maxwell's equations in a preexisting flat space-time may be said in a loose way of speaking to have N_{EM} solutions,

$$N_{EM} = \left[\begin{pmatrix}\text{Number of values}\\ \text{open to one infor-}\\ \text{mation at one point}\end{pmatrix}^{\begin{pmatrix}\text{number of infor-}\\ \text{mations per point}\end{pmatrix}}\right]^{\begin{pmatrix}\text{number}\\ \text{of points}\end{pmatrix}} = \infty^{4\infty^3}, \tag{57}$$

then the equations of geometrodynamics—the equations of combined gravitation physics and electromagnetism—can be said in the light of the foregoing discussion to have N_{GMD} solutions,

$$N_{GMD} = \infty^{8\infty^3}. \tag{58}$$

The initial value data on a 3-surface serve to pick out a unique history from amongst this collection of solutions, and ordinarily serve in addition to pick out a unique 3-surface within the thus selected 4-dimensional space-time continuum.

The formulation of the initial value problem discussed so far is closely related to that familiar in the dynamics of a particle with a single degree of freedom. At a given time t it is enough to give the co-ordinate x and the momentum p to predict the whole future and past of the particle. Despite the fact that 3 numbers come into discussion, it is customary to speak of the number of dynamical co-ordinates as only two. At a different time, t', a different position x' and momentum p' can be so specified that the resulting history is identical with the original history. In other words, there are ∞^2 possible histories, not ∞^3. The new feature in geometrodynamics is the difficulty of breaking down in any simple way the analogue of these 3 numbers into 2 that refer to dynamical variables and one that refers to time. No one has found a way to take the

$$N_{\text{Init}\ GMD} = \infty^{9\infty^3}, \tag{59}$$

different statements of an initial value problem—all consistent with the initial value equations of gravitation and electromagnetism (53), (54) and (52)—and dividing them into classes (Table V) such that all statements of the initial value problem that belong to one class belong to the *same one* of the

$$N_{GMD} = \infty^{8\infty^3},$$

possible histories. Take *one* history. In other words, take one great class of initial value problems. Two initial value problems in this class are distinguished

TABLE V. – *The « one-surface » formulation of the conditions required to fix a history compared and contrasted with the» two-surface » formulation.* Omitted from the Table is the case where both electromagnetic and gravitational degrees of freedom come into play.

	Mechanics of a single degree of freedom	Source-free electromagnetic field in a		Source-free gravitational field
		Lorentz space-time	Curved space-time	
Data adequate to fix history of system (« one-surface » formulation)	$x=x'$ and $p=p'$ at $t=t'$	$\boldsymbol{e}=\boldsymbol{e}'(x, y, z)$ $\boldsymbol{h}=\boldsymbol{h}'(x, y, z)$ at T'	$f_{\mu\nu}=f'_{\mu\nu}$ on space-like surface $x^{\alpha}=x^{\alpha}(u, v, w)$	$\left.\begin{matrix} {}^{(3)}g'_{mn}(u, v, w) \\ {}^{(3)}P'_{mn}(u, v, w) \end{matrix}\right\}$ (*)
Significant data per space point	3	6	7	$6+6-3$ (**) $=9$
Are these data freely disposable	Yes	$\text{div}\,\boldsymbol{e}=0$ $\text{div}\,\boldsymbol{h}=0$	$\text{div}\,\boldsymbol{e}=0$ $\text{div}\,\boldsymbol{h}=0$	No
Number of conditions per space point	0	2	2	4
Number of freely disposable and significant pieces of data per space point required to specify initial value problem	3	4	5	5
Equations of motion plus these data specify history	$x=x(t)$ $p=p(t)$	$\boldsymbol{e}=\boldsymbol{e}(T, x, y, z)$ $\boldsymbol{h}=\boldsymbol{h}(T, x, y, z)$	$f_{\mu\nu}(x^{\alpha})$	${}^{(4)}g_{\mu\nu}(x^{\alpha})$
The data specity more than the history; they single out a special slice of this history	$t=t'$	$T=T'$	$x^{\alpha}=x^{\alpha'}(u, v, w)$	$x^{\alpha}=x^{\alpha'}(u, v, w)$
A different slice out of the same history	x'' and p'' at t''	$\boldsymbol{e}''$ and $\boldsymbol{h}''$ at T''	$f''_{\mu\nu}(x''^{\alpha}(u, v, w))$	${}^{(3)}g''_{mn}$ and ${}^{(3)}P''_{mn}$

Number of distinct choices for initial value data	∞^3	$\infty^{1+4\infty^3}$	$\infty^{5\infty^3}$	$\infty^{5\infty^3}$
« Two-surface » formulation gives « coordinates », no « momenta »	$x=x'$ at t' $x=x''$ at t''	$\boldsymbol{h}'(x,y,z)$ at T' $\boldsymbol{h}''(x,y,z)$ at T''	$(f_{\mu\nu})'_{\text{surf}}$ on $x=x'(u,v,w)$ and $(f_{\mu\nu})''_{\text{surf}}$ on $x=x''(u,v,w)$	${}^{(3)}g'_{mn}(u,v,w)$ and ${}^{(3)}g''_{mn}(u,v,w)$
Number of physically significant pieces of data per space point	$(2\cdot1)+(2\cdot1)=4$	$2\cdot3=6$	$(2\cdot3)+(2\cdot1)=8$	$2\cdot(6-3)=6$
Are these data freely disposable?	Yes	div $\boldsymbol{h}=0$	div $\boldsymbol{h}=0$	Yes
Number of conditions per space point	0	$2\cdot1=2$	$2\cdot1=2$	0
Number of freely disposable pieces of data per space point	4	4	6	6
Number of distinct choices for initial value data	∞^4	$\infty^{2+4\infty^3}$	$\infty^{6\infty^3}$	$\infty^{6\infty^3}$
Number of distinct *pairs* of slices that can be made in one history	∞^2	∞^2	$\infty^{2\infty^3}$	$\infty^{2\infty^3}$
Number of distinct histories	∞^2	$\infty^{4\infty^3}$	$\infty^{4\infty^3}$	$\infty^{4\infty^3}$

(*) Metric and its extrinsic curvature on a 3-surface that is not itself *directly* specified.
(**) Arbitrary coordinates.

from each other in this, that they are two different ways of slicing a 3-surface through the *same* curved 4-dimensional manifold. Evidently the entire dynamics of the gravitational field and of the source-free electromagnetic field is summarized in the geometry of a single space-time continuum—a single history. This summary is also far more compact than the collection of all possible 3-dimensional slices—the collection of all possible initial value problems—consistent with that history. In this sense the history can be said to be more fundamental than either the initial value data or the dynamical equations. Nevertheless these data and these equations are more familar as the working material of dynamics than is the history itself.

6·4. *Initial value equations plus covariance gives field equations.* – Further insight into the relation between the initial value data and the history comes from looking at the requirements which must be satisfied by the data on the 3-surface σ. In the case of electromagnetism these requirements—the vanishing of div $\boldsymbol{h}$ and div $\boldsymbol{e}$—are most readily written in covariant form by use of the electromagnetic field tensor $f_{\mu\nu}$ and its dual $^*f_{\mu\nu}$, as follows:

(60*a*) $$\partial f_{23}/\partial x' + \partial f_{31}/\partial x^2 + \partial f_{12}/\partial x^3 = 0$$

and a similar equation (60*b*) for $^*f$. Now the left hand side of (60*a*) is—apart from a factor $(-g)^{-\frac{1}{2}}$—the time component V^0 of a 4-vector V^μ; that is, the component of the vector V^μ perpendicular to the 3-surface σ. Let it be agreed that the field $f_{\mu\nu}$ and the vector V^μ and the form of the initial value equations (60*a*) are to be subject to covariant transformation in the sense of tensor calculus. Then at any given point P in space-time the initial value equations (60*a*) are to hold not only on one 3-surface σ through that point, but on every 3-surface through that point. In other words, the time component of the vector V^μ is to vanish not only in one Lorentz frame of reference, but in every Lorentz frame. This condition cannot be satisfied unless *all* components of the vector V^μ vanish. In other words, the one condition (60*a*) on the initial value data at a typical point P, plus the principle of covariance, demand that at that point all *four* quantities of the type (60*a*) shall vanish:

$$\partial f_{23}/\partial x^1 + \partial f_{31}/\partial x^2 + \partial f_{12}/\partial x^3 = 0 \;\} \sim \text{« div } \boldsymbol{h} \text{ »} = 0\,,$$

$$\left.\begin{array}{l} \partial f_{03}/\partial x^2 + \partial f_{32}/\partial x^0 + \partial f_{20}/\partial x^3 = 0 \\ \cdots\cdots\cdots\cdots \\ \cdots\cdots\cdots\cdots \end{array}\right\} \sim \text{« curl } \boldsymbol{e} + \partial h/\partial T \text{ »} = 0,$$

or more briefly

(61*a*) $$[\alpha\beta\gamma\delta]\, \partial f_{\gamma\delta}/\partial x^\beta = 0$$

and similarly for the quantities of the type (60b)

$$[\alpha\beta\gamma\delta]\,\partial * f_{\gamma\delta}/\partial x^{\beta} = 0 \,. \tag{61b}$$

Thus out of the divergence relations, plus the principle of covariance, it is possible to derive *all* of Maxwell's equations for the electromagnetic field. The dynamic equations can be said to do no more nor less than to guarantee that the relations $\mathrm{div}\,\boldsymbol{e} = 0$, $\mathrm{div}\,\boldsymbol{h} = 0$ shall hold on *every* 3-surface drawn through every point P in space-time. In this sense *all of source-free electromagnetism is contained in the one statement « lines of force never end ».*

If the eight equations of Maxwell can be compressed in this way down to two elementary relations, the equations of general relativity, being tensorial, can be compressed even more, from 10 equations down to 1. It is enough that the (00) component of the tensor

$$R^{\nu}_{\mu} - \tfrac{1}{2}\,\delta^{\nu}_{\mu} R - (8\pi G/c^4) T_{\mu}^{\ \nu}, \tag{62}$$

shall vanish in every frame of reference in order to guarantee that every component of this tensor shall vanish in one—and all—frames of reference. This simple requirement, the analogue of the divergence relation in electrodynamics, has the form

$${}^{(3)}R - P_m^{\ k} P_k^{\ m} + (P_m^{\ m})^2 = 2*(\boldsymbol{e}*\boldsymbol{e} + \boldsymbol{h}*\boldsymbol{h})\,, \tag{63}$$

or in words,

$$\begin{pmatrix}\text{intrinsic curvature}\\ \text{invariant of any}\\ \text{3-surface through } P\end{pmatrix} - \begin{pmatrix}\text{extrinsic curvature}\\ \text{invariant of that}\\ \text{3-surface through } P\end{pmatrix} =$$

$$= 16\pi \begin{pmatrix}\text{energy density (cm}^{-2}\text{) of}\\ \text{electromagnetic field at } P\\ \text{referred to this 3-surface}\end{pmatrix}.$$

All the field equations of general relativity are derivable from the statement that intrinsic curvature minus extrinsic curvature equals energy density.

If 4-manifolds are compared to automobile fenders, then eq. (63) can be compared to a special curved ruler or template which is used to test whether the fender has been properly made. The test is complete only if the template has been applied to the fender everywhere and in all possible directions—North-South, East-West, and everything between. In a similar way simple condition (63)—plus the relations $\mathrm{div}\,\boldsymbol{e} = 0$ and $\mathrm{div}\,\boldsymbol{h} = 0$—is enough to test whether any arbitrarily specified electromagnetic field history, and metric history, together satisfy all the laws of electromagnetism and general relativity. In a word, *the initial value equations supply the equations of dynamics without the equations of dynamics.*

7. – Sandwich formulation of the initial data and its bearing on freedom of topology.

7·1. *Boundary conditions suited to a variational principle.* – Dynamical equations are derived more often from a variational principle than from initial value equations. With these two ways of deriving equations go two ways of characterizing solutions. The features of the variational analysis are recalled most readily from the example of a particle with one degree of freedom. The integral

$$\int_{x_1, t_1}^{x_2, t_2} L(x, \dot{x}, t)\, \mathrm{d}t\,, \tag{64}$$

is extremized subject to boundary conditions of the « sandwich » variety:

$$\begin{cases} x = x_1 & \text{at} \quad t = t_1\,, \\ x = x_2 & \text{at} \quad t = t_2\,. \end{cases} \tag{65}$$

These data alone characterize the resulting history. In contrast, in the « one time » formulation of the initial value data, one gives co-ordinate *and* momentum at the single time $t = t_1$. Correspondingly, in the one time formulation of electrodynamics the part of the co-ordinate is taken by the magnetic field $\boldsymbol{H}$ over the initial 3-dimensional space like hypersurface, and the part of the momentum is taken by the electric field $\boldsymbol{E}$. In applying a variational principle to electrodynamics, however, it is generally convenient to think of the magnetic field alone—or the vector potential alone—as specified over *two* space like hypersurfaces. The relation between the two forms of analysis is seen most readily by going to the limit where the two times or the two surfaces have a very small separation, Δt or $\Delta T = c\,\Delta t$. Giving x at both times is equivalent then to giving x and $\mathrm{d}x/\mathrm{d}t$ at one time; that is to say, to giving co-ordinate and momentum; similarly in the case of the magnetic field.

7·2. *Equivalence of sandwich and one-time formulations of initial value data of geometrodynamics.* – In the case of geometrodynamics the situation is analogous, as is most easily seen by considering the special case where no electromagnetic fields are present. The configuration co-ordinates are in this case the quantities which specify the 3-dimensional geometry $\mathcal{G}$ *intrinsic* to the initial

3-dimensional space-like hypersurface—all those quantities contained in the 3-dimensional metric ${}^{(3)}g_{mn}$ which are independent of choice of co-ordinate system. The momenta are the numbers needed to specify the *extrinsic* curvature of this 3-space in a co-ordinate-free way. In the sandwich formulation it is again reasonable to believe that one specifies co-ordinates alone—in other words, 3-geometries $\mathcal{G}_1$ and $\mathcal{G}_2$ alone—on two space-like 3-surfaces ([26]). As one check on this view, SHARP has considered the case where the two 3-surfaces are close together, and verified here in all detail as one does in electrodynamics that the sandwich formulation and the one time formulation are equivalent. Of course surprises could be in store in the case where the two surfaces are well separated. If not, then in setting a problem in geometrodynamics one can dispense with having to find on *one* surface a 3-geometry $\mathcal{G}$ *and* an extrinsic curvature P which shall be consistent with each other in the sense of the initia-value eq. (63). Instead, *it is enough to give with complete freedom any two 3-geol metries one pleases, $\mathcal{G}_1$ and $\mathcal{G}_2$; the equations of geometrodynamics then fill in around these two geometries a four dimensional geometry, determining in this process itself the spacing between the two 3-surfaces, and determining also their extrinsic curvature.* What an extraordinarily simple and beautiful situation!

7·3. *Subtle way time appears in sandwich data.* – In the sandwich formulation of the one particle problem there was a clear distinction between the time co-ordinates t_1, t_2 and the configuration co-ordinates x_1, x_2. Not so here! It is enough to specify the geometries $\mathcal{G}_1$ and $\mathcal{G}_2$—and nothing more—in order to tell not only the spatial geometry at these two times but also *where* these two 3-features are with respect to each other and with respect to all the other features of the space-time that they determine. The data in $\mathcal{G}_1$ and $\mathcal{G}_2$, though on the surface purely space-like, is nevertheless an indissoluble combination of information about both space *and* time. SHARP, for example, was able to limit attention to a pair of 3-surfaces close to each other by limiting himself to the case where the two 3-geometries were nearly the same. In this case he could *derive* an explicit expression for the time-like separation between the two 3-surfaces.

7·4. *Re-count of histories.* – It is easy to make one more check on the consistency of this analysis by counting up again the number of distinct histories—say still for simplicity for the special case where there are no electromagnetic fields. Per space point on one surface these are

$$6({}^3g_{mn}) - 3 \text{ (freedom of choice of 3 co-ordinates)} = 3 \tag{66}$$

([26]) Appreciation is expressed to D. SHARP for communication of unpublished results on this problem and to him and Professor C. MISNER for much valuable discussion of it.

data. Of these, two can be considered to give the amplitude of the gravitational waves of the two distinct states of polarization: and any change in the third datum produces a motion of this particular part of the hypersurface forward or backward in time. Though Fourier analysis is inappropriate in a curved space, it can be recalled for the sake of correspondence with familiar pictures that specification of the amplitude of a field oscillator on two parallel space-like surfaces is normally sufficient to give its amplitude and position at one time. An estimate along this or related lines evidently gives for the number of distinct histories

$$N_{\text{Grav}} = \infty^{(4\infty^3)} . \tag{67}$$

Thus the count checks out. Yet it is never possible to say *which* of the 3 data at a point of $\mathcal{G}_1$ describes *time*!

7·5. *Relation to quantum theory.* – The sandwich formulation of a dynamical problem is of great interest because the variables which are specified on the two surfaces are exactly the same variables which on one surface enter as independent variables into the wave function of quantum theory:

$$\begin{cases} \psi(x, t) & \text{for a harmonic oscillator;} \\ \psi(H(x), t) & \text{for the electromagnetic field (eq. (12));} \\ \psi(\mathcal{G}) & \text{for pure gravitational disturbances (}^{27}\text{)} . \end{cases} \tag{68}$$

7·6. *How much freedom of topology?* – The close relation of the 2-surface formulation to quantum theory raises the question, how *general* can the geometry $\mathcal{G}$ be? How wide a variety of topologies must be considered? It may be permissible to seek a little insight into this issue by returning to the classical variational problem: How much freedom of choice is there for the topologies at the two faces, $\mathcal{G}_1$ and $\mathcal{G}_2$, of the sandwich? I am informed by Professor CHARLES MISNER that Professor RENÉ THOM, as part of his theory of cobordism, has proven a theorem which, loosely stated, is as follows: Given any two non-singular topological (not necessarily metric) 3-spaces, one can fill in between them with a non-singular topological 4-space. It is not at all necessary that the topologies of the two 3-spaces should be the same. This circumstance suggests that *on both surfaces in classical geometrodynamics one is completely free to pick any topology he pleases.* It also suggests that the wave functional $\psi(\mathcal{G})$ *has to be considered to be defined over all topologies.*

---

(27) Appreciation is expressed to Professor B. DEWITT, Professor C. MISNER and D. SHARP for illuminating discussions of this third case. See especially C. W. MISNER: *Rev. Mod. Phys.*, **29**, 497 (1957).

8. – A new topology revealed in an old solution: the Schwarzschild metric.

8·1. *The exterior solution; its application and its maximal extension.* – Best known of all deductions from Einstein's field equations is the Schwarzschild line element—the solution for the special case of spherical symmetry and

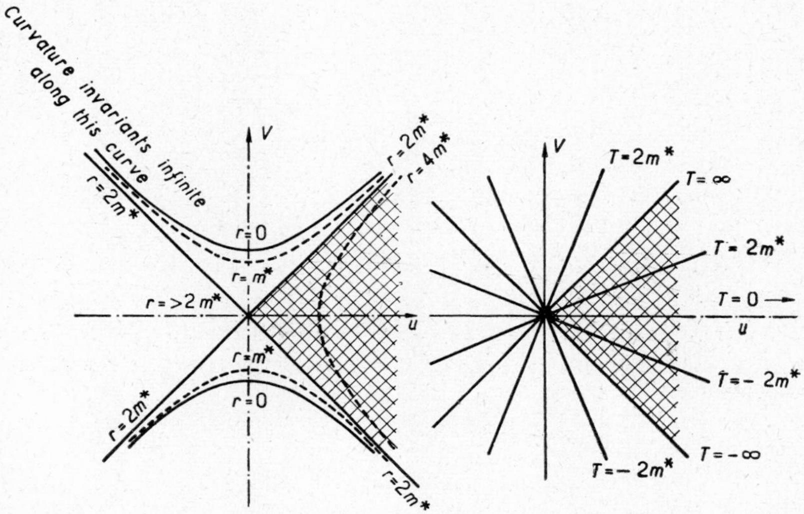

Fig. 10. – Kruskal's remapping of the Schwarzschild metric in coordinates u (space-like) and v (time-like) better adapted than the usual coordinates to bringing out the lack of any intrinsic geometrical singularity at $r=2m^*$, and emphasizing the intrinsic singularity at $r=0$. The metric is rewritten in the form

$$\mathrm{d}s^2 = f^2(-\,\mathrm{d}v^2 + \mathrm{d}u^2) + r^2(\mathrm{d}\theta^2 + \sin^2\theta\,\mathrm{d}\varphi^2)\,,$$

with

$$[(r/2m^*) - 1]\exp[r/2m^*] = u^2 - v^2\,,$$

and

$$(T/2m^*) = \operatorname{arctgh} 2uv/(u^2+v^2)\,,$$

and

$$f^2 = (32m^{*3}/r)\exp[-\,r/2m^*] = (\text{a transcendental function of } u^2 - v^2)\,.$$

Null geodesics are inclined at $\pm 45°$. For a finite range — but only for a finite range — of the time-coordinate v the metric is free of all singularities. The geometry of space inescapably associated with Schwarzschild's solution is most readily seen by considering the time $v=0$. The space part of the metric describes *two* Euclidean spaces smoothly joined together by a throat (Fig. 11). To restrict attention to the region $r \geqslant 2m^*$ in the conventional representation of the Schwarzschild metric (cross hatched region of diagram) is to cut away a large and perfectly regular part of the space-time manifold, a part which moreover is indispensible for tracing out the history of all possible geodesics.

TABLE VI. – *Status of some predictions of general relativity.*

Effect	Prediction	Observation
Deflection of light which grazes sun	1.751″ of arc for light which just grazes sun	Many observations ([a]) of which two typical recent ones ([b]) are: 2.01″ ± 0.27 1947 1.70″ ± 0.10 1952
Gravitational red shift translated into equivalent Doppler effect	Sun ($M_\odot$, $R_\odot$) 0.6 km/s	Too small to detect reliably because of velocity of gas currents ([c]).
	40 Eri B($0.43 M_\odot$, $0.016 R_\odot$) (17 ± 3) km/s	(21 ± 4) km/s ([d]).
	Sirius B ($1.0 M_\odot$, $0.008 R_\odot$) 79 km/s	Unsuited to reliable measurement ([d]).
	Two elevations on earth separated by 22.5 m: $\Delta\nu/\nu = 4.92 \cdot 10^{-15}$	Measured via Mössbauer effect ([e]): $\Delta\nu/\nu = (5.13 \pm 0.51) \cdot 10^{-15}$
Precession of the perihelion in seconds of arc per century	Mercury 43.03 Venus 8.63 Earth 3.84 Mars 1.35	42.56 ± 0.94 ([f]) 4.6 ± 2.7 ([f])
Dynamic universe	Universe of uniform curvature will expand and recontract. Extrapolated time back to start of expansion will exceed actual time by a factor of at least 1.5. Both numbers together allow lower and upper bounds to be predicted for density of mass energy.	Expansion observed. Values for the two relevant times are uncertain by factors of at least two. No decisive test is yet possible as to whether their ratio is consistent with prediction. The density of mass-energy is also too uncertain to test the theory decisively ([g]).

([a]) An excellent summary of the observations at times of eclipses and of results of alternative reductions of the same data appears in G. C. MC VITTIE: *General Relativity and Cosmology* (London, 1956), Chap. V, adapted from M. W. OVEDEN.

([b]) G. VAN BIESBROEK: *Astron. Journ.*, **55**, 49 (1950); **58**, 87 (1953).

([c]) Miss ADAMS: *Month. Not. Roy. Astron. Soc.*, **118**, 106 (1958). See however C. E. ST. JOHN, *Astrophys. J.* **67**, 195 (1928).

([d]) Observations on 40 Eri by D. M. POPPER: *Astrophys. Journ.*, **120**, 316 (1954); on Sirius B by J. H. MOORE, *Proc. Ast. Soc. Pac.* **40**, 229 (1928). Radiation scattered in the earth's atmosphere, due originally to Sirius A mixes with direct radiation from Sirius B to give radiation with altered red shift which requires correction, according to G. KUIPER as quoted by MC VITTIE in reference (*a*). For white dwarfs and further discussion see W. J. LUYTEN: *White Dwarfs and Degenerate Stars* in *Vistas in Astronomy* (London, 1957). Appreciation is expressed to Prof. W. C. BIDELMAN and Prof. M. SCHWARZSCHILD for discussion of the astrophysical evidence.

([e]) R. V. POUND and G. A. REBKA jr.: *Phys. Rev. Lett.*, **4**, 337 (1960).

([f]) G. M. CLEMENCE: *Rev. Mod. Phys.*, **19**, 361 (1947); *Proc. Am. Phil. Soc.*, **93**, 532 (1949).

([g]) Further discussion later in present article (Sect. **5**).

vanishing electromagnetic field:

$$\mathrm{d}s^2 = -(1 - 2m^*/r)\,\mathrm{d}T^2 + \frac{\mathrm{d}r^2}{(1 - 2m^*/r)} + r^2(\mathrm{d}\theta^2 + \sin^2\theta\,\mathrm{d}\varphi^2)\,. \tag{69}$$

From this solution in the region exterior to a mass follow the three most familiar predictions of general relativity—the gravitational red shift, the bending of light by the sun, and the precession of the perihelion of an orbit (Table VI).

The solution (65) is sometimes called the « exterior solution » to distinguish it from another solution—to which it is joined—valid in a region endowed with a non-zero density of « real » mass. It is appropriate to consider such an « interior » solution if applications are at stake. But of more interest here is a question of principle: What are the consequences of assuming an *everywhere empty* curved space?

In the absence of « real » masses the demand of spherical symmetry inescapably leads to a metric which—with allowance for the possibility of co-ordinate transformations—is equivalent to (65), as shown long ago by BIRKHOFF. This metric has a troublesome feature: g_{rr} becomes infinite, and g_{TT} goes to zero, at $r = 2m^*$. However, several authors have pointed out that the singularity at $r = 2m^*$ is apparent only. It arises from the co-ordinate system employed, not from anything singular about the intrinsic geometry itself at $r = 2m^*$. At that place *all the quantities which describe the curvature of the manifold in an invariant way are finite.* KRUSKAL ([28]) has shown that a co-ordinate system exists in which the metric is regular at an initial instant as judged by curvature invariants, and remains regular for a finite proper time in the past and future (Fig. 10). This metric represents the *maximal extension of the Schwarzschild metric*: only by taking a space so extensive can every geodesic in the original region be continued until it either runs off to infinity or runs into a region (upper and lower hyperbolas in Fig. 10 marked $r = 0$) where the intrinsic curvature is infinite.

8·2. *A new topology, endowed with a wormhole.* – The geometry to which one is inescapably led by this reasoning does not have a Euclidean topology. Instead, it is to be pictured as illustrated in Fig. 11. One sees not one Euclidean space, but two Euclidean spaces, joined together by a « bridge », to use, the terminology of EINSTEIN and ROSEN ([29]). Alternatively, one can think of the two sheets as being in actuality two different portions of the same

([28]) M. KRUSKAL (reported by J. A. WHEELER): *Int. Conf. on Relativistic Theories of Gravitation* (Royaument, July 1959); M. KRUSKAL: *Phys. Rev.*, **119**, 1743 (1960); the work of Kruskal has been anticipated in some respects by C. FRONSDAL: *Phys. Rev.*, **116**, 778 (1959).

([29]) A. EINSTEIN and N. ROSEN: *Phys. Rev.*, **48**, 73 (1935).

Euclidean space, so far removed from one another that no mutual influence of one on the other via the « upper space » ever comes into evidence. In this case the connection may be called a « wormhole » for the sake of vividness of expression, or a « handle », to use a familiar topological term. If the space were static, a bird could fly in one mouth of the wormhole and out the other.

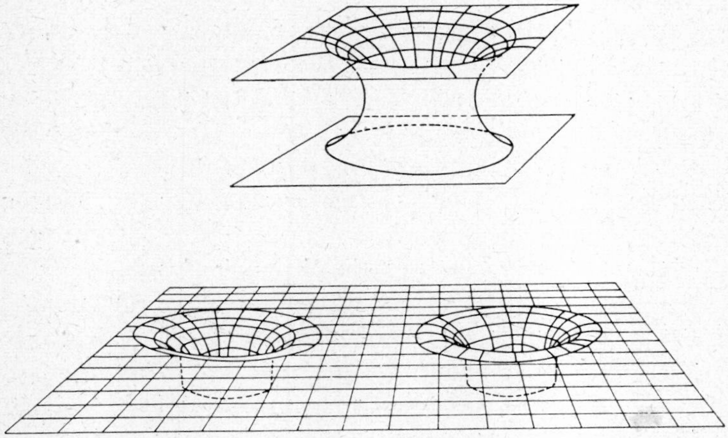

Fig. 11. – Two interpretations of the 3-dimensional « maximally extended Schwarzschild metric » of Kruskal at the cotime $T = ct = 0$. Above: a connection in the sense of Einstein and Rosen between *two* otherwise Euclidean spaces. Below: a wormhole (J. A. Wheeler: *Phys. Rev.*, **97**, 511 (1955)) connecting two regions in *one* Euclidean space, in the limiting case where these regions are extremely far apart compared to the dimensions of the throat of the wormhole.

The distance along the throat of the wormhole from one mouth to the other need have no correspondence whatever with the distance in the open space between the same two mouths. To have an elementary illustration of this point, it is enough to take a sheet of paper, punch a small hole somewhere in the upper half of the sheet (later to be one mouth), a second hole of the same size in the lower half of the sheet, and then smoothly bend the sheet so that the two mouths come back to back. In this case the length of the throat is zero. Yet the geometry intrinsic to the sheet of paper has remained Euclidean. In the analogous 3-dimensional situation the bird would be transported almost instantaneously from one place to another miles away according to the measurement of distance in the upper space. However, the Schwarzschild metric, static though it seems in the co-ordinates of eq. (69), is seen to be far from static in the co-ordinates of Kruskal. Using his co-ordinates, one can prove that there is never time enough for a particle to travel from a far away point in the upper space to a far away point in the lower space. In this sense there is no possibility of contradicting elementary notions of causality.

8·3. *The wormhole allows a purely geometrical description of a two body problem.* – The two far away mouths of a wormhole manifest mass, in the sense that the metric around each is Schwarzschildean in character, as it is around any « real » mass, Therefore they must experience a Newtonian attraction. A wormhole thus provides a singularity-free and purely geometrical version of the Newtonian problem of two equal masses. One is assured by the Einstein-Infeld-Hoffman type of analysis that these two « objects » will be drawn towards each other in the expected way purely as a consequence of the field equations themselves. In other words, curvatures will increase at the near sides of the throats, and decrease at the far sides so that the two regions of curvature will come together.

The two body situation just described is an example of a typical problem of pure geometrodynamics. Once the appropriate geometrical data have been prescribed on an initial space-like surface, then the whole past and future is determinate. The initial data however are not determinate! They can be specified with far wider arbitrariness than might be expected from the Newtonian variables: 6 initial co-ordinates, and 6 initial momenta. The reason is not far to seek. The masses will send out gravitational waves as they accelerate towards each other. But gravitational radiation can, and in the general case will, already be on hand, circulating through space, as the masses start to approach. There is therefore a multiple infinitude of conceivable two body problems to analyse. Among them MISNER (30) has found it possible to pick out some which are particularly simple and to formulate for them precise self consistent initial value data. To go further with one of these cases and follow out the ultimate fate of the wormhole is a demanding problem, subject to possible analysis by an electronic computer.

9. – Charge without charge.

9·1. *Conservation of the flux through a wormhole.* – If the best known of all of the solutions of Einstein's field equations compels one to consider the concept of a multiply connected space, what is the consequence of multiple connectivity when an electromagnetic field is present? This question leads straight on to a classical picture of electric charge (31).

Fig. 12 illustrates a situation where lines of electric force thread through a wormhole. They satisfy everywhere Maxwell's equations. As a consequence, the integrated electric flux out of a mouth cannot change with time, no matter how irregular the electromagnetic field, no matter how violently curved the space, no matter how much the separation or size of the wormhole mouths

(30) C. W. MISNER: *Phys. Rev.* **118**, 1110 (1960).
(31) J. A. WHEELER: *Phys. Rev.*, **97**, 511 (1955).

change with time, so long as the topology itself does not alter [32]. *This flux* therefore satisfies the law of conservation of electric charge and *can be identified with electric charge.* Yet nowhere is there any « real » charge in this situation. One therefore has a purely geometrical description of electric charge in terms of the metric and topology of curved empty space; or in brief, *charge without charge.*

The charge pictured in Fig. 12 is a purely classical type of charge. It has nothing whatsoever directly to do with the quantized charges of elementary particle physics, for which a completely different picture is suggested.

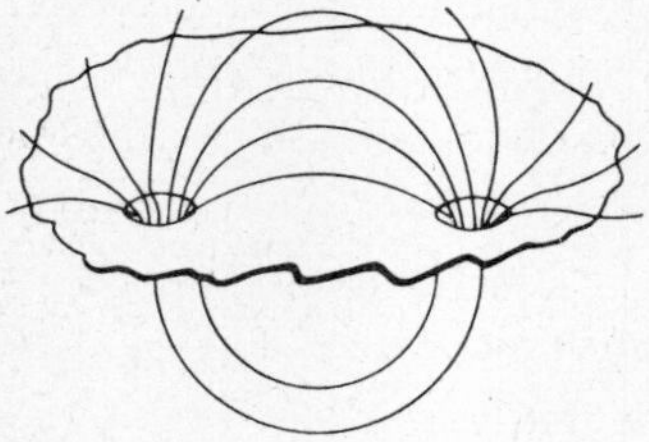

Fig. 12. – Symbolic representation of *classical* electric charge: a wormhole through which there is an electric flux. The two mouths appear to an observer with poor resolving power to be two equal and opposite electric charges. Out of one region of three-space he finds lines of force emerging over the whole 4π solid angle. To quite another region he discovers lines of force converging, also over the full 4π. He may construct a boundary around the right hand charge, determine the flux through this boundary, incorrectly apply the theorem of Gauss, and « prove » that there is a charge inside the « boundary ». It isn't a boundary. Someone caught within it — to speak figuratively — can go into one mouth of the wormhole, through the throat, out the other mouth and return by way of the surrounding nearly Euclidean space to look at his « prison » from the outside. Lines of force nowhere end. Maxwell's equations nowhere fail. Nowhere can one place his finger and say, « Here there is some charge ». This classical type of electric charge has no direct relation whatsoever to quantized electric charge. There is a freedom of choice about the flux through the wormhole, and a specificity about the connection between one charge and another, which is quite foreign to the charges of elementary particle physics (for a conceivable model of which see Fig. 17). For ease of visualization the number of space dimensions in the above diagram has been reduced from three to two. The third dimension, measured off the surface, has no physical meaning — it only provides an extra dimension in which to imbed the surface for more convenient diagrammatic representation.

9·2. *The geometrodynamical zoo.* – A small beginning has now been made in populating the zoological garden of geometrodynamics. It contains 1) electromagnetic waves, 2) electromagnetic geons, 3) gravitational waves, 4) gravitational geons, 5) uncharged wormhole mouths that move like neutral objects (but have an electric polarizability), 6) mouths or wormholes that carry flux, that describe charge, and that move like charged objects and 7) objects which are composites of 1)–6). But none of these entities has the least direct relation to the elementary particles of observational science.

---

[32] This theorem is due to MISNER; see C. W. MISNER and J. A. WHEELER: *Ann. Phys.*, **2**, 525 (1957).

10. – Equations without reasonable solutions?

10·1. *Any algorithm to construct all solutions?* – It is not at all out of the question that a way can some day be worked out to classify and construct all histories which solve Einstein's field equations for 1) the case of pure gravitation and conceivably even for 2) the case of geometrodynamics: gravitation plus source-free electromagnetism. *But are there any non-trivial solutions which are free of singularity?*

It is sometimes said that the equations are extremely complicated, even for the case of pure gravitation. This statement appears justified when the equations are expressed in all detail in terms of derivatives of the $g_{\mu\nu}$ of the first and second order and the matrix reciprocal to $g_{\mu\nu}$. In this form equations are quite non-linear. However, in another sense the equations are extremely simple; they say only that the 4-manifold must be such that at every point P, and on every 3-surface drawn through P, this condition is fulfilled:

$$\begin{pmatrix}\text{intrinsic}\\ \text{curvature}\\ \text{invariant}\end{pmatrix} = \begin{pmatrix}\text{extrinsic}\\ \text{curvature}\\ \text{invariant}\end{pmatrix}. \tag{70}$$

It is difficult to think of any kind of relation more beautifully geometric in character than (70).

One is the more tempted to hope some day for a simple algorithm to solve (70) because there is another famous and slightly analogous problem—also very non linear in character—where such an algorithm has been discovered. Bend a closed loop of wire into some arbitrary shape, dip it into a soap solution, and remove it, along with the soap film that now spans it. The energy of the soap film being equal to the product of the surface tension and the surface, and the energy being a minimum, it follows that the film is a *minimal surface*. The equation of such a surface has the well known and very non-linear form

$$(1+z_x^2)z_{yy}+(1+z_y^2)z_{xx}-2z_xz_yz_{xy}=0 \tag{71}$$

in terms of the elevation z above the xy plane and the partial derivatives of this elevation, $z_x=\partial z/\partial x$, $z_{xx}=\partial^2 z/\partial x^2$, etc. This equation, like the equations of general relativity, reduces to a standard type of linear equation ($z_{xx}+z_{yy}=0$) in the limit of a nearly level surface. Nevertheless, the procedure for solving this equation ([33]) makes no direct use of this circumstance nor of any other approximation. Instead, take « any real plane algebraic curve C in the s, t plane » $s = s(\lambda)$ and $t = t(\lambda)$ (the analog of a potential) and construct the Abelian integrals

$$(72)\qquad \begin{cases} x = \operatorname{Re}\displaystyle\int \frac{2s}{1+s^2}\, it\, \mathrm{d}s\,, \\[2ex] y = \operatorname{Re}\displaystyle\int \frac{1-s^2}{1+s^2}\, it\, \mathrm{d}s\,, \\[2ex] z = \operatorname{Re}\displaystyle\int t\, \mathrm{d}s\,. \end{cases}$$

Consider what was in the beginning the real number s to be a complex number, $s = \alpha + i\beta$. Then the three integrals (72) provide three functions of the two parameters α and β. These functions provide a parametric representation of a surface which automatically satisfies the non-linear eq. (71), provided that the following conditions are satisfied (Lipman Bers):

1) For every point (s, t) on C the reality of s implies that of t.
2) The functions $x(\alpha, \beta)$ and $y(\alpha, \beta)$ are single valued on the part of the Riemannian surface F of C where $\beta \geqslant 0$.

This result out of the theory of minimal surfaces provides a model for the kind of very general solution that one would like to see for Einstein's field equations. One starts with an arbitrary function—in the present case the function $t = t(s)$—and from it generates a solution. From the properties of the generating formalism one can deduce the singularities and other major properties of the solution.

The only everywhere regular solutions of the equation for minimal surfaces which are defined and regular for all values of x and y are trivial; they are flat; $z = c_1 x + c_2 y$. This beautiful theorem of S. BERNSTEIN ([33]) is the analogue of the well known theorem about Laplace's equation: There is no solution of

$$(73)\qquad \nabla^2 \psi = 0$$

which is regular and finite for all values of x, y, and z except the trivial solution $\psi = \text{constant}$. The existence of these theorems raises a deep and impor-

([33]) L. F. LIPMAN BERS: *Proc. Int. Congr. of Math.*, vol. **2** (Cambridge, 1952), p. 157. See R. COURANT: *Ann. Math.*, **38**, 679 (1937) for an earlier account of the problem of the soap film — the famous problem of Plateau. Eq. (71) is one of several ways of writing the equation for the vanishing of the *sum* of the principal curvatures at a point, $\varkappa = (1/R_1) + (1/R_2) = 0$; that is, for the vanishing of the total extrinsic curvature. Here R_1 and R_2 stand for the principal radii of curvature at the given point on the surface. In contrast, general relativity deals with the intrinsic curvatures of 4-space, built up out of *products* of the type $(1/R_m R_n)$, where R_m and R_n are principal radii of curvature. See also G. DARBOUX, *Leçons sur la théorie générale des surfaces*, Part I (Paris, 1941).

tant question. *Do Einstein's field equations possess any everywhere regular solutions apart from the trivial solution that describes flat space-time?* Some evidence can be cited which bears upon this question, even though no final answer is available today.

10'2. *The regular Kruskal-Schwarzschild metric eventually becomes singular.* – The most familiar solution of the geometrodynamical equations for the special case where all electromagnetic fields vanish is described by Schwarzschild's line element, (69). In Kruskal's co-ordinates, at $v=0$, the geometry of 3-spaces is everywhere regular. Moreover, it remains regular for a finite proper time in the past and future. However, after the lapse of a finite proper time the curvature invariants—quantities independent of the co-ordinate system in use—become infinite, corresponding to the point $r=0$ in (68). Moreover, this description of the Schwarzschild solution is *inescapable*, in the sense that it is based upon an account of what happens to the tracks of light rays and material particles. Any non-singular co-ordinate system must describe the same phenomenon. In other words, a solution previously regarded as regular in time and singular in space has been interpreted more properly as initially regular in space, but *intrinsically* singular after a finite proper time. This example is consistent with the conjecture that all but trivial solutions eventually manifest singularity.

10'3. *Singularity in geodesic co-ordinates does not mean singularity in geometry.* – RAYCHAUDHURI and KOMAR deal with a more general situation [34]. They consider any initial 3 surface σ in a 4-manifold that satisfies the equations of general relativity. They consider any co-ordinate system, u, v, w in this 3-space. At the intersections of the co-ordinate surfaces they station infinitesimal test particles. They follow the tracks of these particles as time proceeds. Along each track they measure off the elapsed proper time and use this quantity as time co-ordinate. In geometrical terms, they analyze the 4-space in terms of a family of geodesically parallel space-like hypersurfaces. They show from Einstein's field equations that the surfaces will become singular after the lapse of a finite time, either into the future or into the past (but not necessarily in both), unless the original space is flat and free of concentrations of mass energy. This result could be thought to show that there exist no regular solutions of the field equations except the trivial solution for flat space-time, just as there are no non-singular solutions of the equation for minimal surfaces except those that describe flat surfaces. However, KOMAR stresses that what is known to go singular is not necessarily the intrinsic geometry, but only the representation of this geometry in terms of a family of geodesically parallel space-like hypersurfaces.

([34]) A. RAYCHAUDHURI: *Phys. Rev.*, **98**, 1123 (1955) and **106**, 172 (1957); A. KOMAR: *Phys. Rev.*, **104**, 544 (1956).

10·4. *Time-symmetric gravitational waves, regular everywhere and presumably at all time, as an example.* – It appears reasonable to believe that there actually exist solutions of the equations of geometrodynamics which are asymptotically flat at infinity, and which remain regular for all time, and which have energy content. Despite the regularity of such a solution for all time, the solution will possess only singular representations in terms of a family of geodesically parallel space-like hypersurfaces. Consider by way of simple example a gravitational wave which implodes from a great distance in otherwise flat space, reaches a state of maximum concentration, and re-explodes outward with the speed of light. Let it possess a moment of time symmetry ([35]) in this sense, that there exists a co-ordinate system such that in this co-ordinate system the metric has the property

$$(74)\qquad \begin{cases} g_{00}(T, x, y, z) = g_{00}(-T, x, y, z)\,, \\ g_{m0} = g_{0m}(T, x, y, z) = -\,g_{0m}(-T, x, y, z)\,, \\ g_{mn}(T, x, y, z) = g_{mn}(-T, x, y, z)\,. \end{cases}$$

Then the whole past and future of the metric, all the intrinsic geometry of the 4-manifold, is determined by one piece of information and no more: the intrinsic *three*-dimensional geometry of the 3-space of time symmetry, $T=0$. Thus, for this particular hypersurface the *extrinsic* curvature—governed by the manner of imbedding in the surrounding 4-space—is obviously zero:

$$(75)\qquad {}^{(3)}P_{mn}(\sim \text{«}\, \partial g_{mn}/\partial T\, \text{»}) = 0\,.$$

This value for the extrinsic curvature automatically fulfills three of the four conditions ((53) and (54)) that have to be specified by the initial value data. The fourth condition demands only that the *intrinsic* curvature of the 3-dimensional surface of time symmetry shall be zero:

$$(76)\qquad {}^{(3)}R = 0\,.$$

The counting of degrees of freedom is simple. There are 6 disposable metric components per space point in the hypersurface $T=0$. However, the three co-ordinates are freely disposable. Therefore there are only $6-3=3$ intrinsically geometrical data per space point. They moreover must satisfy the one condition (76) per space point. Therefore there are only two disposable numbers per space point.

A time-symmetric gravitational wave is quite analogous to an electromagnetic field with a moment of time symmetry:

$$(77)\qquad \begin{cases} \boldsymbol{e}(T, x, y, z) = -\,\boldsymbol{e}(-T, x, y, z)\,, \\ \boldsymbol{h}(T, x, y, z) = \,\boldsymbol{h}(T, x, y, z)\,. \end{cases}$$

([35]) J. Weber and J. A. Wheeler: *Rev. Mod. Phys.*, **29**, 509 (1957).

At the moment of time-symmetry the electric field vanishes identically. The magnetic field, subject to the condition $\operatorname{div} \boldsymbol{h} = 0$, provides only two disposable numbers per space point. In the language of Fourier analysis, 1) there are two states of polarization per point in wave number space, 2) there is one oscillator for each state of polarization, and 3) there is one co-ordinate and one momentum for each oscillator, but 4) all the momenta vanish at the instant of time symmetry in the special case of a field that *possesses* a moment of time symmetry. In this case the usual four disposable quantities per point reduce in number to two.

10·5. *The effective energy distribution for a gravitational wave.* – BRILL has shown how to construct everywhere regular 3-dimensional metrics which satisfy the condition (76) and which can therefore serve as initial value data for a time-symmetric gravitational wave [36]. He restricts attention to the case where the 3-space has an axis of symmetry. He writes the metric in the form suggested by BONDI,

$$\mathrm{d}s^2 = \psi^4(\varrho, z)\left[\exp\left[2\lambda q_1(\varrho, z)\right](\mathrm{d}\varrho^2 + \mathrm{d}z^2) + \varrho^2\,\mathrm{d}\varphi^2\right]. \tag{78}$$

Here the factor $q_1(\varrho, z)$ may be considered qualitatively to describe the distribution of the effective energy of the gravitational field at the moment of time symmetry. Only those distributions q_1 are considered which vanish outside of a certain finite radius:

$$(\varrho^2 + z^2)^{\frac{1}{2}} = r \leqslant a\,. \tag{79}$$

The quantity λ determines the strength of the gravitational wave. The function $\lambda q_1(\varrho, z)$ summarizes the one disposable quantity that remains per space point (*i.e.*, per point in the (ϱ, z) or meridian plane) in the case of axial symmetry. The factor ψ is not freely disposable. It is fixed by the initial value equation of vanishing intrinsic curvature, ${}^{(3)}R = 0$, which takes the form

$$(1/r)(\partial/\partial r)r(\partial\psi/\partial r) + (\partial^2\psi/\partial z^2) + [(\lambda/4)(\partial^2 q_1/\partial r^2 + \partial^2 q_1/\partial z^2)]\psi = 0$$

or more briefly,

$$ {}^{(3)}\nabla^2\psi + (\lambda/4)({}^{(2)}\nabla^2 q_1)\psi = 0\,. \tag{80}$$

The factor ψ may be considered qualitatively to describe the gravitational field produced by a distribution of effective mass-energy in the gravitational wave, this distribution itself being governed by the function $\lambda q_1(\varrho, z)$.

([36]) D. BRILL: *Ann. Phys.*, **7**, 466 (1959); see also H. ARAKI: *Ann. Phys.*, **7**, 456 (1959).

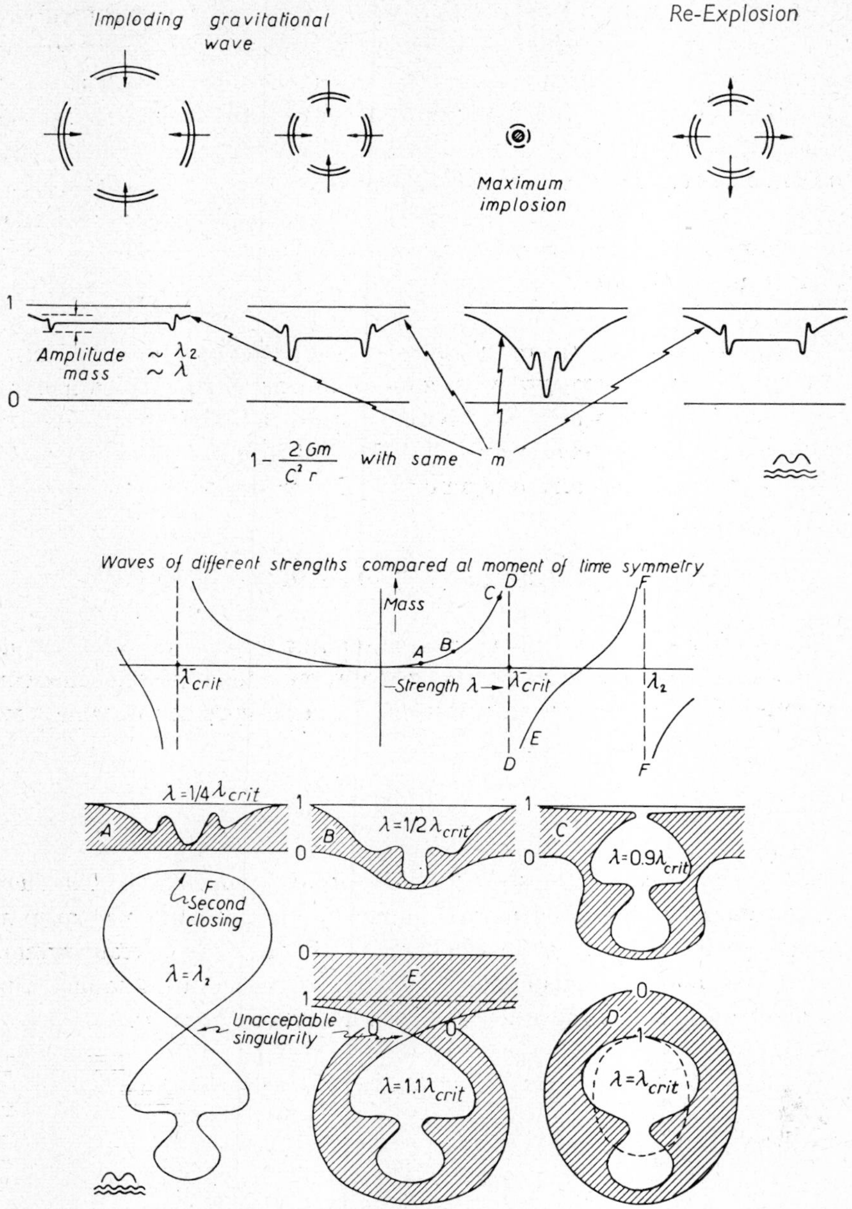

Fig. 13. – Above: qualitative diagram of a gravitational wave which comes in from great distances, reaches a stage of maximum contraction at a moment of time symmetry, and re-expands outwards. Middle: qualitative diagram of how metric varies with time in the course of this implosion and explosion, showing Schwarzschild type of asymptotic approach to flatness at great distances. The mass associated with this $1/r$ approach to flatness remains unchanged throughout the entire evolution of the gravitational wave. Below: more detail about such a wave at the moment of time sym-

Eq. (80) might be thought to allow an infinite number of solutions for the field factor ψ. However, solutions which are bounded at finite distance typically have nodes at finite distances, or become infinite at great distances. In either case they describe 3-geometries that are intrinsically singular. The 3-geometry is only then free of singularity, and describes a localized concentration of energy in an asymptotically flat space, when 1) the factor ψ at large distances has the asymptotic form

$$\psi(\varrho, z) \sim A(\lambda) + \frac{1}{r} B(\lambda) = A(\lambda)\left[1 + \frac{m^*(\lambda)}{2r}\right], \tag{81}$$

and 2) when the strength λ of the distribution factor $q(\varrho, z) = \lambda q$, does not exceed a certain critical limit $\lambda = \lambda_1$. For every positive value of λ less than this critical limit, there exists one and only one regular solution $\psi(\varrho, z)$ that satisfies requirement (81), according to BRILL. This solution describes a localized gravitational wave whose mass-energy is m^* (cm) or $(c^2/G)m^* = m$(g).

10·6. *Type of imploding and re-exploding gravitational wave which is regular for all time.* – This kind of gravitational wave stands in close analogy with a time-symmetric electromagnetic wave which implodes—as towards the focus of a lens of aperture in excess of 2π—reaches a configuration of extremal concentration, and then spreads out and returns to great distances. No imploding electromagnetic wave can be uniform in intensity over the whole 4π of solid angle; no field of polarization vectors of uniform magnitude can be laid down on the surface of the unit sphere in a singularity-free way. Similarly, there is no such thing as an exactly spherically symmetric gravitational wave. Nevertheless, there exist solutions of the initial value problem, for gravitation as for electromagnetism, which have nearly spherical symmetry. Starting with one or other arbitrary choice for the moment of time symmetry, one has some reason to believe that the wave spreads out and becomes weaker and weaker as time advances (Fig. 13) much as does an electromagnetic wave. In other words, it is natural to *presume that there exist singularity free but non trivial*

---

metry. A slice through 4-space at this moment has a characteristic 3-dimensional geometry of its own. A typical component of the metric associated with this 3-geometry departs from unity the more, the greater is the strength of the gravitational wave at this moment (different problems, not the same problem at different moments). For a certain critical value of the strength of the gravitational wave the space is curved up into a closed universe. For any greater value of the strength the metric is singular and inadmissible. For the critical value of the strength, the 3-geometry is everywhere perfectly regular, and it remains so for a finite proper time. However, it is conjectured here that as this *closed-space* metric evolves with time, however it is originally chosen, it will always develop a singularity in its intrinsic geometry.

space-time manifolds which satisfy Einstein's field equations for source-free gravitational waves in situations where the space is asymptotically flat.

A time-symmetric gravitational wave of finite energy content, whose mathematical existence BRILL has proven, and whose regularity for all past and future times one has reason to presume, will not by reason of that regularity violate the theorem of Raychaudhuri and Komar. To examine this question consider a spherical array of test particles centered on the point of implosion and at rest long before the arrival of the wave. Examine these particles after the wave has imploded and re-exploded and gone for away and left the space in the neighborhood of these particles once more flat. The particles will have acquired velocities which, though small and constant in time are finite and non-uniform in direction and magnitude ([37]). As a consequence the sphere will slowly change shape and become singular. Or in geometrical terms, the geodesics normal to a 3-sphere far in the distant past – and the family of subsequent geodesically parallel surfaces perpendicular to these geodesics—eventually evolve into a singular pattern. Evidently this singularity in no way implies any intrinsic singularity in the geometry of space-time.

We judge that there are non-singular solutions of the geometrodynamical equations for gravitational waves which are non-trivial, whereas every non-singular and boundary-free solution of the equations for a soap film is trivially flat. The parallelism between the two problems therefore at first sight appears to become fainter. However, the parallelism seems again stronger when among solutions of the equations of geometrodynamics attention is limited to those that describe *manifolds closed in space.* In this case some circumstantial evidence can be cited to suggest that *the intrinsic geometry always becomes singular within a finite proper time* when the space is *properly* closed.

10·7. *Universe closed in Einstein's general relativity.* – EINSTEIN gives the following arguments in favor of the conception of a universe bounded in space ([38]):

1) « From the standpoint of the theory of relativity, the condition for a closed surface is very much simpler than the corresponding boundary condition at infinity of the quasi-Euclidean structure of the universe.

2) « The idea that MACH expressed, that inertia depends upon the mutual action of bodies, is contained, to a first approximation, in the equations of the theory of relativity; it follows from these equations that inertia depends, at least in part, upon mutual actions between masses. As it is an unsatisfactory assumption to make that inertia depends in part upon mutual actions, and

([37]) For a study of the response of test particles in the analogous case of a cylindrical gravitational wave, see ref. [35].

([38]) A. EINSTEIN: *The Meaning of Relativity*, 3rd ed. (Princeton, 1950), p. 107.

in part upon an independent property of space, Mach's idea gains in probability. But this idea of Mach's corresponds only to a finite universe, bounded in space, and not to a quasi-Euclidean, infinite universe. From the standpoint of epistemology it is more satisfying to have the mechanical properties of space completely determined by matter, and this is the case only in a space-bounded universe ».

10·8. *Spherical universe expands and recontracts.* – To gain some impression of the geometrodynamics of a 4-manifold bounded in space, it is helpful to consider the idealization of a spherically symmetrical universe, so well known in cosmology. Today the status of this problem is simpler than it was in the past. In the earliest days EINSTEIN examined the stability of a universe uniformly filled with dust. He found that the system could not remain at rest; that contraction would begin. In other words, a spherically symmetric universe, like a collection of mutually attracting rocks thrown apart, should be expanding or contracting but never static. This conclusion seemed at the time so unreasonable that he later added an artificial negative pressure, or « cosmological term » to the field equations to give a static universe. Later Hubble found evidence from the red shift of spectral lines that the universe actually *is* expanding. This observation might have served as a fourth way to test general relativity (over and above solar deflection of starlight, precession of Mercury, and gravitational red shift) had the original predictions of the theory been made with sufficient confidence. After HUBBLE and others had established the existence of a recessional red shift nearly proportional to the distance between the receptor and the emittive galaxy, EINSTEIN discarded the arbitrary cosmological term as mathematically artificial and physically without justification. The equations of geometrodynamics without this added term define what is today usually meant by the term « general relativity ». However, a different connotation attached to general relativity during the 1920's and early 1930's when cosmological models were under most intense study; the cosmological term was added to the equations; and a great number of models resulted, according as the « cosmological constant » that multiplied this extra term had one or another value. Today the situation is very much simpler.

10·9. *Dynamics uniquely determined by equation of state.* – If Einstein's equations are accepted in their original simple form, and Einstein's arguments are accepted that the universe is closed, and spherical symmetry is assumed for purposes of convenient idealization, then *the dynamics of expansion and recontraction is uniquely determined by the equation of state of the source of mass-energy that fills the space.* Let a represent the radius of curvature. Let $T = ct$ represent the cotime elapsed since the start of expansion. Let the distance travelled by a photon in a short time interval be divided by the radius of curvature at that time to define an angular parameter η, for the measurement of time, arbitrarily taken to be zero at the start of the expansion:

$$d\eta = a^{-1}d \quad \text{(distance in 3-space)}\,. \tag{82}$$

Then the initial value requirement on the data on successive space-like surfaces,

$$-\begin{pmatrix}\text{extrinsic}\\ \text{curvature}\\ \text{invariant}\end{pmatrix} + \begin{pmatrix}\text{intrinsic}\\ \text{curvature}\\ \text{invariant}\end{pmatrix} = \text{constant}\begin{pmatrix}\text{energy}\\ \text{density}\end{pmatrix} \tag{83}$$

takes the form

$$(3/a^4)\left[(da/d\eta)^2 + a^2\right] = (8\pi G/c^4)\begin{pmatrix}\text{energy}\\ \text{density}\end{pmatrix}. \tag{84}$$

The equation of state determines the way the pressure and density change during adiabatic expansion and recontraction [39]:

$$\frac{3\,da}{a} + \frac{d(\text{energy density})}{(\text{energy density}) + (\text{pressure})} = 0\,. \tag{85}$$

Eqs. (82), (84), (85) together completely determine the dynamics of this change.

Any equation of state will give a pressure which lies between the two extremes of zero pressure (« dust-filled universe ») and maximum pressure (« radiation-filled universe »). In these two cases the equations possess the following exact solutions:

a) Friedmann universe. Dust. Zero pressure.

$$\begin{cases} T = \tfrac{1}{2}a_0(\eta - \sin\eta)\,, \\ a(T) = \tfrac{1}{2}a_0(1 - \cos\eta)\,. \end{cases} \tag{86}$$

These equations give a parametric representation of a cycloid. The parameter η runs from 0 to 2π. A photon has just time enough to go around and come back to its original angular co-ordinates on the spherical space during the entire time of expansion and recontraction. The mass of the universe is connected with radius of curvature a_0 at the moment of maximum expansion by the relation

$$M = 3\pi c^2 a_0/4G\,. \tag{87}$$

Constant during the expansion is a quantity analogous to the sum of the rest energy, kinetic energy and potential energy of the system,

$$Mc^2 + Mc^2(da/dT)^2 - 4GM^2/3\pi a = 0\,. \tag{88}$$

---

(39) L. LANDAU and E. LIFSHITZ: *The Classical Theory of Fields* (Cambridge, 1951), p. 338.

However, the quantity defined by the left hand side—analogous to *the total energy of the universe—is not a disposable constant of integration.* There is no way to give the closed universe enough energy to allow it to keep on expanding forever. In this respect it is not adequate to compare the dynamics of the universe with the motion of a system of rocks thrown apart and drawn back together again by their mutual gravitational pull.

b) Tolman universe. Filled with radiation. Pressure equal to one third of energy density.

$$(89)\qquad \begin{cases} T = a_0(1-\cos\eta)\,, \\ a(T) = a_0 \sin\eta\,. \end{cases}$$

These equations describe a circle on which the parameter η runs from 0 to π. During the time of expansion and recontraction a photon has only time enough to go around to the antipodal point on the 3-dimensional sphere.

10·10. *Conjecture: every closed metric becomes singular with time.* – These two limiting cases have been described here in such detail because both cases lead to a true singularity in the intrinsic geometry of space after the lapse of a finite proper time. The same is presumably true for any intermediate equation of state. This situation is compatible with the *conjecture that in every closed universe which has the topology of the 3-sphere, and which obeys the equations of geometrodynamics, there always exist test-particle geodesics which cannot be continued indefinitely, because they run into a region where the metric is singular.*

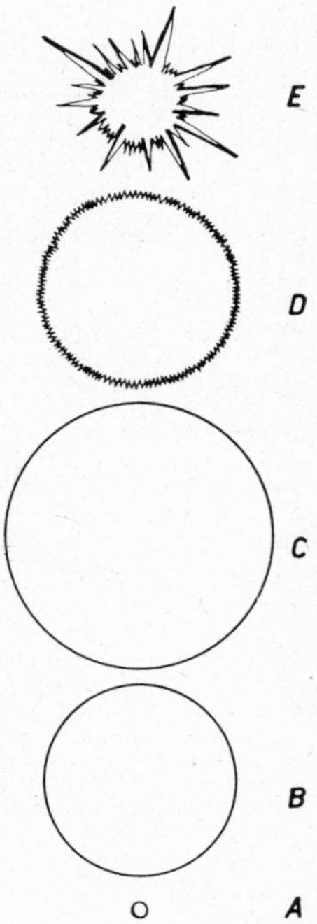

Fig. 14. – Schematic representation of behavior of an undersea bubble as it contracts towards a minimum size and re-expands. This line drawing was made with one eye on the photographs of such bubbles given in the book of Cole (ref. (40)). Is it right to assume that this drawing also gives a schematic representation of the behavior of a closed universe near the phase of maximum contraction? Does the step-by-step integration of the equations of geometrodynamics lead on through this phase by way of a metric that is always free of intrinsic geometrical singularity? In the text the conjecture is discussed that this uniquely determined continuation of the initial value data can *never* be free of singularity.

---

(40) See R. H. Cole: *Underwater Explosions* (Princeton, 1948), for an account of the physics at the phase of maximum contraction.

This conjecture about the intrinsic singularity of closed-space solutions deserves deeper examination because the blame for the singularity might be attributed to an unjustified use of the concept of equation of state in the analysis of Friedmann and Tolman. Neither dust nor radiation looks homogeneous under microanalysis. The scale of the irregularities might determine —it could be argued—a minimum distance down to which the recontraction process can proceed as predicted. Thereafter—it might be assumed—the dynamics follows the course of events familiar in the case of an undersea bubble. Horns and spikes develop during the course of the recontraction of such an object (Fig. 14). As a consequence the inward motion reverses itself not everywhere simultaneously, but at different times in different places, after the fashion of a glove being turned inside out one finger at a time. To be able to give this more detailed account of what goes on nevertheless proves in no way that the hydrodynamical turn-about is singularity-free. Cavitation is one of the most singular of hydrodynamic phenomena, and cavitation presumably occurs during the successive cycles of maximum contraction of an undersea bubble formed in an energetic explosion [see reference ([40])]. In so far as this hydrodynamic model furnishes any guide as to what to expect of the solutions of Einstein's equations, it suggests this *conjecture: every solution for the problem of a properly closed universe develops somewhere a singularity after the lapse of a finite proper time.* Evidently only plausibility arguments are available to support this conjecture. 1) A qualified analogy with the theory of minimal surfaces (Table VII). 2) Observed instabilities in the implosion of an underwater bubble. 3) Similar instabilities in the implosion of a nearly spherical dust-filled relativistic universe when it approaches the phase of maximum contraction ([41]). 4) Unpublished analysis by Dieter Brill of the dynamics of a universe closed up entirely by its content of pure gravitational radiation. BRILL deals with the special case of a universe which admits a moment of time symmetry and an axis of rotational symmetry (eqs. (78)–(81)). He proves there exist closed 3-spaces which satisfy the initial value requirement

$$ {}^3R = 0 \tag{90} $$

and which are free of all singularity. It follows from the work of LICHNEROWICZ and FOURÈS on the Cauchy problem of general relativity ([42]) that this initial value data can be extended for a *finite* time into the future and past without developing a singularity. As the dynamics proceed in either direction from the moment of time symmetry the volume of the 3-space—BRILL has proven ([43])—

([41]) J. B. ADAMS, R. MJOLSNESS and J. A. WHEELER. Onzième Conseil de Physique Solvay. *La structure et l'évolution de l'univers* (Brussels, 1958).

([42]) A. LICHNEROWICZ: *Théories relativistes de la gravitation, et de l'électromagnétisme* (Paris, 1955); Y. FOURÈS-BRUHAT: *Journ. Rational Mech. Anal.*, **4**, 951 (1956).

([43]) The author is indebted to Dr. BRILL for permission to mention his result here.

always begins decreasing. In other words, *time symmetry* is not inconsistent with a stage of maximum expansion, but it *is always inconsistent with a stage of maximum implosion.* This result does not prove, but it suggests, that there exists *no* singularity free solution of Einstein's source-free gravitational equations which runs through the stage of maximum contraction and on into an ensuing phase of re-expansion. The last plausibility argument that every closed-universe solution ultimately develops a singularity comes from (5) the Schwarzschild solution, as already discussed.

TABLE VII. – *Qualified analogy suggested here between theory of minimal surfaces and theory of solutions of Einstein's source-free field equations.*

Bernstein's theorem on minimal surfaces	Trial formulation of analogous statement about Einstein's equations.	Tentative position taken here on this formulation.
Every non-trivial (non-flat) minimal surface possesses a singularity	1. - Every solution which is not flat possesses somewhere a singularity.	1. - False. Note regular behavior of a weak time-symmetric pure gravitational wave in an asymptotically flat space.
	2. - Every solution which is not asymptotically flat possesses somewhere a singularity.	2. - False. Consider infinite plane wave (BONDI, ROSEN, ROBINSON, PENROSE, TAKENO, KOMPANEYETS).
	3. - Every solution which describes a closed space develops sometime a singularity.	3. - False. Consider 3-cube in flat 3-space and identify opposite faces, thus obtaining a closed space with the topology of a 3-torus. Being flat, the metric does not evolve in time, and no singularity ever develops.
	4. - Every solution which describes a properly closed space develops sometime a singularity. The concept « properly closed » is not yet a clearly defined concept and presumably requires for its definition some consideration of Mach's principle.	4. - This is the present conjecture. « Properly » closed includes topology of 3-sphere, (topology of 2-sphere) × (topology of circle), and a whole class of related topologies; excludes topology of Euclidean 3-space, topology of 3-torus, and possibly other topologies.

10'11. *In what ways can classical space-time become singular?* – If the conjecture is right that every properly closed space that satisfies Einstein's equations becomes singular after a finite proper time, then the special case where this space contains a Schwarzschild throat illustrates at least one way this singularity can come about by the curvature gradually becoming infinite. What alternative ways there are for singularities to develop is not known. Quite lacking today is any systematic and co-ordinate independent analysis of all the kinds of singularities which can be encountered in solutions of Einstein's equations which are regular elsewhere.

10·12. *New and truly fundamental features of general relativity.* – If Einstein's arguments are right that only a properly closed universe is physically reasonable (44), and if the conjecture is correct that such a universe, evolving according to the classical relativistic field equations, always develops a singularity, then geometrodynamics differs in character even more decisively than previously suspected from any linearized version of field theory. Being so different, Einstein's general relativity has to be discussed on its own terms, in the light of the most general principles—not in terms of the workaday tools and concepts used for a linear theory. 1) The total energy is not a defined quantity for a closed universe. The usual derivation of the law of conservation of energy considers a 3-space and in this 3-space considers a 2-surface which contains all relevant parts of the system in question. However, in a closed universe, surfaces drawn at greater and greater distances from a given point P ultimately have to contract and shrink to nothingness in some antipodal region of space. The law of conservation of energy reduces to the trivial entity $0 = 0$. By way of contrast, consider the dynamics of a great collection of small masses thrown outward with a common velocity from a common center under Newtonian forces in a flat space. Here the total energy,

$$E = (M/2)(\mathrm{d}a/\mathrm{d}t)^2 - GM^2/2a\,, \tag{91}$$

can be either positive or negative or zero; the masses may fall back onto each other, or they may fly apart forever. No such freedom exists in the case of the closed universe! (eq. (88)). 2) Not only is total energy a defined quantity for a linearized field, but also this energy is representable as the sum of contributions from individual modes of excitation. In contrast, there is not the least evidence that a geometrodynamical universe naturally admits any description in terms of normal modes of excitation.

No total energy and no normal modes are two novel features of classical geometrodynamics. There is a third: 3) There exist situations in which there are *pairs of points in space-time which cannot be connected by a geodesic.* Of such a situation the Schwarzschild metric furnishes the best studied example. In Fig. 15 no geodesic going out from A can ever reach B, and conversely. Closely associated with this feature is another. A sequence of equidistant events P_1, P_2, P_3, ... may occupy a perfectly finite and possibly very small

(44) A. Einstein: *The Meaning of Relativity*, 5th ed. (Princeton, 1955).

proper time and yet not be observable at great distances even for an observer who waits there for an infinite proper time. In particular, he can wait forever and yet receive no light signal to tell him that the curvature at the throat of the Schwarzschild metric is going to infinity. He can discuss the precession of the perihelion of a test particle, the red shift, and the deflection of light in the curved space well outside the throat without ever seeing any reason to trouble about the possibility that the metric may go singular. It will, but not

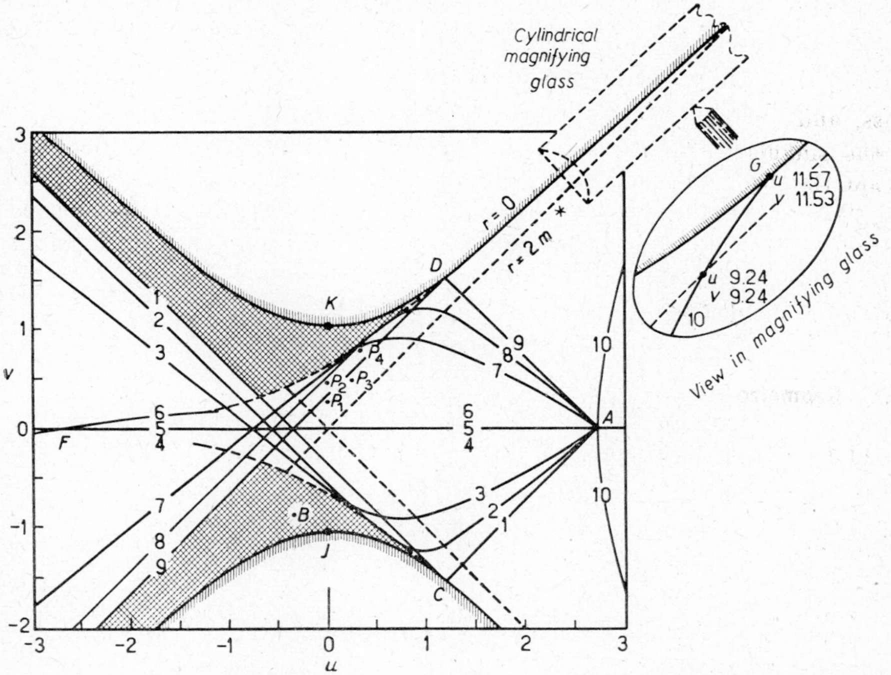

Fig. 15. – Shadow zone (cross hatched) unreachable by any radial geodesic that issues from A. Radial geodesics are plotted here in terms of Kruskal's space-like and time-like coordinates u and v, such that the Schwarzschild metric is $ds^2 = f^2(du^2 - dv^2)$ with $f^2 = (32m^{*3}/r) \exp[-r/2m^*]$ and $[(r/2m^*) - 1] \exp[r/2m^*] = u^2 - v^2$. Space like geodesics: 2, 3, 4, 5, 6, 7, 8. Limiting case of space-like geodesic give light-like geodesics 1 and 9. *There exists no radial geodesic that connects A and a typical point B in the shadow zone.* - Space-like geodesics from A never strike the region $r = 0$ (shaded hyperbolas $v^2 - u^2 = 1$) where the intrinsic curvature becomes infinite. A time-like geodesic through A, on the other hand (path of ideal test particle) always runs on at least *one* end into this barrier, and runs into this barrier at both ends when the energy of the test-particle is insufficient for escape from the center of attraction. Geodesic 10 corresponds to the special case where the test particle reaches its maximum Schwarschild co-ordinate r just at A itself. This geodesic ends at point G *not* tangent to the hyperbola in the (u, v) plane. - An observer far away in the region to the right will never receive light signals from P_1, P_2, P_3, P_4 no matter how long he waits. - The interval of proper cotime from J to K is however perfectly finite ($2\pi m^*$). The calculations which went into the construction of this graph were made by R. W. FULLER and are to be submitted for publication elsewhere.

in his future! In other words, in curved space-time the whole infinite range of proper time available to an observer may not suffice to pick up the signals given off by a light source in a finite proper time.

10·13. *Importance of the issue of singularities.* – If geometrodynamics has such unexpected features, must it not be concluded to be physically unreasonable, or internally inconsistent, or both? This question is obviously central to any assessment of what general relativity has to contribute to the advance of physics. In such an assessment it is not enough to point to the scope of geometrodynamics—to the ability of Einstein's theory to describe gravitation without gravitation, electromagnetism without electromagnetism, mass without mass, and charge without charge. It is necessary to face up to the question of the singularities. If this issue did not arise it would not be difficult to accept the other unusual features of the theory—the absence of a well defined energy for a closed universe, the failure to supply any analysis into independent modes of excitation, and the infinitely different scales of time on different world lines. With this issue unsolved, is not the whole outlook of geometrodynamics clouded?

11. – Geometrodynamics and the quantum of action.

11·1. *Analogous problem of singularity from early days of atomic physics.* – It is not possible to state a final position on the question of singularities today because the more general implications of Einstein's field equation have not yet been sufficiently investigated ([45]). However, it is possible to cite a problem of an older era in physics which has received an answer from quantum mechanics and which supplies an interesting analog to the problem of geometrodynamical singularities. In the 1910's it was well understood from Earnshaw's theorem that a system of charged particles possesses no configuration of equilibrium. The apparent contradiction between this conclusion and the stability of atomic systems led to the greatest variety of proposals for changing the law of force between particles. Today it is of course clear that the Coulomb law holds over a fantastic number of powers of ten in the distance. In the 1910's it was also understood from classical electrodynamics that an electron should spiral in towards a nucleus faster and faster as the moving charge radiates energy. Attempts were made to avoid this difficulty too, by arbitrary changes in the laws of electrodynamics. Today the laws of interaction with the radiation field have been checked to enormous accuracy by the concordance of experiment and theory for the Lamb shift of the 2*s* level of hydrogen.

([45]) A summary of the present status of work on the quantization of general relativity was presented by P. G. Bergmann and A. Komar at the Royaumont Conference of 1959 (unpublished).

The singular state for a pair of charged particles is avoided, not by changing the law of interaction between the electron and the nucleus, not by giving up the laws of electromagnetic radiation, but by adding the quantum principle. The electron cannot be confined to too small a localization distance L without making the associated spread in momentum, $\Delta p \sim \hbar/L$, so great, and the corresponding kinetic energy, $\hbar^2/2mL^2$, so large, as to overcompensate the Coulomb binding, $-e^2/L$. The electron stops radiating, not because the electromagnetic field is incapable of absorbing further energy, but because there is no lower state to which the electron can drop. In loose terms, the quantum of action forces on physical processes a smoother dependence on space and time than would have been expected from the unquantized version of the laws of motion.

11·2. *Probable bearing of quantum effects on the question of singularities.* – Does the quantum principle, as applied to geometrodynamics, likewise prevent the development of any singular situation? Is it reasonable to compare the singularities which arise in the geometry in the recontraction phase of a closed universe with the curling crests and cusps which develop on an ocean wave as it moves into shallow water? In the hydrodynamic case a limit is set to the sharpness of any incipient singularities by the action of capillarity. The lengthening and thinning sheet of water at the overturning crest is broken up into droplets and foam by surface tension. Is there a similar effective limit set to the sharpness of the curvature of space-time by the quantum of action? In the hydrodynamic case there is an enormous disparity in size between the many meter wave lengths of an ocean breaker and the millimeter scale of the droplets which it forms when it crashes on the beach. In the case of geometrodynamics there is an even greater disparity in scale between the dimensions which it is most natural to consider as relevant 1) the radius of curvature of the universe—perhaps $\sim 10^{10}$ light years or $\sim 10^{28}$ cm—or of any macroscopic portion of the universe and 2) the natural scale of quantum fluctuations in the metric, a scale given by the simplest dimensional arguments as

$$L^* = (\hbar G/c^3)^{\frac{1}{2}} = 1.6 \cdot 10^{-33} \text{ cm} . \tag{92}$$

The important fact is not the smallness of this length, but the circumstance that there is any characteristic length at all. It guarantees that the curvatures of space cannot develop all the way to the singularities predicted by classical geometrodynamics. These singularities do not indicate that classical general relativity lacks internal self-consistency. Instead, they show that the classical dynamics of curvature leads head-on into phenomena of which only quantum theory can give a satisfactory account. In this respect there is the closest analogy between the sharpening curvature of geometrodynamics and the inward spiralling electron ot atomic physics.

11·3. *Does quantum geometrodynamics shed any light on the elementary particle problem?* – Curved empty space going through its dynamical evolution with time thus must show quite new features at small distances as a necessary consequence of the quantum principle. To say this much is easy. To say what these features are is much more difficult. Yet this question cannot be escaped. To explain why electrons do not forever spiral inward is to explain why atoms can exist and why the physical world can have any substantiality at all. Similarly to explain why curvature cannot become infinite may be the key to understanding why there is any such thing as matter in the world.

Geons are not matter, although they are immaterial objects which have mass. They are so big, and their constitution is so classical in character, that they cannot have any direct connection whatsoever with elementary particles. Neither do the *classical* charges manifested by a curved empty space with multiply connected topology have the least direct connection with the *quantized* charges of elementary particle physics. This circumstance does not mean that elementary particles have to be considered for all time as basic unexplained and unexplainable entities. Neither does it mean instead that the basic substrate of physics will always be regarded—as it is in today's provisional account of particle phenomenology—as a collection of fields interacting with each other: electron fields, meson fields, neutrino fields and other kinds of fields. In that event, too, physical theory would forever be encumbered with a collection of primitive unexplained constants: the characteristic mass values associated with the constituitive fields, and the strengths of the couplings between these fields. To accept either position would be to accept the idea of space-time as an *arena* for physics and to give up Einstein's inspiring vision of curved empty space-time as *all* of physics. Of course no one can make a final assessment at this time of the relative promise of different lines of investigation. However, to overlook the promise of a purely geometrical description of nature would seem less justified than ever before at a time when geometrodynamics—and geometrodynamics alone—has been found to explain not only

> gravitation without gravitation and
> equations of motion without equations of motion, but also
> mass without mass,
> electromagnetism without electromagnetism,
> coupling constant without coupling constant, and
> charge without charge.

Can then elementary particles be understood as quantum aspects of curved empty space, and nothing more?

11·4. *Necessity of seeking guidance from elementary particle physics and quantum electrodynamics.* – It would seem a misguided hope at the present stage of physics to think of proposing anything in the way of a concrete quantum geometrodynamical model for an elementary particle. Of course regions of space-time in which the curvature is growing ever sharper can be imagined to break up into particles much as the crest of an ocean wave breaks up into foam and droplets. But such a picture is far too fuzzy and speculative in character to supply anything with the sharpness of a model. Moreover, if the analogy with hydrodynamics is any guide to dealing with the non-linear equations of general relativity, it will be a long time before the wealth of phenomenology to be read from the equations is actually read from them. Vortices, shock waves, Helmholtz instability, Rayleigh-Taylor instability and the generation of sound by turbulence were all found by observation before they were analyzed by theory (46). Therefore, in looking for a purely geometrical description of elementary particles, it is reasonable to take as a guide not only all that one knows about the implications of Einstein's field equations, but also all that one knows about elementary particles from both experiment and theory.

11·5. *All space the seat of violent disturbance according to quantum electro dynamics.* – Nothing is more striking about elementary particle theory than the circumstance that it takes all space for its territory. A world containing a single electron, for example, does not make sense. The electron would drop to a negative energy state in a fantastically short time, as Dirac long ago showed. The observed stability of electrons against this type of radiative catastrophe demands that all negative energy states be occupied. Out of this infinite but unobservable sea it is possible anywhere to raise up an electron into tangible being. To this possibility, familiar experiments on pair production stand witness.

All space is permeated not only by electron physics, but also by fluctuations in the electromagnetic field, even in the « vacuum state » or ground state of the electromagnetic field. These fluctuations are as inescapable as the well tested zero point vibrations of atoms in crystal lattices. The field fluctuations act for example upon the electron in the $2s$ state of hydrogen and cause it too to fluctuate by a mean squared distance $\langle r^2\rangle_{AV}$ about the position that would otherwise be expected for it. Thereby the energy of the electron in the atomic potential $V(\boldsymbol{r})$ is raised by the amount

$$\Delta E_{\text{Lamb}} = \langle r^2/6\rangle_{AV}\langle\nabla^2 V\rangle_{AV}\,. \tag{93}$$

The quantity $\langle\nabla^2 V\rangle_{AV}$ being known, and the Lamb-Retherford shift ΔE_{Lamb} being measured, a value is obtained for $\langle r^2\rangle_{AV}$. This value checks the theory of electromagnetic field fluctuations in the most impressive way (47).

(46) See E. A. Power and J. A. Wheeler: *Rev. Mod. Phys.*, **29**, 480 (1957) for a table of the analogies between hydrodynamics and geometrodynamics (pp. 137-138 of text).

(47) See F. Dyson: *Lecture Notes on Quantum Electrodynamics* (photolithographed notes) (Ithaca, N. Y., 1954), for this way of describing the Lamb shift; also T. Welton: *Phys. Rev.*, **74**, 1157 (1948).

11·6. *Central status of the « undressed » electron.* - If any purely geometric description of elementary particles physics is ever to be possible, it cannot escape making all space the seat of violent electron and electromagnetic and other fluctuation phenomena—this is one inescapable conclusion out of quantum electrodynamical experiment and theory. A second conclusion is this. The « undressed electron » or some related concept must occupy a place more prominent, not less prominent, than the position which that concept occupies today—because this is the point at which quantum electrodynamics fails of being a closed theory. This theory deals with mathematical objects—« undressed elecctrons »—whose mass and charge deviate from the mass and charge of the experimental electron by factors which are formally infinite, and which in reality are presumably very large. The interaction of one such Dirac particle with the electromagnetic field—and through its intermediation with the other particles of an infinite sea of negative energy electrons—brings into being a coupled charge cluster, a complicated collection of virtual pairs and virtual photons, which is identified with the experimental or « dressed » electron. Most calculations of electron theory can be arranged in such a way that only the « renormalized » charge and mass of this dressed electron come into evidence (48)—satisfying evidence that the physical picture is reasonable in its main features. However, no such escape from the problem of the structure of the electron—« dressed » or « undressed »—is possible when one asks why the electron has the particular charge and mass which it happens to have.

In conclusion, geometrodynamics can offer something significant to the solution of the elementary particle problem only if it can provide some understanding of what an undressed electron is, and only if it can make it clear in what sense all space is the seat of violent fluctuations. Are the two questions related to each other?

Poincaré and Lorentz long ago showed that new issues come to the fore when an attempt is made to account for the structure of a charged particle (49). The energy and momentum of the electromagnetic field are components of a tensor, and in a certain sense transform under change of reference system twice as fast as the components of a 4-vector. Poincaré reformulated this conclusion in physical terms: tensions of non-electric character are required to hold the charged object together. In view of this conclusion it is interesting to see

---

(48) H. A. Kramers: *Non-relativistic quantum electrodynamics and correspondence principle*, Solvay Congress, 1948 (Rapport et Discussions, Bruxelles, 1950) and subsequent developments in quantum electrodynamics due to Tomonaga, Schwinger, Feynman and Dyson, summarized for example in W. Thirring: *Principles of Quantum Electrodynamics* (New York, 1958).

(49) H. Poincaré: *Rendiconti Palermo*, **21** (1906); H. A. Lorentz: *Versl. Kon. Ac. Amsterdam*, **26**, 981 (1917). For a survey of the history of this problem, see A. Pais: *Developments in the Theory of the Electron* (Princeton, 1948).

that two well separated mouths of a flux-bearing wormhole provide a self consistent model of a pair of charged objects. Here the gravitational forces provide the tensions of which Poincaré spoke. A geon is another object where gravitational pulls work against electromagnetic pressures in such a way that the total momentum and energy transform properly under change of reference system. The universe itself is a third system whose structure depends in an essential way upon the presence of gravitational forces. Yet none of these three examples is relevant in any direct way to the problem of the undressed electron nor to the phenomenon of violent fluctuations throughout all space. If either undressed electrons or vacuum fluctuations have anything to do with gravitation and the geometry of curved empty space, it is not by reason of any direct contribution from classical gravitational fields, or classical curvatures of space, but because *quantum fluctuations in these quantities give rise to decisively new effects.*

11'7. *Nature and consequences of fluctuations in the metric.* – It is possible to discuss the order of magnitude and qualitative character of geometrodynamical fluctuation phenomena ([50]). The intensity of the field variations depends upon the dimensions of the region under study. When its extension in space and in cotime are both of the order of magnitude L, then the quanta of most importance for the fluctuations have energy of the order of magnitude $\hbar c/L$. The energy density of the field is of the order $\hbar c/L^4$. The fields themselves are therefore of the order $(\hbar c)^{\frac{1}{2}}/L^2$, with or without appropriate dimensional factors for transformation into familiar units (Table VIII).

TABLE VIII. – *Order of magnitude of field fluctuations in the special case where the space and cotime extensions of the region under study both have the same magnitude L.* The quantity L^* is an abbreviation for $(\hbar G/c^3)^{\frac{1}{2}} = 1.6 \cdot 10^{-33}$ cm. In the case of electromagnetism capital letters signify quantities expressed in cgs units, such as electrostatic V and electrostatic V/cm, whereas lower case quantities refer to geometrized units: dimensionless potentials and fields with the units cm^{-1}.

	Electromagnetism	Gravitation
Potential	$\Delta A_\mu \sim (\hbar c)^{\frac{1}{2}}/L$ or $\Delta a_\mu \sim L^*/L$	$\Delta \varphi_{\text{newton}} \sim c^2 L^*/L$ or $\Delta g_{\mu\nu} \sim L^*/L$
Field	$\Delta F_{\mu\nu} \sim (\hbar c)^{\frac{1}{2}}/L^2$ or $\Delta f_{\mu\nu} \sim (L^*/L^2)$	$\Delta(\text{acceleration}) \sim c^2 L^*/L^2$ or $\Delta \Gamma^\alpha{}_{\beta\gamma} \sim L^*/L^2$
Space curvature	—	$\Delta R^\alpha{}_{\beta\gamma\delta} \sim L^*/L^3$

([50]) J. A. WHEELER: *Ann. Phys.*, **2**, 604 (1957).

At distances L of the order of magnitude of the reduced Compton wave length,

(94) $$L_m = \hbar/mc = 3.85 \cdot 10^{-11} \text{ cm},$$

from an electron the static gravitational field, and static alteration in the metric, is of course fantastically small:

(95) $$\Delta g_{\text{static}} \sim 2Gm/c^2 L_m \sim (L^*/L_m)^2 \sim 10^{-44}.$$

The fluctuation in the metric is also exceedingly small:

(96) $$\Delta g_{\text{fluct}} \sim L^*/L_m \sim 10^{-22}.$$

At still smaller distances the calculated static field of the electron does not increase further in order of magnitude because the energy and mass of the particle are not localized to a distance much smaller than L_m.

In contrast, the calculated fluctuations in the metric are unaffected by proximity to a particle. They have only to do with the extension of the region under study. On an atomic scale the metric appears flat, as does the ocean to an aviator far above. The closer the approach, the greater the evident degree of irregularity. Finally, at distances of the order L^*, the fluctuations in the typical metric component, $g_{\mu\nu}$, become of the same order as the $g_{\mu\nu}$ themselves. Then the character of the geometry shows new features, as indicated schematically in Fig. 16.

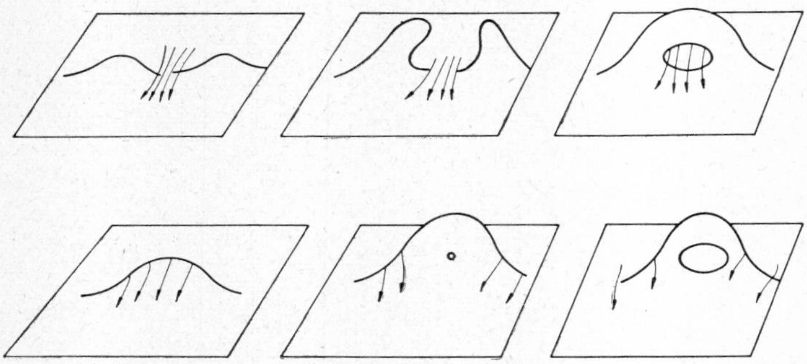

Fig. 16. – Growth of a fluctuation in the geometry of space to a point where space becomes multiply connected, schematically illustrated. Above, left to right: fluctuation of a type which traps lines of force in a wormhole. The integral of the field over the mouth of the wormhole has a non-zero value. The wormhole is endowed with a charge. Below, left to right: development of the same type of multiple connectedness via a sequence of geometries such that lines of force never have an opportunity to thread through the wormhole. The charge is zero.

Multiple connectedness develops, as it does on the surface of an ocean where waves are breaking. Of course it is not necessary to propose a method to observe these fluctuations in order to note how directly and inescapably they follow from the quantum theory of the metric. One does not have to use the word « observation » at all. Instead, one can say: 1) The quantum mechanical state of the metric field is a functional of the three-dimensional geometry $\mathscr{G}$ intrinsic to a space like surface σ:

$$\Psi = \Psi(\mathscr{G})\,. \tag{97}$$

2) The probability amplitude Ψ typically falls off rapidly for *large scale* departures from a smoothly behaved metric, but falls off very little for departures from smoothness which are of the scale $L^* = (\hbar G/c^2)^{\frac{1}{2}}$ or less. Moreover, it has to be expected that the fall-off will proceed at a not very different rate regardless of whether the departures from smoothness leave the topology unchanged or whether they introduce multiple connectedness of a high order—or even an infinitely ramified topology. As WEYL remarked [51], « ... a more detailed scrutiny of a surface might disclose that, what we had considered an elementary piece, in reality has tiny handles attached to it which change the connectivity character of the piece, and that a microscope of ever greater magnification would reveal ever new topological complications of this type, *ad infinitum*. »

11'8. *Meaning of fluctuations.* – In this discussion the word « fluctuation » is only a shorthand language to speak of configurations of the system in question —here the geometry—for which there is an appreciable probability amplitude. According to this way of speaking, an elementary harmonic oscillator of mass m and circular frequency ω, described by a wave function

$$\Psi = N \exp\left[- m\omega x^2/2\hbar\right], \tag{98}$$

« undergoes fluctuations in position » ot the order

$$\Delta x \sim (\hbar/m\omega)^{\frac{1}{2}}\,.$$

In the same way the electromagnetic field in a nearly flat space-time is often described in terms of the co-ordinates ξ_1, ξ_2, ξ_3, ... of an infinite set of harmonic oscillators. The ground state wave function becomes a normalized product of Gauss functions:

$$\Psi = N \exp\left[-\sum_n \mu_n \xi_n^2/2\hbar\right]. \tag{99}$$

The fluctuations in the amplitudes of the respective field oscillators are then

---

[51] H. WEYL: *Philosophy of Mathematics and Natural Science* (original German in 1927; revised for English edition; translation by O. Helmer) (Princeton 1949), p. 91.

of the order

(100) $$\Delta\xi_n \sim (\hbar/\mu_n)^{\frac{1}{2}}\,,$$

where the μ_n are simple constants.

11·9. *Gauge invariance in the state functional for electromagnetism.* – Another mode of analysis is more suited to a space-like description of the electromagnetic field fluctuations, such as is also of interest in geometrodynamics. The amplitude of the co-ordinate ξ_n of the typical field oscillator can be expressed as an integral over all space of the product of the magnetic field $\boldsymbol{H}(x)$ multiplied by the appropriate periodic function of position. In this way the wave function (99) for the ground state of the electromagnetic field becomes expressed as a *functional* of the magnetic field ([52]):

(101) $$\Psi = N \exp\left[-(16\pi^3\hbar c)^{-1}\right]\iint \boldsymbol{H}(x)\cdot\boldsymbol{H}(y)\,|x-y|^{-2}\,\mathrm{d}^3x\,\mathrm{d}^3y\,.$$

This expression provides a means to evaluate and compare the probability amplitudes for any arbitrarily specified configurations of the magnetic field $\boldsymbol{H}_1(x)$, $\boldsymbol{H}_2(x)$, ..., $\boldsymbol{H}_k(x)$, ... which are defined throughout all space and have zero divergence. Of course it is not necessary to restrict attention to the ground state of the electromagnetic field; a state of higher energy can be considered; or also a state which is not an eigenstate of the energy at all, such as the functional

(102) $$\Psi = N \exp\left[-\varepsilon^{-2}\right]\int\left(\boldsymbol{H}(x) - \frac{\boldsymbol{k}\times\boldsymbol{x}}{a^2+x^2}\right)^2\mathrm{d}^3x\,;$$

supplementary condition $\operatorname{div}\boldsymbol{H} = 0$;

where ε is a very small number. This functional describes a state in which the magnetic field has maximum probability to be found in the configuration

(103) $$\boldsymbol{H}(x) = \frac{\boldsymbol{k}\times\boldsymbol{x}}{a^2+x^2}\,,$$

where a and $\boldsymbol{k}$ are constants.

Often the dynamics of the electromagnetic field is discussed in terms of the vector potential $\boldsymbol{A}$, connected with $\boldsymbol{H}$, by the equation

(104) $$\boldsymbol{H} = \operatorname{curl}\boldsymbol{A}\,.$$

Then the probability amplitude is evaluated in the first instance as a functional of $\boldsymbol{A}$. Only later is it discovered as a consequence of gauge invariance, that $\boldsymbol{A}$ comes into evidence in the state functional only in the form $\boldsymbol{H} = \operatorname{curl}\boldsymbol{A}$.

([52]) Appreciation is expressed to members of a class in quamtum mechanics, particularly to H. Dempster, for evaluation of the exponent in this expression. In it, the divergence of the magnetic field is required to vanish.

11·10. *Gauge invariance in the state functional for geometrodynamics.* – In a similar way the probability amplitude for any given 3-dimensional geometry $\mathscr{G}$ on a space-like surface σ will be considered at the start as a functional of the metric components.

$$ {}^{(3)}g_{mn} \tag{105}$$

over this surface. However, a change in the co-ordinate system used within this surface will change the metric components ${}^{(3)}g_{mn}$ without changing the intrinsic geometry $\mathscr{G}$. The situation is completely analogous to that in electromagnetism, where the substitution

$$ \boldsymbol{A} = \boldsymbol{A}_{\text{new}} + \operatorname{grad} \lambda \tag{106}$$

changes the potential A without changing the field $\boldsymbol{H}$. It follows that the state functional for source-free relativity depends after all not on the 6 functions ${}^{(3)}g_{mn}$, but only on the intrinsic geometry:

$$ \Psi = \Psi(\mathscr{G}) \, . \tag{107}$$

The magnitude of fluctuations may be small or large, to judge from the case of a single mechanical oscillator and from the variety of quantum states which are open to that elementary system. An even greater multiplicity of states is available to the electromagnetic field ([53]). Therefore it might be thought that the fluctuations of the electromagnetic field require for their description an even greater number of parameters. This is certainly the case

---

([53]) Can the metric field also be prepared in any one of a great number of quantum states? Great freedom of choice would seem to exist if states are allowed which describe a metric which in the large is asymptotically flat. Thus, if there exists a Schwarzschild mass that characterizes the rate of approach to large scale flatness, then this mass can have one or another value, corresponding as in the case of electromagnetism to some of the freedom open in the original preparation of the state of the system. However, it is not at all clear that this freedom remains when in accordance with the consideration of Einstein attention is restricted to a « properly closed space ». The energy of a closed universe is not even a definable quantity, so there can be no possibility of preparing the system in any one of a number of alternative states of different proper energies. More important, however, is a new issue of principle about the closed universe of general relativity (H. EVERETT III: *Rev. Mod. Phys.*, **29**, 454 (1957); J. A. WHEELER: *Rev. Mod. Phys.*, **29**, 463 (1957)). There is no place to stand outside the system to observe it. There is nothing outside it to produce transitions from one state to another. Therefore the question raises itself, how to distinguish one state from another. Or are the boundary conditions in the case of a closed universe such, that there is only one permissible quantum state for the system? Whether there exists in this sense a unique « *universal wave function* » is perhaps the most challenging of all questions associated with the quantization of general relativity. (In this connection see also C. W. MISNER: *Rev. Mod. Phys.*, **29**, 497 (1957)).

so far as concerns field fluctuations of substantial scale. They can have small amplitude or large amplitude, depending upon the state in which the system is prepared. However, the state functional of a continuous field presents a new feature when fluctuations of small scale are considered, provided that the state functional is not singular. The amplitude of the fluctuations of small scale approaches a standard level characteristic of that scale alone (Table VIII) provided that the scale in question is smaller than the scale of any particularities built into the state functional itself (54).

11·11. *Virtual foam-like structure of space.* – So much for the formal machinery to describe state functions and for the inevitability of small scale fluctuations in electrodynamics and in geometrodynamics; now back to the physical consequences of these fluctuations for the nature of space and for the nature of the « undressed electron ».

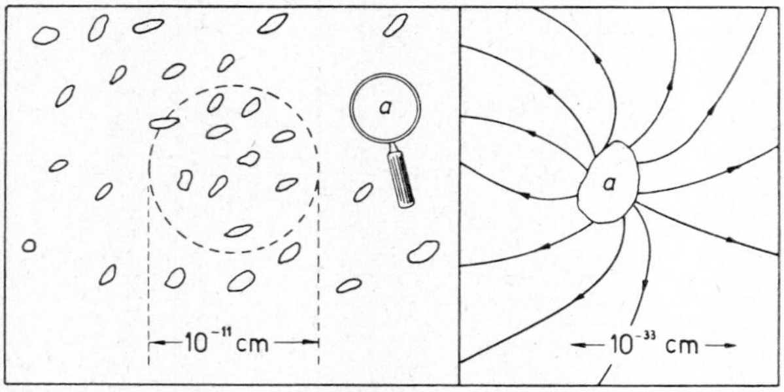

Fig. 17. – Configuration of the 3-space geometry — and electromagnetic field — of the type for which the probability amplitude is reduced only very little compared to the peak value of the probability amplitude. The small circles indicate wormhole mouths associated with the multiple connectedness of the space. The typical dimension characteristic of this topology is of the order $L^* = (\hbar G/c^3)^{\frac{1}{2}} = 1.6 \cdot 10^{-33}$ cm, far smaller than any dimension with any direct relevance to the elementary particle problem, $(\hbar/mc) = 3.9 \cdot 10^{-11}$ cm. Associated with a typical wormhole such as a is not only a great curvature of space, but also a great field, as indicated by the lines of force in the enlarged view of a at the right.

Fig. 17 provides a symbolic representation of the typical configuration to which the state functional of the combined gravitational and electromagnetic field will assign a probability amplitude of only little less than peak value. In this configuration 1) Space has a foam-like structure, being endowed not only with a macrocurvature on the scale of the universe, but also a microcurvature on the scale L^*. 2) Wormhole mouths occur almost everywhere,

(54) For a discussion related to this point, see N. Bohr and L. Rosenfeld: *Kgl. Dan. Viden. Sels., Mat.-fys. Medd.*, **12**, no. 8 (1933).

with typical spacings and typical dimensions of the order of L^*. 3) A wormhole of dimension L—not necessarily exactly of the order L^*—typically has threading through it a field of the order $E \sim (\hbar c)^{\frac{1}{2}}/L^2$. In consequence the wormhole is endowed with a flux and its two ends with effective charges of the order $\sim L^2 E \sim (\hbar c)^{\frac{1}{2}} \sim 12e$. 4) This charge is one order of magnitude greater than the elementary quantum of charge, is not quantized, and has no direct relationship whatever to the charge of an elementary particle. 5) The densities of energy, $E^2/8\pi$, and of mass, $E^2/8\pi c^2$, associated with the typical field are enormous, $\sim \hbar c/L^{*4}$ and $\sim \hbar/cL^{*4} = c^5/\hbar G^2 = 5 \cdot 10^{93}$ g/cm^3, compared to anything familiar from the elementary particle problem. 6) So is the electrical mass-energy of a worm hole:

$$m_1 = (\hbar/cL^{*4})L^{*3} = (\hbar c/G)^{\frac{1}{2}} = 2.2 \cdot 10^{-5}\ \text{g (or} \sim 10^{28}\ \text{eV)}\,. \tag{108}$$

7) The gravitational energy of interaction of two typical nearby worm holes is of the order

$$E_{\text{grav}} \sim -Gm_1^2/L^*\,. \tag{109}$$

The associated lowering of mass,

$$E_{\text{grav}}/c^2 \sim -(G/c^2)(\hbar c/G)(c^3/\hbar G)^{\frac{1}{2}} = -m_1 \tag{110}$$

is of the same order as the positive mass of the two interacting concentrations of *electromagnetic energy.* In other words, *gravitational interactions make a decisive contribution towards compensating the zero point energy of the electromagnetic field,* an energy which in so many ways of calculation turns out to be infinite. For example, if each field oscillator is assigned an energy $\hbar\omega/2$, then the electromagnetic energy up to the circular frequency $= c/L$ is

$$2\int_0^{\omega} (\hbar\omega/2)\, 4\pi(\omega/2\pi c)^2\, \mathrm{d}(\omega/2\pi c) \sim \hbar c/L^4\,, \tag{111}$$

—a divergent quantity if the analysis is extended to indefinitely small distances. However, at distances L of the order of magnitude of L^* and smaller, completely new geometries come into consideration which entirely change the analysis of the problem of the electromagnetic zero point energy. That problem cannot be escaped here by arbitrarily subtracting off the zero point energy. There is no disposable additive constant of energy in general relativity because energy has mass and mass curves space. Therefore it is significant to discover that *quantum* geometrodynamics imposes fundamentally new and more hopeful considerations on the problem of divergent field energy.

11·12. *Identification of the fluctuation wormhole with the undressed electron.* – Quantum geometrodynamics has thus this much point of contact with the much more thoroughly analyzed theory of quantum electrodynamics, that all space in both accounts is the seat of violent fluctuations. But what of the other characteristic feature of electrodynamics—the « undressed electron »? *If there is to be any correspondence between pure quantum geometrodynamics* —with no extra fields, no coupling constants, and no arbitrary inventive elements—*and quantum electrodynamics, then the « undressed electron » must be identified with the elementary wormhole.* Its mass must be said to be of the order of $m_1 = 2.2 \cdot 10^{-5}$ g, its charge of the order of $(\hbar c)^{\frac{1}{2}} \sim 12e \sim 56 \cdot 10^{-10}$ esu, its dimensions of the order $L^* = 1.6 \cdot 10^{-33}$ cm. Only this identification can provide in straight quantized general relativity a natural picture for the virtual pairs throughout all space which are demanded in the most compelling way by quantum electrodynamics.

11·13. *Renormalization of mass and charge.* – It is not an objection to such a geometrical account of the « undressed electron » that it does not provide a sharply defined charge or mass for this object. The theory of renormalization in quantum electrodynamics already has place [55] for the concept of a distribution in mass values for the « undressed electron ». Likewise the spread in charge values for this entity in no way contradicts the atomicity in the charge of the experimental electron.

11·14. *Implications of small scale of fluctuations for phenomenological theory.* – If this picture of the undressed electron has any relation to reality, then it follows that the vacuum—already in the absence of any experimental electrons—has going on in it the most fantastic wealth of physics, with enormous concentrations of electromagnetic energy, multiply connected topology, and fluctuations of exceedingly small scale. All these phenomena differ in scale by many powers of ten from anything encountered in normal atomic or elementary particle processes. Therefore a phenomenological theory of these processes should make sense which contains no explicit reference to the mass m_1 and the length L^*. This kind of theory is analogous to a phenomenological theory of elasticity which never mentions atoms or molecules or their laws of interaction. Quantum electrodynamics—or subtraction physics—is such a theory. It is able to deal with a wide range of questions without having to ask from what source undressed and dressed electrons derive their charge and mass. The theory's most striking success and most striking failure—its accuracy of prediction and its divergence in principle—are a little more understandable if the geometrodynamical picture of the dressed electron makes sense. On this view they are both due to the same cause—the extreme smallness of

---

[55] G. KÄLLÉN: *Quantenelektrodynamik*, in *Handb. d. Phys.*, edited by S. FLÜGGE, vol. 5, part I (Berlin, 1958); and W. THIRRING: *Principles of Quantum Electrodynamics* (New York, 1958).

the characteristic length of vacuum physics, L^*, compared to the characteristic length of electron physics, $L_m = \hbar/mc$ ([56]).

11·15. *Particles interpreted as collective disturbances superposed on vacuum physics.* – A particle, according to this purely geometrical interpretation of nature, makes percentagewise an almost negligible perturbation upon the violent physics of the vacuum. If this vacuum is compared to a solid body, then the electron is to be compared to a passing phonon. That collective disturbance contributes almost nothing to the relatively enormous energies of circulation of the electrons in any atom of the solid. Similarly an electron—and any other particle—is to be regarded on the microscopic scale of geometrodynamics as relatively unimportant in the scheme of things. For if the re-evant density of mass-energy is of the order

$$m/L_m^3 \sim m^4c^3/\hbar^3 = 1.57\cdot 10^4 \text{ g/cm}^3 \; ; \tag{102}$$

for the vacuum it is

$$m_1/L^{*3} \sim 5\cdot 10^{93} \text{ g/cm}^3 \; . \tag{103}$$

To explain the mass of the electron, on this view, is like explaining the speed of a collective disturbance such as a phonon; and the existence of particles with different characteristic masses is somewhat analogous to the existence in liquid helium of different types of collective disturbance, or different branches in the curve of frequency as a function of wave number. The specific and non-electric forces between some particles, and the weak specific forces that act on the electron and μ-meson, are to be compared with the interaction between phonons or excitons or spin waves that differ in mode of polarization or otherwise ([57]).

This purely geometrodynamical description of elementary particles does not have the status of a theory definite enough in its predictions to be confirmed or denied by experiment. Moreover, it has no relation to a recent attempt to explain elementary particles in terms of the states of a single fundamental spinor field. This field is conceived to evolve within the arena of a flat space-time. Therefore it has no evident connection with geometry. The proposal

---

([56]) The possible significance of gravitation physics for the elementary particle problem, and the effective cut-off it imposes at small distances for the otherwise divergent self-energy of the electron, have been pointed out by L. D. LANDAU, A. A. ABRIKOSOV and I. M. KHALATNIKOV: *Dokl. Akad. Nauk SSSR*, **95**, 497 (1954); D. IVANENKO: *Suppl. Nuovo Cimento*, **6**, 349 (1957) and *Max Planck Festschrift* (1958), p. 353, and W. PAULI: *Helv. Phys. Acta Suppl.*, **4**, 267 (1956). See also S. DESER: *Rev. Mod. Phys.*, **29**, 417 (1957).

([57]) For the interaction of excitons, see for example R. E. MERRIFIELD: *Journ. Chem. Phys.*, **31**, 522 (1959).

in question goes back to IWANENKO ([58]) and has recently been taken up actively in a modified form by HEISENBERG ([59]). A non-linear equation ([60]) is introduced containing a quantity l with the dimensions of a length,

$$\gamma^{\mu}\,\partial\psi/\partial x^{\mu}_{+}\, l^2\gamma_{\sigma}\gamma_5\,\psi(\overline{\psi}\gamma^{\sigma}\gamma_5\psi) = 0$$

having no connection whatsoever with the characteristic distance L^* of quantum geometrodynamics. It is of course possible that the solution of the particle problem lies in this or in some quite different direction. However, if a more conservative approach has any validity; if there is any hope of understanding elementary particles within the framework of ideas due to MAXWELL and

---

([58]) D. IVANENKO: *Sov. Phys.*, **13**, 141 (1938); A. SOKOLOV and D. IVANENKO: *Kwantowaja Theorija Polja*, part. II, Sect. **3** (Moskow and Leningrad, 1952); D. IVANENKO: *Suppl. Nuovo Cimento*, **6**, 349 (1957) and *Max Planck Festschrift* (1958), p. 353.

([59]) W. HEISENBERG: *Rev. Mod. Phys.*, **29**, 269 (1957); *Padua-Venice Conference* (Oct. 1957); Leipziger Vortrag (April 1958); H. P. DÜRR, W. HEISENBERG, H. MITTER, S. SCHLIEDER and K. YAMAZAKI: *Zeits. f. Naturfor.*, **14a**, 441 (1959).

([60]) It is sometimes jokingly said, « Nature is complicated; non-linear equations are complicated; therefore nature should be described in terms of non-linear equations ». However, it should be noted in what an important way the non-linearities of general relativity differ from those of the proposed non-linear spinor equation. The spinor equation is locally non-linear. In contrast, the « non-linear » equations of gravitation theory are locally *linear* in this sense, that a coordinate system can always be introduced at any point P such that the metric at this point has locally a Lorentz character. Derivations from the Lorentz metric come in only as the square of the distance from P. The equations for these deviations from flatness in this neighborhood and in this coordinate system are linear. In other words, the so-called non-linear features of general relativity are actually of a very special and subtle kind in that they show themselves only over *extended regions* of space-time. This circumstance comes particularly to the fore when one discusses the global and topological properties of the solutions of Einstein's equations. A solution is normally treated as acceptable in a given region only if in the vicinity of every point in that region the metric is perfectly regular. This locally Lorentz character of space-time is of course demanded by Einstein's principle of equivalence, according to which one can always eliminate accelerations at a given point by transformation to a suitable local frame of reference. The accelerations were only of gravitational origin in the original formulation of the equivalence principle. Charged particles received another analysis. However, charged objects from the point of view of classical geometrodynamics are non-localized objects. At any local point there never appears anything with the character of charge. In any vicinity with dimensions l small compared to a wormhole mouth the question of acceleration of a charge can never arise. Also in such a neighborhood and in an appropriate coordinate system the electromagnetic field makes a non-Lorentzian contribution to the metric which is only of order l^2. In this microscopic sense and in the framework of classical geometrodynamics the equivalence principle applied as well in the presence of electromagnetic fields as in the case of pure gravitational fields. In other words in a wider sense than ever before Einstein's deeply fundamental principle of equivalence would seem to demand strict *local linearity* of field equations.

TABLE IX. – *Present geometrodynamical concepts of classical and quantized charge compared and contrasted.*

Nature of elementary charged object	Classical	Quantum
Name	Wormhole mouth	Elementary particle
Observed	No	Yes
Dimensions, L	Macroscopic, L	$L \sim 10^{-12}$ or 10^{-13} cm
Wormhole description of object	Mouth of a single wormhole	Of order of 10^{60} to 10^{63} virtual wormhole mouths in a region of dimensions 10^{-12} cm, the surroundings of which to infinite distances are endowed with a practically equal density of virtual wormholes
Flux of lines of force through a single wormhole (charge of wormhole)	Anything from 0 up to $\sim (c^2/G^{\frac{1}{2}})L$ or $\sim (c^2/G^{\frac{1}{2}})[(G/c^2)\cdot(\text{mass})]$ $\sim G^{\frac{1}{2}}\cdot(\text{mass})$	Varies from wormhole to wormhole, but typically of the order of $\sim(\hbar c)^{\frac{1}{2}} \sim 12e$ and therefore enormous compared to the classical limit of $G^{\frac{1}{2}}\cdot(10^{-27}\text{ g})$ or $\sim 10^{-21}\,e$
Overall charge of charged object	Same as foregoing	A quantized multiple of e; value of quantum of charge independent of fields to which object is subject, according to quantum electrodynamics
Importance of quantum fluctuations in metric for description of this charged object	Fluctuations do not come into consideration in classical geometrodynamics	All important
Ratio of root mean squared fields far from object to root mean squared fields in immediate vicinity	Negligible so long as discussion is entirely classical and so long as actual fluctuations in real physical vacuum are overlooked	Unity to one part in $10^{\sim 80}$
Extra curvature of space due to presence of charged object, relative to curvature that would exist in its absence	Enormous	Negligible to one part in $10^{\sim 80}$
Wormhole connection between charge of this object and an opposite charge somewhere else in space	Well defined connection to a specific wormhole mouth somewhere else in space	Not one wormhole but an enormous number of them. Not real and classical but virtual and quantum. The connections they establish extend all over everywhere, not to a single well defined opposite charge
Oversimplified recapitulation of this concept of charged object	Simple topological handle that traps lines of force	Collective disturbance of almost negligible strength in a foam-like medium

EINSTEIN and modern quantum theory, without additions and changes; if there are no supplementary fields and coupling parameters to be brought in from outside; if all physics is pure geometry—then it would seem difficult to bring the battle-tested conclusions of quantum electrodynamics into correspondence with the most evident features of quantum geometrodynamics except along such lines as those sketched out here. In this case there would seem to be no escape from the picture of *elementary particles as exceedingly weak collective disturbances in a physics-rich curved empty space of virtual foam-like constitution.*

11·16. *Completely different character of classical and quantum charged objects.* – This brief sketch of almost all one knows today about the nature of quantum geometrodynamics emphasizes how very great is the difference between a physical charged particle and one of the geons, or one of the wormhole mouths, of classical geometrodynamics (Table IX). EINSTEIN and ROSEN in more recent times ([61]), as well as REISSNER and NORDSTRØM in the early days of Einstein's theory, concluded that the charged particles in nature do not admit a description in terms of general relativity. The geometrized mass of the electron, for example,

$$m^* = Gm/c^2 = (9.1\cdot 10^{-28}\ \text{g})(0.74\cdot 10^{-28}\ \text{cm/g}) = 6.8\cdot 10^{-56} \tag{115}$$

and its geometrized charge,

$$e^* = G^{\frac{1}{2}}e/c^2 = (4.8\cdot 10^{-10}\ \text{esu})(2.9\cdot 10^{-25}\ \text{cm/esu}) = 1.4\cdot 10^{-34}\ \text{cm} \tag{116}$$

do not satisfy the energy criterion

$$(m^*)^2 > (e^*)^2 \tag{117}$$

which applies to the spherically symmetric solution of the coupled equations of gravitation and electromagnetism. From this circumstance they concluded that they ought to change the equations of general relativity or go over to some completely different point of view. However, no problem arises on this score if one gives up any idea that the electron is to be compared with a *classical* object (distinction between last two columns in the table). It is therefore essential to maintain a sharp distinction between two absolutely different pictures of an electrically charged object: 1) a single classical wormhole and 2) a collective disturbance of a highly quantum character in a medium topologically so densely connected that it resembles a foam. What is suggested

([61]) A. EINSTEIN and N. ROSEN: *Phys. Rev.*, **48**, 73 (1935).

by this distinction about the nature of elementary particles? First, there is no reason at this point to fear that a purely *geometrical* description lacks the richness to describe the manifold features of the physical world. There may be deep subtleties in the nature of « geometry » in a final analysis, but the four-dimensional Riemannian space-time continuum of geometrodynamics already offers a descriptive framework of previously unsuspected scope. Second, *topology* has proved indispensable in giving a purely geometrical description of charge. Therefore there is good reason to search further for the implications of multiple connectivity for spin, for neutrinos, and for the symmetry properties of elementary particles. Third, renewed reasons have shown themselves to regard the *physics of the vacuum* as a rich subject and also as a vital foundation for understanding the constitution of particles. Finally, out of pure geometry and nothing more one discovers that he can *derive quantities* of the most lively physical significance.

To date only an infinitesimal beginning has been made on applying to neutrino and elementary particle physics these concepts of pure geometry, topology, the vacuum, and derived quantities.

And of more concern, nowhere in the scheme of geometrodynamics does there today appear any completely natural place for the neutrino. Therefore issues of neutrino physics, unsolved and solved, form the subject of the rest of this account. But before turning to them it is appropriate to cast a backward glance over the central themes of the present section—geometrodynamics and the quantum principle—to ask for any clue to a larger framework of ideas that might include them both.

11·17. *Topological aspect of quantum theory.* – One feature about the quantization of a classical system turns out to be topological in character ([62]). This feature shows up most directly when quantum mechanics is formulated by Feynman's method of sum over histories ([63]). *The value of the sum over histories depends upon the topology of the class of histories over which the sum is extended* (Fig. 18). The difference between the value of the sum for two different classes of histories gives the commutator of the operator formulation of quantum mechanics. Yet non-commutative operators never explicitly put in an appearance in the foundations of the Feynman method. Commutators receive instead a topological analysis.

([62]) This way of stating the matter arose in presenting field theory to a class in quantum mechanics in 1955 and was described in the Lorentz lectures at Leiden in 1956 (unpublished). Appreciation is expressed to H. Dempster for clearing up many features of this formulation of the quantum mechanics of particles and fields.

([63]) R. P. Feynman: *Ph. D. Thesis* (Princeton, 1942); *Rev. Mod. Phys.*, **20**, 367 (1948); J. C. Polkinghorne: *Proc. Roy. Soc.*, A **230**, 272 (1955); P. Choquard: *Helv. Phys. Acta*, **28**, 89 (1955).

To see topology appear in quantum mechanics after it has put in such a striking appearance in geometrodynamics raises the question whether there is some deep and today only partially revealed topological unity between these

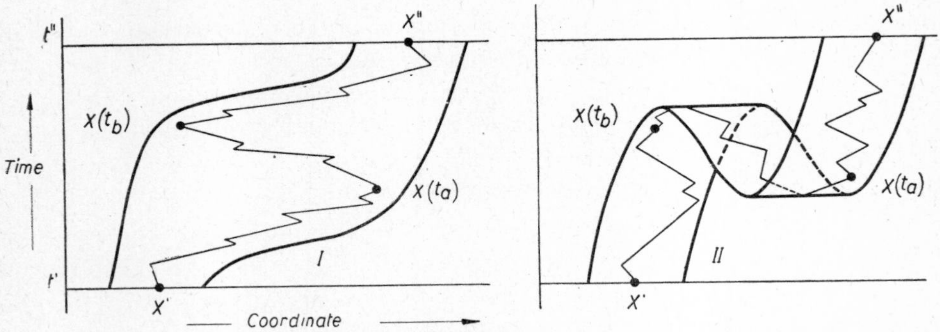

Fig. 18. – The fabric of history is unrolled differently at I and at II. Histories themselves therefore have different topologies in the two cases, as witness two different histories that lead from the same initial configuration to the same final configuration. Let I_H denote the classical action for the history H of a harmonic oscillator. Let $\underset{H}{S}$ denote the operation of summing over all histories, with equal weight for each, and with such a normalization that the sum $\langle x''t''|x't'\rangle = \underset{H}{S} \exp[iI_H/\hbar]$ is unitary. Then this expression is the propagator. It has the same value whether the sum goes over histories of the type I or histories of the type II. Not the same, however, are the values of the sum

$$\langle x''t''|x(t_b)x(t_a)|x't'\rangle = \underset{H}{S}\, x(t_b)x(t_a) \exp[iI_H/\hbar]\,,$$

for the two classes of histories. The difference is equal to the commutator of the *operators* $x(t_b)$ and $x(t_a)$ of the operator formalism, despite the fact that $x(t_b)$ and $x(t_a)$ are ordinary c-numbers, not operators.

two aspects of physics. It is not clear in what direction to look for an answer. Therefore the following brief resumé of the sum over histories and the topological description of commutators will be limited to the bare facts, plus some details which will later be of use in considering the quantum theory of the neutrino.

11˙18. *Feynman's method of the sum over histories.* – It will be enough to consider a dynamical system with a single degree of freedom to survey the main ideas. The *configuration* of the system at the time t' is described by the single number x'. A *history* H is described by a function $x_H(t)$. Attention will be limited to histories H which are compatible with specified initial and final configurations, in the sense

$$x_H(t') = x'\;;$$

$$x_H(t'') = x''\,.$$

The central idea in quantum mechanics is the existence of a *probability amplitude* $\psi(x, t)$ which evolves in time in accordance with the Schrödinger differential equation or equivalently, in accordance with an integral equation,

$$\psi(x'', t'') = \int \langle x''t'' | x't' \rangle \, \psi(x', t') \, dx' . \tag{118}$$

The quantity $\langle x''t'' | x't' \rangle$, the *propagator*, can be found from any classical Lagrange function, $L(x, \dot{x}, t)$, which is of second degree in the velocities, by either of two procedures. 1) Define the momentum $p = \partial L/\partial \dot{x}$ and the Hamiltonian $H = p\dot{x} - L = H(p, x, t)$. Write down the equation

$$i\hbar \, \partial \langle xt | x't' \rangle / \partial t = H(-i\hbar \, \partial/\partial x, x, t) \langle xt | x't' \rangle , \tag{119}$$

where it may be necessary to consider the question of proper ordering of the non-commutative factors in H. Solve this Schrödinger equation subject to the boundary condition that the propagator at the time $t = t'$ shall vanish everywhere except at $x = x'$. Multiply the solution by such a normalization factor that the propagators for different times shall satisfy the *composition law*

$$\int \langle x'''t''' | x''t'' \rangle \, dx'' \, \langle x''t'' | x't' \rangle = \langle x'''t''' | x't' \rangle . \tag{120}$$

2) Define alternatively a *skeleton history* by distinguishing a set of intermediate times $t' < t_1 < t_2 < \ldots < t_n < t$ and by specifying the configuration at these times: $x_1, x_2, \ldots, x_n$. By differences of the type

$$v \to \frac{x_{k+1} - x_k}{t_{k+1} - t_k} ,$$

rather than by derivatives compute a Lagrange function and the difference version of the classical action integral,

$$I_H = \int L(x_H(t), \dot{x}_H(t), t) \, dt . \tag{121}$$

On occasion there is a certain ambiguity in how derivatives shall be re-expressed as differences, this ambiguity being closely related to the question of ordering of factors in the Hamiltonian. Sum the expression $\exp[iI_H/\hbar]$ over skeleton histories by integrating over the co-ordinates $x_1, x_2, \ldots, x_n$ (x' and x'' being fixed), including in front of the integral an appropriate normalizing factor. Proceed to the limit of infinitely fine subdivision of time. The limiting value of the integral, the « sum over all histories », gives the propagator

$$\langle x''t'' | x't' \rangle = \underset{H}{S} \exp[iI_H/\hbar] . \tag{122}$$

In the case of a free particle the propagator found by either method turns out to have the same value it would have for the most primitive conceivable skeleton history, a displacement linearly dependent upon time,

$$\langle x''t''\,|\,x't'\rangle = \left(\frac{m}{2\pi i\hbar(t''-t')}\right)^{\frac{1}{2}} \exp\left[\frac{im(x''-x')^2}{2\hbar(t''-t')}\right]. \tag{123}$$

For a particle bound by a harmonic oscillator potential the exponent in the propagator is again equal to the extremal value of the classical action; that is, to Hamilton's principal function:

$$\langle x''t''\,|\,x't'\rangle = \left(\frac{m\omega}{2\pi i\hbar \sin\omega(t''-i')}\right)^{\frac{1}{2}} \exp\frac{im\omega(x''^2+x'^2-2x''x'\cos\omega(t''-t'))}{2\hbar\sin\omega(t''-t')}. \tag{124}$$

A generalization of this procedure suffices to quantize a classical *field*, as for example the electromagnetic field. Space is subdivided as well as time. There results a 4-dimensional lattice of points in space time. It is bounded in past and future by space-like surfaces σ' and σ''; that is, by two 3-dimensional lattices. To specify the value of the field at each point of σ' is to give a *field configuration*, C'. Fixing the field at each point of the 4-lattice determines a *field history*, H. Attention is limited to histories H which agree on σ' with the configuration C' and which match C'' on σ''. At all lattice points between σ' and σ'' the appropriate field quantities are now treated as variable, of integration, and in this way the sum of histories is once more evaluated to give the field propagator

$$\langle C''\sigma''\,|\,C'\sigma'\rangle = \mathop{S}_{H} \exp\left[iI_H/\hbar\right], \tag{125}$$

in the limit of finer and finer subdivision of space and time. The propagator is again normalized to satisfy the composition law.

$$\mathop{S}_{C''}\langle C'''\sigma'''\,|\,C''\sigma''\rangle\langle C''\sigma''\,|\,C'\sigma'\rangle = \langle C'''\sigma'''\,|\,C'\sigma'\rangle. \tag{126}$$

In the case of source free general relativity the configuration variables C and the parameters which specify the surface σ are inextricably intertwined into a single simple concept, the intrinsic 3 geometry, $\mathscr{G}$.

11·19. *Topologically distinct histories.* – In the application of the composition law—say the composition law in the elementary form (120)—it is not required that the time t'' be intermediate between t' and t'''. The propagator for the evolution of the system from t' to a t'' *greater* than t''' can be folded together with a propagator for the backwards evolution from t'' to t''' to get the propagator for going directly from t' to t'''; it makes no difference what value t'' has. While the propagators have this composition property, matrix elements in general have not.

The matrix element of the product of the co-ordinates x at two specified and distinct times t_a and t_b is defined ([64]) as the sum over histories,

$$\langle x'''t''' \, | x(t_b)\, x(t_a) \, | x't' \rangle = \underset{H}{S}\, x(t_b)\, x(t_a) \exp\, [iI_H/\hbar] \; ; \tag{127}$$

similarly for the matrix element of other operators. However, *the definition is complete only if the topology of the history is specified* to the extent necessary to distinguish between cases I and II in Fig. 18. In the case of the harmonic oscillator the two definitions differ from each other by the amount

$$(\hbar/im\omega) \sin \omega(t_b - t_a) \, . \tag{128}$$

This agrees with the value of the commutator between the *operator* quantities $\boldsymbol{x}(t_b)$ and $\boldsymbol{x}(t_a)$ in the usual operator formulation of quantum mechanics.

11·20. *Commutators without commutators*; *operators without operators.* – In a similar way for the electromagnetic field it is possible to calculate two inequivalent values for the matrix element of the product

$$A_\mu(x_a, t_a)\, A_\nu(x_b, t_b) \, . \tag{129}$$

The difference between histories of the two distinct topologies agrees with the usual value for the commutator of two electromagnetic field quantities. Thus, starting from a sum over histories in which no operator quantity ever makes an appearance, one secures the equivalent of the usual commutation relations; or briefly, finds « *commutators without commutators* ».

Of course commutators have a stature in Feynman's description of quantum mechanics which is secondary to their part in the operator form of the theory. In that form of the theory, the commutators are needed in order to define the algebra of the operators, this algebra in turn being needed so that one can derive relations between observables. These relations typically lead to differential equations. Feynman's procedure concentrates less on writing down equations to be solved and more on writing down formal—and often very useful—expressions for the solutions. In short, it provides « *operators without operators.* »

Quantum mechanics thus lends itself naturally to topological considerations. What kind of inner connection therefore is there, if any, between this sort of topology and the topology of geometrodynamics? This question stands unanswered.

([64]) F. J. Dyson: *Lecture Notes on Quantum Electrodynamics* (Cornell University, 1954).

II. – Does there Exist a Purely Geometrical Description of the Neutrino Field?

1. – If not, geometrodynamics is deficient.

Many elementary particles have half integral spin. It is impossible to accept any description of elementary particles that does not have a place for spin $\frac{1}{2}$. What then has any purely geometrical description to offer in explanation of spin $\frac{1}{2}$ in general? More particularly and more importantly, what possible place is there in quantum geometrodynamics for the neutrino—the only entity of half integral spin which is a pure field in its own right, in the sense that it has zero rest mass and moves with the speed of light? No clear or satisfactory answer is known to this question today. Unless and until an answer is forthcoming, *pure quantum geometrodynamics must be judged deficient as a basis for elementary particle physics*. Therefore it is appropriate to list and discuss some of the attempts to find a natural place for the neutrino in quantum geometrodynamics.

2. – Correspondence principle inapplicable to neutrino field; « non-classical two-valuedness ».

It is not possible to find any classical description of the neutrino field along correspondence principle lines. In this respect this third field of zero rest mass is quite different in character from gravitation and electromagnetism. For them it is possible to go from the quantum theory to the classical limit, for example in the sense that the vibrational quantum numbers or « occupation numbers » of the various modes of oscillation of the electromagnetic field are allowed to become very large. But the neutrino satisfies Fermi statistics and cannot have occupation numbers greater than unity. Thus there is no obvious classical starting point for an analysis of the neutrino field. A wider framework of ideas seems necessary. To extract the concept of spin out of classical geometry alone would appear as impossible as the faded hope of a few early investigators to derive quantum mechanics *out of* relativity. So far as one can judge, quantum considerations must be accepted from the beginning in dealing with the neutrino and with spin. No one was more aware of this than PAULI. His wonderfully descriptive term « non-classical two-valuedness » antedated the term « spin ».

3. – Composition of fields of higher spin out of fields of spin $\frac{1}{2}$ not found workable.

Not to try to derive a spinor field out of geometry, but to try to derive gravitational—and electromagnetic—fields out of a spinor field is an approach sometimes advocated. Instead of going in the direction

$$\text{Tensor} \to \text{Vector} \to \text{Spinor}\,,$$

it has in the past seemed more natural to go in the direction

$$\text{Spinor} \to \text{Vector} \to \text{Tensor}\,.$$

However, the best studied attempt to proceed in this direction—the neutrino theory of light (65)—has been abandoned. PRYCE discovered (66) that such a theory in any form so far discussed does not possess proper relativistic invariance. The theory assumes that there exists between neutrinos a physical interaction, never introduced explicitly and never discussed, such that a photon is described by a pair consisting of one neutrino and one antineutrino; or rather, by a linear superposition of very many such pairs of states.

Quite a different coupling of neutrinos, the much more explicit coupling of β decay theory, the exchange of neutrinos between nucleons, was proposed as a mechanism for the generation of gravitational forces, after this coupling was found to be too weak to account for nuclear forces. HEISENBERG, shortly after putting forward the view that nucleons are the elementary constituents of nuclear matter, held together by exchange forces, suggested that the neutrino might be the intermediary in such a coupling (67). This interaction was analysed in more detail by BETHE and BACHER (68). They found that the resulting effective nucleon-nucleon coupling 1) diverges, 2) can only be made finite by a cut off, 3) then varies as the inverse seventh power of the distance between nucleons, and 4) for a cut off distance of the order of $2\cdot10^{-12}$ cm, is too weak by a factor $\sim 10^{12}$ to account for nucleon-nucleon binding. That two neutrino exchange is connected with gravitational rather than nuclear

(65) P. JORDAN: *Ergeb. exakt. Naturwiss.*, **7**, 158 (1928); *Zeits. Phys.*, **105**, 229 (1937); P. JORDAN and R. DE L. KRONIG: *Zeits. Phys.*, **100**, 569 (1936); R. DE L. KRONIG: *Physica*, **3**, 1120 (1936); also L. DE BROGLIE, W. HEISENBERG and H. A. KRAMERS in: *L. de Broglie, Physicien et Penseur* (Paris, 1953).

(66) M. H. L. PRYCE: *Proc. Roy Soc.*, **165**, A. 247 (1938). Additional comments in J. A. WHEELER: *Phys. Rev.*, **97**, 534 (1955) (p. 181 of present text). See also publications of A. SOKOLOV and K. M. CASE.

(67) Lectures at Cavendish Laboratory (Cambridge, 1934), unpublished.

(68) H. A. BETHE and R. F. BACHER: *Rev. Mod. Phys.*, **8**, 201 (1936).

forces was a later proposal of GAMOW and TELLER (69). An artificial hypothesis to remove divergences from the interaction integrals was proposed by BOCCHIERI, GULMANELLI and MONTALDI (70). The consequences of this hypothesis are not known. Without such a hypothesis, on the basis of the Fermi interaction as it presently exists, KAWAGUCHI arrived at an effective interaction potential which 1) for some unexplained reason differs from that of BETHE and BACHER in having a $1/r$ rather than a $1/r^3$ dependence but which still, 2) « does not produce any detectable correction to the gravitational force » (71).

4. – Spinor as square root of a vector?

Attempts to proceed from spin $\frac{1}{2}$ to larger spins—the spin 1 of electromagnetism and the spin 2 of gravitation (72)—having thus been thwarted, what can be said of attempts to go the other way? In already unified field theory the electromagnetic field strength is represented as the « Maxwell square root » of Ricci curvature tensor, a quantity unique up to the angle α of the complexion:

$$f_{\mu\nu} = \xi_{\mu\nu} \cos\alpha + * \, \xi_{\mu\nu} \sin\alpha \, ,$$

where

$$\xi_{\mu\alpha}\xi^{\varkappa\alpha} + * \, \xi_{\mu\alpha} * \xi^{\varkappa\alpha} = R_{\mu}^{\varkappa} = (8\pi G/c^4)\cdot(\text{stress energy tensor}) \, . \tag{130}$$

In this sense a field of spin 1 can be said to be derivable from a field of spin 2. Is it then possible to « take a second square root » to derive a spinor field? Or equivalently, can one transcribe all the content of neutrino theory into a formalism that uses only vectors and tensors, as already unified field theory expresses Maxwell's equations entirely in terms of the metric tensor and its derivatives?

5. – Inconsistent with Fermi character of neutrino field.

Out of the wave function ψ of a spinor field, such as the neutrino field and the associated quantity $\psi^\dagger$ it is easy and natural to construct the familiar bilinear combinations that give a scalar, a vector, a tensor, a pseudovector

---

(69) G. GAMOW and E. TELLER: *Phys. Rev.*, **51**, 289 (1937); G. GAMOW: *Phys. Rev.*, **71**, 550 (1947); H. C. CORBEN: *Nuovo Cimento*, **10**, 1485 (1953).

(70) P. BOCCHIERI and P. GULMANELLI: *Nuovo Cimento*, **5**, 1016 (1957); P. GULMANELLI and E. MONTALDI: *Nuovo Cimento*, **5**, 1716 (1957).

(71) M. KAWAGUCHI: *Nuovo Cimento*, **8**, 506 (1958).

(72) M. FIERZ and W. PAULI: *Helv. Phys. Acta*, **12**, 297 (1939).

and a pseudoscalar. Moreover it is possible to work back from these combinations—provided that they satisfy certain consistency conditions—to ψ itself (73). However, no useful point of view has developed along these lines to connect spinor fields with the geometry of space. This negative outcome might be expected from the circumstance that the correspondence principle applies to geometry but not to a spinor field.

6. – Duality rotations for electromagnetism and neutrinos.

It would not be right to leave the « square root process » without noting one striking analogy between the neutrino field and the electromagnetic field. If $\boldsymbol{e}$ and $\boldsymbol{h}$ denote the electric and magnetic parts of the field tensor $\boldsymbol{f}$, and if they satisfy Maxwell's equations for curved empty space, then it is well known that the same equations are also satisfied by new fields, $\boldsymbol{e}'$ and $\boldsymbol{h}'$, defined by the *duality rotation* (9)

$$\boldsymbol{e}' + i\boldsymbol{h}' = \exp[*\alpha_0](\boldsymbol{e} + i\boldsymbol{h}) , \tag{131}$$

where α_0 is an additive constant of complexion. In the same way, if ψ satisfies the neutrino wave equation in curved space-time, so does (74) the *duality rotated spinor*,

$$\psi' = \exp[\tfrac{1}{2} i\beta_0\gamma_5]\psi . \tag{132}$$

Therefore it is natural to ask an unanswered question: does there exist any deeper connection between the two kinds of duality rotation?

7. – Spinors give tool to describe local rotations.

Another fundamental issue is this: What geometric function do *spinors* serve that is not already served by co-ordinate transformations? They *permit one*, MARCEL RIESZ replies, *to describe—as co-ordinate transformations with their element of continuity never can—a rotation (or Lorentz transformation) at one point in 4-space that has nothing to do with any localized rotation at any*

(73) T. TAKABAYASI: *Progr. Theor. Phys.*, **8**, 143 (1952); **9**, 187 (1953). See also E. WHITTAKER: *Proc. Roy. Soc. London*, A **158**, 38 (1937) (discussed by J. L. SYNGE in *Proc. Edinburgh Math. Soc.*, **11**, 39 (1958)); D. BOHM, R. SCHILLER and J. TIOMNO: *Suppl. Nuovo Cimento*, **1**, 48 (1955); and K. IMAEDA: *Progr. Theor. Phys. Japan*, **5**, 133 (1950).

(74) Case of flat space: B. F. TOUSCHEK: *Nuovo Cimento*, **5**, 1281 (1957); A. SALAM: *Nuovo Cimento*, **5**, 299 (1957); D. IVANENKO and A. BRODSKI: *Žurn. Ėksp. Teor. Fiz.*, **33**, 910 (1957); case of curved space. D. R. BRILL and J. A. WHEELER. *Rev. Mod. Phys.*, **29**, 465 (1957).

other point in space (75). How then could this kind of localized rotation be of importance in passing from classical geometrodynamics to quantum geometrodynamics? Two trial answers suggest themselves.

8. – No evidence for half spin representations of group of coordinate transformations.

Trial 1: « Spinor fields are to geometrodynamics what a single spinor is to the rotation of a single rigid body » (76). The wave functions of a symmetric rotator, for example,

$$\psi^{(J)}{}_{mK}(\varphi, \theta, \chi) , \tag{133}$$

for given J and K, are transformed by a rotation of the frame of reference into new wave functions which are linear combinations of the old ones. The coefficients are labelled by two indices, m and m', and are functions of the parameters of the rotation. In dealing with normal rigid body rotations one demands single valued wave functions. The coefficients of transformation must therefore depend in a single valued way upon the choice of the element R of the rotation group:

$$\mathscr{D}^{(J)}{}_{mm'}(R) . \tag{134}$$

One finds in consequence that J must be integral. This requirement is given up in the case of electron spin. The topology of the rotation group, it is noted, is that of a 3-sphere imbedded in a 4-dimensional Euclidean space (x, y, z, w), with opposite points identified with each other. If α, β, γ denote the direction cosines of the angle of rotation, and θ denotes the magnitude of the rotation, then in the Hamilton-Cayley-Klein representation of a rotation

$$\left\{\begin{aligned} x &= \sin \tfrac{1}{2}\theta \cos \alpha , \\ y &= \sin \tfrac{1}{2}\theta \cos \beta , \\ z &= \sin \tfrac{1}{2}\theta \cos \gamma , \\ w &= \cos \tfrac{1}{2}\theta . \end{aligned}\right. \tag{135}$$

(75) M. RIESZ: *L'équation de Dirac en relativité générale*, Lund Univ. Math. Sem., **12** (1954); also in Comptes Rendus du douzième congrès des mathématiciens Scandinaves tenu à Lund, 10-15 Août 1953, p. 241 (1954). Dr. R. PENROSE kindly stresses that spinors resemble vectors much more than this interpretation of Riesz's remarks would imply; the real distintion is the $\pm$ ambiguity of spinors: *Ann. Phys.*, **10**, 171 (1960). See also E. CARTAN: *Selecta* (Paris, 1939), p. 112.

(76) For the use of the Cayley-Klein parameters in describing the orientation of a rigid body see for example H. B. G. CASIMIR: *Rotation of a Rigid Body in Quantum Mechanics* (The Hague, 1931).

An increase of θ by 2π gives the same rotation but an antipodal point on the sphere. If now these antipodal points are no longer identified ([77]), a group results—the « covering group »—which is larger than the rotation group. To demand that the coefficients of transformation be merely single valued functions of the element chosen from this larger group is to accept as permissible not only integral values for the spin J, but also half integral values. The extra wave functions then allowed show the « non-classical two-valuedness » of PAULI.

With a system of two rotators it is possible in this way similarly to associate a product of two spin $\frac{1}{2}$ wave functions; and so on. Therefore *an infinite set of rotational degrees of freedom might seem a natural object to take as progenitor of a spinor field.*

A simple orthogonal transformation at one point is associated with *one* rotation. In general relativity, with its infinitude of points, will not a change in the curvilinear co-ordinate system bring about at *every* point a rotation of local frame of reference? Will not an infinite set of rotational degrees of freedom thereby be put into evidence? In other words, cannot the general element T of the group of co-ordinate transformations be expressed in some sense as the direct product of an infinite number of rotations, each associated with an individual point? If then one permits each elementary rotation to have associated with it a spin $\frac{1}{2}$, will he not end up with a spinor field, and will not this spinor field be associated in some inescapable way with the group of general co-ordinate transformations in general relativity? Apparently not. The topology of the group of the T's is not the same as the topology of the infinite product of covering groups, each associated with a single rotation. LAURENT finds no representation of the co-ordinate transformation group which has any of the qualities one would associate with a spinor field ([78]).

9. – Spinor field connected with existence of fine grained topology?

Trial 2: There is another kind of two valuedness that could be of interest in connection with the origin of spin. Consider a single wormhole. In other words, consider two well separated spheres in 3-space. « Cut away the space interior to each » and identify corresponding points on the surfaces of the two spheres. At the moment that a finger is slowly inserted into the left hand

(77) E. P. WIGNER: *Group Theory and Its Application to the Quantum Mechanics of Atomic Spectra*, translated by J. J. GRIFFIN (New York and London, 1959).

(78) B. E. LAURENT: kind private communication, *International Conference on Relativistic Theories of Gravitation* (Royaumont, 28 June 1959).

sphere, it is seen emerging—in the non-dynamic and classical world under discussion—from the right hand sphere. There are however two inequivalent ways to perform the identification according as rotations about the surfaces of the two spheres proceed in the same sense or in opposite senses. A right handed glove thrust through the sphere in one case remains right handed, in the other case reverses parity. In the one instance the space is said to be orientable; in the other, non-orientable. It may well be that non-orientable spaces, or « parity-non-conserving spaces », are ruled out by a principle which has been briefly alluded to and which today is not yet very well formulated, the principle that « space shall be properly closed »—a principle for the selection of topologies that presumably has a deep going connection with Mach's principle. If however both spaces are permissible, then a space with one wormhole has one classical two-valuedness associated with it, and one with n wormholes has n-fold duplicity. If it should turn out that there are 2^n inequivalent ways to get to a geometry with n wormholes, and if it should make sense to assign 2^n distinct probability amplitudes to the same macroscopic field configuration, then one would be in possession of a non-classical two valuedness with as many spin-like degrees of freeedom as there are wormholes. Therefore this direction of analysis is of considerable interest. A number of options shows up which is qualitatively of the same order as the number of degrees of freedom of a spinor field, when one goes to the virtual foam-like space of quantum geometrodynamics. It is difficult to say anything more specific about the reasonableness or unreasonableness of this conceivable « correlation of spin with parity » until more is known about the formalism of quantum geometrodynamics. FINKELSTEIN and MISNER [79] have given an interesting discussion of the possibility of getting a wave function that shows a non-classical two valuedness in a multiply connected space. Their investigation leads them to the conjecture that a 3-space unendowed with torsion, in the topological sense of that term, cannot show spin $\frac{1}{2}$.

10. – No fundamental theory of neutrino.

In conclusion, it is not at present possible to point to a natural and decisive connection between a spinor field and the quantum geometrodynamics of curved empty space.

---

[79] D. FINKELSTEIN and C. W. MISNER: *Ann. Phys.*, **6**, 230 (1959) and report at Royaumont Conference (30 June 1959).

11. – Neutrino provisionally treated as foreign field in a pre-existing space-time continuum.

Electrodynamics, on the other hand, in the scheme of already unified field theory, is very directly connected with geometry. Yet for most purposes it is simplest not to express the electromagnetic field quantities explicitly in terms of the metric. It is more convenient to use the familiar and equivalent dual language of « field within a space. » Similarly to speak of a neutrino field as going through its dynamical evolution within the arena of a space may therefore also make sense. At any rate, that is the only way in which it is possible to formulate neutrino theory today sufficiently definitely so as to permit concrete physical results to be deduced.

12. – Relativistic wave equation for neutrino.

The wave equation of the neutrino in curved space can be written either in the Dirac 4-component form

$$\gamma^\mu \nabla_\mu \psi = 0 \tag{136}$$

or in the Pauli-Lee-Yang 2-component form

$$S^\alpha \nabla_\alpha \psi = 0 . \tag{137}$$

Here the matrices satisfy the relations

$$\begin{cases} \gamma_\mu \gamma_\nu + \gamma_\nu \gamma_\mu = 2g_{\mu\nu} , \\ \bar{S}_\mu S_\nu + S_\nu \bar{S}_\mu = 2g_{\mu\nu} . \end{cases} \tag{138}$$

In addition to the usual Christoffel symbols formed by differentiation of the metric,

$$\Gamma_{\alpha\beta}{}^{\gamma} = \tfrac{1}{2} g^{\gamma\sigma}(\partial g_{\beta\sigma}/\partial x^\alpha + \partial g_{\alpha\sigma}/\partial x^\beta - \partial g_{\alpha\beta}/\partial x^\sigma) \tag{139}$$

it is necessary to define matrices or Fock-Ivanenko coefficients Γ_k, such that

$$\partial\gamma_\alpha/\partial x^\beta - \Gamma_{\alpha\beta}{}^{\mu}\gamma_\mu - \Gamma_\beta \gamma_\alpha + \gamma_\alpha \Gamma_\beta = 0 ; \tag{140}$$

then the covariant derivative ∇, when applied to a spinor, gives

$$\nabla_\alpha \psi = \partial\psi/\partial x^\alpha - \Gamma_\alpha \psi \, . \tag{141}$$

The wave equation [80] (136) (or (137)) gives formalism adequate to discuss many features of the interaction between gravitational fields and neutrinos.

III. - Spacelike Description of the Neutrino Field.

1. - How to evaluate disturbance of neutrino field in vacuum state?

When the neutrino field is regarded as a foreign object in a pre-existing space-time geometry, and when that geometry is idealized as nearly flat, then it is possible to analyze the states of excitation of this field into normal modes in a familiar way. To each mode is assigned an occupation number which may be either 0 or 1, but which is 0 for the ground or « vacuum » state of the neutrino field. To be in the ground state does not imply that the neutrino field—any-more than a harmonic oscillator or the electromagnetic field—is in a state of zero disturbance. Can the state functional for this condition of the neutrino field be expressed in a space-like representation—analogous to eq. (12) for the space-like representation of the ground state of the electromagnetic field—which allows this state of disturbance to be brought more directly into evidence? Yes, as KLAUDER has shown [81]. Just as the state functional Ψ_{vac} of the electromagnetic field supplies a number for every choice of the magnetic field $\boldsymbol{H}(x)$, so the state functional for the neutrino field supplies a number for

---

(80) See W. L. BADE and H. JEHLE: *Rev. Mod. Phys.*, **25**, 714 (1953) for a general review of the literature on the Dirac wave equation in curved space, also V. FOCK and D. IVANENKO: *Compt. Rend.*, **188**, 1470 (1929); V. FOCK and *Zeits. f. Phys.*, **57**, 261 (1929); P. G. BERGMANN: *Phys. Rev.*, **107**, 624 (1957); J. G. FLETCHER: *Nuovo Cimento*, **8**, 451 (1958); also D. BRILL and J. A. WHEELER: *Rev. Mod. Phys.*, **29**, 465 (1957). In connection with eq. (8) in this latter paper appreciation is expressed to F. L. SCARF for pointing out that a factor $\frac{1}{4}$ is missing; the corrected equation should read

$$\Gamma_k = (g_{\mu\alpha}/4)\,[(\partial b_\nu{}^\beta/\partial x^k)\,a^\alpha{}_\beta - \Gamma_{\nu k}{}^\alpha]\,s^{\mu\nu} + a_k l \, ,$$

and agrees with eq. (17) of V. BARGMANN: *Sitzber. Preuss. Akad. Wiss., Phys.-Math. Klasse*, 346 (1932).

(81) J. R. KLAUDER: *The Action Option and a Feynman Quantization of Spinor Fields in Terms of Ordinary c-Numbers*, *Ph. D. Thesis* (Princeton, May 1959); *Ann. Phys.*, **11**, 123 (1960).

every choice of a « χ-field. » Here χ is a field with two components, both of which depend upon position:

$$\chi_1 = \chi_1(x) \; ; \qquad \chi_2 = \chi_2(x) \, . \tag{142}$$

For fields χ which are regular in a sense defined more precisely by KLAUDER, it is possible to write

$$|\Psi_{\text{vac}}(\chi)|^2 = N \exp\left[-\frac{1}{4\pi^2}\int \frac{\chi^*(z)\,\{\sigma\cdot(-i)\overleftrightarrow{\nabla}\}\,\chi(y)}{(z-y)^2}\,\mathrm{d}^3z\,\mathrm{d}^3y\right], \tag{143}$$

in close analogy to the corresponding expression for the state functional for the electromagnetic field. Here N is a normalization constant; σ_x, σ_y and σ_z are the Pauli spin matrices; and the arrow has this significance:

$$A(\overleftrightarrow{\partial/\partial x})B \equiv A(\partial B/\partial x) - (\partial A/\partial x)B \, . \tag{144}$$

For fields χ which depend upon position in a non-regular manner, it is necessary—Klauder shows—to give a formula more comprehensive than (143):

$$|\Psi_{\text{vac}}(\chi)|^2 = \exp\left[\mathrm{Tr}\ln(1-K)\right], \tag{145}$$

where Tr symbolyzes the operation of taking the trace, and K is an operator which depends upon the c-number fields χ and χ^* and which is given by KLAUDER.

2. – No reference to anti-commuting c-numbers.

Klauder's description of a spinor field has two interesting and very new features: 1) the χ-field describes an overcomplete family of states and 2) on this very account it allows a field to be quantized by Feynman's method of sum over histories without any reference to the so-called anticommuting c-numbers which have previously been required in this connection, and which are mathematically indefensible objects [82].

---

[82] As K. SYMANZIK writes in *Zeits. Naturfor.*, **9a**, 809 (1954), « Bei der Behandlung von Fermionfeldern werden spinorielle Funktionen eingeführt, die mit sich selbst, mit ihrer Adjungierten und mit anderen spinoriellen Funktionen antikommutieren. In dieser Antivertauschbarkeit mit der konjugiert komplexen Funktion liegt eine Schwierigkeit, da hieraus das identische Verschwinden dieser spinoriellen Funktionen folgt ... ».

3. – Sum over histories expressed in terms of an overcomplete family of states.

Ordinarily the state function associated with a single Fermi-Dirac degree of freedom is expressed as two complex numbers, one giving the probability amplitude for that state being empty, the other for it being occupied. In other words, the two states $|0\rangle$ and $|1\rangle$ form a complete basis for describing all possible states for this one degree of freedom. The propagator which describes the evolution in time of one of these two states, or any state, has the form

$$\langle b''t''|b't'\rangle \equiv \langle b''|\exp[-i(t''-t')]H/\hbar|b'\rangle . \tag{146}$$

The law of composition of propagators takes the form

$$\langle b'''t'''|b't'\rangle = \sum_{b''=0}^{1} \langle b'''t'''|b''t''\rangle\langle b''t''|b't'\rangle . \tag{147}$$

This law of composition can be rewritten in another form, KLAUDER points out. Define the state

$$|b\rangle \equiv (1-|b|^2)^{\frac{1}{2}}|0\rangle + b|1\rangle . \tag{148}$$

Then as b runs through all complex numbers b_r+ib_i of absolute magnitude less than 1, the state vector $|b\rangle$ runs through an *overcomplete family of states*. In terms of an integration over this family the law of composition becomes

$$\langle b'''t'''|b't'\rangle = \int_{|b|<1} \langle b'''t'''|bt''\rangle \, \mathrm{d}b \, \langle bt''|b't'\rangle , \tag{149}$$

where $\mathrm{d}b$ is a symbol for the volume element

$$\mathrm{d}b \equiv (2/\pi)\,\mathrm{d}b_r\,\mathrm{d}b_i . \tag{150}$$

This point of view makes it possible to define in a useful way a *skeleton history* of the Fermi-Dirac degree of freedom between an initial time t' and a final time t''. The values of the complex number b are specified not only at t' and t'' but also at a regular succession of times in the intervening interval:

$$b'', \quad b_n, \quad b_{n-1}, \quad \dots, \quad b_2, \quad b_1, \quad b' .$$

The process of summation over histories is then expressed in terms of an n-fold integration over volume elements of the type (150) and passage to the limit of an indefinitely fine subdivision in time. Generalizing this procedure from one to an infinity of Fermi-Dirac degrees of freedom, KLAUDER defines the concept of *sum over histories for a Fermi-Dirac field.* Yet nowhere in this analysis is it necessary to introduce operators or the so-called anticommuting c-numbers.

Owing to the circumstance that a Fermi-Dirac field has a spinor, not a scalar character, it is necessary to introduce *two* complex numbers in Klauder's analysis to describe the overcomplete family of states associated with one spinor degree of freedom. To specify Klauder's two component field $\chi(x)$ at the time t' provides a means to give the pair of complex numbers b_1' and b_2' at t' for each of an infinite number of spin sytems.

4. – Klauder's new formulation of the distinction between Fermi-Dirac and Einstein-Bose statistics.

Nothing in Klauder's analysis forces Fermi-Dirac fields to have a spinor character. Therefore no new insight is won into the connection between spin and statistics. What is gained instead is a new formulation of the distinction between Fermi and Bose statistics. This KLAUDER illustrates by the example of a single harmonic oscillator with the classical equations of motion

$$\left\{\begin{aligned} i\,\dot{a}\,(t) &= a\,(t)\,,\\ -\,i\,\dot{a}^*(t) &= a^*(t)\,. \end{aligned}\right. \tag{151}$$

The classical action has the value

$$I=\int[(i/2)\,(a^*\,\overleftrightarrow{\partial/\partial t}\,a)-a^*a]\,\mathrm{d}t\,, \tag{152}$$

and the quantum mechanical Hamiltonian is

$$\boldsymbol{H}=\boldsymbol{a}^*\boldsymbol{a}=\boldsymbol{N}\,. \tag{153}$$

The correct propagator in the Fermi-Dirac case from a state $|b'\rangle$ to a state $|b''\rangle$ is

$$\langle b''t''|b't'\rangle=(1-|b''|^2)^{\frac{1}{2}}(1-|b'|^2)^{\frac{1}{2}}+b^{*''}\exp\,[-i(t''-t')]\,b'\,, \tag{154}$$

where both $|b'\rangle$ and $|b''\rangle$ belong to the overcomplete family of states and are defined by (148). This result can be won straight out of the sum over histories, Klauder shows, if the propagator is written formally as

$$\langle b''t''|b't'\rangle=N\!\int\exp\left[i\!\int[(i/2)\,(b^*\,\overleftrightarrow{\partial/\partial t}\,b)-b^*b]\right]\mathrm{d}t\,\mathscr{D}b(t)\,. \tag{155}$$

This expression is understood to be the limit of a corresponding sum over skeleton histories when the subdivision in time is made infinitely fine:

(156) $$(t''-t')/(n+1) = \Delta t = \varepsilon \to 0\,.$$

The volume element before passage to the limit is the product of expressions of the form (151):

(157) $$\mathrm{d}b_1\,\mathrm{d}b_2 \ldots \mathrm{d}b_n\,.$$

The integrand has the following simple value in the case of a skeleton history which goes over into a continuous history on passage to the limit:

(158) $$\exp i \sum \left[(i/2)b^*_{k+1}(b_{k+1}-b_k)-(i/2)(b^*_{k+1}-b^*_k)b_k-\varepsilon\, b^*_{k+1}b_k\right].$$

However, it is a very important circumstance that most of the contribution to the Feynman sum comes from histories which are *not* continuous in this sense. To calculate propagators consistently for such histories, KLAUDER recalls out of the operator formulation of quantum mechanics the formula

(159) $$\langle b''t''\,|\,b't'\rangle = \langle b''\,|\exp\left[-i(t''-t')\boldsymbol{H}\right]|\,b'\rangle$$

and therefore writes the integrand in (154)—before passage to the limit—as a product of $(n+1)$ numerical—not operator—factors of the form

(160) $$\langle b_{k+1}|\exp\left[-i\varepsilon\boldsymbol{H}\right]|\,b_k\rangle$$

or

(161) $$\left\{\langle b_{k+1}|\,b_k\rangle - i\varepsilon\,\langle b_{k+1}|\boldsymbol{H}|\,b_k\rangle\right\}.$$

In the special case in question, where $H = a^*a$, this expression has the value

(162) $$\left\{(1-|b_{k+1}|^2)^{\frac{1}{2}}(1-|b_k|^2)^{\frac{1}{2}}+b^*_{k+1}b_k - i\varepsilon\, b^*_{k+1}b_k\right\}.$$

It is *this formula* which *really defines what is meant by the integrand in* (155). Expression (162) of course reduces to (158) for skeleton histories which in the limit approach *continuous* histories.

The same sum over histories (155) *applies* equally well *to* the case of *Bose statistics*! Only let the letter a be substituted into (156) and (158) in place of b, and let the individual volume element $\mathrm{d}b = (2/\pi)\,\mathrm{d}b_r\,\mathrm{d}b_i$, with $1 \geqslant |b| \geqslant 0$, be replaced by $\mathrm{d}a = (1/\pi)\,\mathrm{d}a_r\,\mathrm{d}a_i$, with $\infty \geqslant |a| \geqslant 0$. The propagator $\langle a''t''\,|\,a't'\rangle$ obtained by the new process of integration is now to be understood as connecting a state $|a'\rangle$ with a state $|a''\rangle$, where the states $|a\rangle$ again belong to an overcomplete family of states, but this time states of a Bose system. The familiar complete set of orthogonal states for describing a Bose system has for state identification label an occupation number, N:

$$|0\rangle, \quad |1\rangle, \quad ..., \quad |N\rangle, \quad ...$$

In terms of this basic set of state vectors, the typical state of the overcomplete family of states is

$$|a\rangle = \exp\left[-\tfrac{1}{2}|a|^2\right] \sum_{N=0}^{\infty} (N!)^{-\frac{1}{2}} a^N |N\rangle \,. \tag{163}$$

The propagator between states of this category is defined just as well as the propagator between states of any other kind and suffices moreover completely to describe the dynamics of the system.

5. – The action option.

The mathematics of Einstein-Bose quantization looks identical to that for Fermi-Dirac quantization in this formalism. Where is the difference? The important point, KLAUDER points out, is not the circumstance that the complex number a in the one case is unbounded while the complex number b in the other case is restricted to lie in the unit circle. Instead, the decisive difference lies here: that 1) *the classical action integral in* (155) *or* (158) *must be given a meaning for discontinuous histories before the sum over histories can even be defined*; and 2) *this extension of the action principle to unruly histories is made differently for Einstein-Bose than for Fermi-Dirac fields.* Specifically, the integrand of the Feynman sum over histories (155) is again the product of $(n+1)$ factors, each of a form completely analogous to (161):

$$\langle a_{k+1}|a_k\rangle - i\varepsilon\langle a_{k+1}|\boldsymbol{H}|a_k\rangle \;;$$

but the concrete expression of this quantity (as a consequence of (153) and (163)) is completely different,

$$\exp\left[-\tfrac{1}{2}|a_{k+1}|^2 + a^*_{k+1}a_k - \tfrac{1}{2}|a_k|^2 - i\varepsilon a^*_{k+1}a_k\right], \tag{164}$$

from the value (162) used in the Fermi-Dirac case. Nevertheless, for *continuous* histories the elementary propagators for the two kinds of statistics agree completely in the limit $\varepsilon \to 0$ of fine subdivision of time.

In summary, as KLAUDER puts it,

« The Feynman procedure demands a numerical action value for histories outside the domain for which the action integral was intended, *e.g.* for histories which are discontinuous with respect to space or time. One is therefore presented with an "action option," *i.e.* the action value for such "unruly" histories may be defined in various ways. Depending on the choice made, the resulting quantum theory can be made to manifest either Bose or Fermi statistics. This ambiguity is inherent in the formalism itself; but the proper choices to extend the classical information are most readily determined by constructing the sum over histories by a summation over multiple products of matrix elements of the unitary operator which advances the state an infinitesimal time. This summation need not be limited to the familiar discrete basis vectors; one can employ a "generalized representation" which involves, for each Fermion degree of freedom, continuously many, non-independent vectors. By choosing a suitable parametrization for this "overcomplete family of states, the appropriate action functional will appear in the exponent of the integrand which defines the *c*-number sum over histories." »

That classical physics is a limiting case of quantum physics has long been understood, but it is new to see the extent of arbitrariness that is open in passing in the reverse direction—an arbitrariness in interpreting an action integral sufficiently great to spell the difference between opposite kinds of statistics. It is not inconceivable that this circumstance may be a clue to the deeper significance of Fermi-Dirac—and spinor—fields. Quite apart from this question of principle, KLAUDER's work would seem for the first time to extend to Fermi fields a technique of quantization—a sum over histories free of any reference to operator quantities—which is particularly well suited to a space-like description of the neutrino field, especially in curved space. However more elementary methods are sufficient and more appropriate for anaysing the elementary processes now to be examined.

6. – No geometrodynamical explanation apparent for law of conservation of lepton number.

In connection with the space like description of the neutrino field, one final question is suggested by the analogy of the electromagnetic field. Can this spinor field manifest anything like a conserved flux through a wormhole in a multiply connected space, like the charge defined by the electric flux? If a spinor flux could be defined and were found to be conserved, this circumstance could have a bearing on the interpretation of leptonic charge. It does not exist. A case has been investigated ([83]) where it was possible to solve

([83]) J. R. KLAUDER and J. A. WHEELER: *Rev. Mod. Phys.*, **29**, 516 (1957).

exactly the equations for a spinor field of zero rest mass in a space with a multiply connected topology. It was shown in this example that no quantity can be defined covariantly which has properties analogous to those of a total flux. Therefore no way is presently apparent to understand from the viewpoint of geometrodynamics why anything like lepton number is conserved ([84]).

IV. – Elementary Interaction of Neutrinos and of Gravitational Radiation.

1. – Production of real and virtual pairs out of the vacuum.

The production of pairs in the collision of two photons ([85]),

$$\hbar\omega_1 + \hbar\omega_2 \rightarrow e^- + e^+ \tag{165}$$

and the scattering of light by light ([86]),

$$\hbar\omega_1 + \hbar\omega_2 \rightarrow \hbar\omega_3 + \hbar\omega_4\,, \tag{166}$$

were two of the processes analysed early in the development of quantum electrodynamics. That the cross section for forward scattering in the second process—of high order—could be deduced directly from the cross section for the more elementary process (165); that the Kramers-Kronig dispersion relation is valid for *relativistic* energies—this was the point established for the first time by TOLL ([87]). These results tell in clear language something about the rich physics of the vacuum. What can be said of neutrino analogs to these electrodynamical processes?

The existence of the process

$$\nu + \tilde{\nu} \rightarrow \mu^- + e^+ \tag{167}$$

follows directly from the spontaneous decay of the μ-meson and the principle of microscopic reversibility. Well above the threshold,

$$(\hbar\omega_1)\cdot(\hbar\omega_2) \geqslant (208\, mc^2/2)^2\,, \tag{168}$$

([84]) In this connection see especially R. P. FEYNMAN and M. GELL-MANN: *Phys. Rev.*, **109**, 193 (1958).

([85]) G. BREIT and J. A. WHEELER: *Phys. Rev.*, **46**, 1087 (1934).

([86]) A. ACHIESER: *Phys. Zeits. Sow.*, **11**, 263 (1937).

([87]) J. S. TOLL: *The Dispersion Relation for Light and Its Application to Problems Involving Electron Pairs, Ph. D. Thesis* (Princeton, 1952); also an earlier statement of results, J. S. TOLL and J. A. WHEELER: *Phys. Rev.*, **81**, 654 (A) (1951).

the calculated cross section for this reaction increases (88) as

$$\sigma_{\text{absn}} \sim (g^2/\hbar^2 c^4)\omega_1\omega_2 . \tag{169}$$

In the case of light the cross section for the production of pairs at first goes up with energy, but then goes down, so that the dispersion integral converges. Not so here, where a literal application of the same formula leads to the scattering cross section

$$(\mathrm{d}\sigma/\mathrm{d}\Omega)_{\text{forward}} = \left| \frac{\omega_2^2}{2\pi^2 c} \int\limits_0^\infty \frac{\sigma_{\text{absn}}(\omega_1, \omega_2')\,\mathrm{d}\omega_2'}{\omega_2'^2 - \omega_2^2} \right|^2 \sim (\omega_1\omega_2^2 g^2/\hbar^2 c^5)^2 \ln^2 (\hbar\omega_\infty/100\, mc^2). \tag{170}$$

This divergence says that the dispersion relation should not be used for neutrinos as it is used for light; or that the cross section for the pair production process (167) cannot continue to increase indefinitely in proportion to the invariant product $\omega_1\omega_2$; or both. In similar situations, as for example in oversimplified theories of stopping power of matter, or of the dynamics of a plasma, divergent logarithms are encountered, which in more careful analyses are found to have values of the order of 10. Assumption that the logarithm here is of a similar order leads of course to a cross section for the forward scattering of neutrinos by neutrinos which is fantastically small, but still relevant to the theory of geons composed of neutrinos (88).

2. – Form factor. Direct Fermi coupling?

The existence of a value for the integral (170) which is bounded at all depends on the assumption that some kind of form factor cuts off the Fermi interaction at high energies and small distances. YANG and LEE have discussed (89) possible experimental implications of such a form factor. It enters in a way much more decisive than the logarithm in formulas for the cross sections of other neutrino processes, a number of which have been analyzed by EUWEMA (90). However, the present neutrino-neutrino scattering process already on its own account calls attention to another ambiguity in estimates of the cross sections for certain elementary processes of neutrino physics. It is perfectly conceivable that the scattering occurs by way of a *direct* Fermi interaction, based on a possible identity in coupling constants between

$$\nu + \tilde{\nu} \to \nu' + \tilde{\nu}' \tag{171}$$

(88) J. A. WHEELER: *Phys. Rev.*, **97**, 511 (1955); D. R. BRILL and J. A. WHEELER: *Rev. Mod. Phys.*, **29**, 465 (1957).

(89) T. D. LEE and C. N. YANG: *Phys. Rev. Lett.*, **4**, 307 (1960).

(90) R. N. EUWEMA: *Neutrinos and Their Interaction with Matter, Ph. D. Thesis* (Princeton, April 1959).

and

$$p + e^- \to n + \nu\,. \tag{172}$$

Then the contribution of a second order process, via production and reannihilation of a μ^-, e^+ pair, would be negligible by comparison.

3. – Elastic scattering of neutrinos by electrons and protons.

Not so fantastically difficult to investigate experimentally is a similar direct coupling in the process

$$\tilde{\nu} + e^- \to \tilde{\nu}' + e^{-\prime}\,. \tag{173}$$

A direct Fermi type of interaction here, if it exists, should outweigh any second order coupling that takes place, via the intermediate virtual states $n+\tilde{n}$ and $p^+ + p^-$. A direct interaction, if it takes place at all, might reasonably be expected to have the same coupling constant (91), $g = 1.37 \cdot 10^{-49}$ erg cm^3, as that which characterizes the reactions in the « triangle diagram » (92):

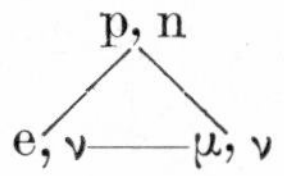

In this case the scattering cross section will be of the order

$$\sigma \sim (g/\hbar^2 c^2)^2 (\hbar\omega) \cdot (mc^2) \tag{174}$$

for neutrino energies $\hbar\omega$ of the order of the rest energy of the electron and larger, and

$$\sigma \sim (g/\hbar^2 c^2)^2 (\hbar\omega)^2 \tag{175}$$

for smaller energies, with

$$\sigma \sim 10^{-44}\ \text{cm}^2 \tag{176}$$

for $\hbar\omega = mc^2 = 0.5$ MeV.

A cross section similar to (175) will be expected for the elastic scattering of anti-neutrinos by protons if here too there happens to be a direct Fermi coupling. WOLLAN searched for this reaction (93). He had two similar con-

---

(91) O. KOFOED-HANSEN and R. GATTO: *Rendiconti S.I.F.*, XI, pp. 251, 336 for the status of measurements of this constant.

(92) O. KLEIN: *Nature*, **161**, 897 (1948); G. PUPPI: *Nuovo Cimento*, **8**, 587 (1948); J. TIOMNO and J. A. WHEELER: *Rev. Mod. Phys.*, **21**, 144 (1949); T. D. LEE, M. N. ROSENBLUTH and C. N. YANG: *Phys. Rev.*, **75**, 905 L (1949); E. C. G. SUDARSHAN and R. E. MARSHAK: *Phys. Rev.*, **109**, 1860 (1958).

(93) E. O. WOLLAN: *Phys. Rev.*, **72**, 445 (1947).

tainers, one filled with CH_4 at 11 atmospheres, the other filled with argon to such a pressure as to give an equal response to γ–rays. No detectable difference in ionization current could be found when the two chambers were placed just outside the shielding of a reactor producing a large flux of anti-neutrinos. From this negative result it followed that the cross-section for the scattering of anti-neutrinos by protons must be less than about $2\cdot10^{-30}$ cm². A new experiment to study the same effect may be possible with a sensitivity sufficient, and a nuclear reactor power great enough, to detect a cross section of the order of 10^{-44} cm², according to a kind personal communication of REINES (94).

4. – Form factor; detection of anti-neutrino.

Fission product neutrinos presumably have energies far too low to disclose any energy dependence of the Fermi coupling constant in this scattering experiment, or a form factor such as has been discussed by LEE and YANG (89). Neither does it seem feasible to investigate the important question of the form factor experimentally in the famous anti-neutrino absorption reaction (95)

(177) $\tilde{\nu} + p \rightarrow e^+$ (annihilated with a short but characteristic time delay to give two photons) + n (captured in Cd dissolved in water to produce several γ rays after a longer characteristic time),

owing to the low count rate. This reaction, so decisive in establishing the reality of the anti-neutrino, may however come to serve as a tool to measure the flux of anti-neutrinos in space. REINES and COWAN measured at a high power Du Pont reactor at Savannah River a cross section of

$$\sigma = (11 \pm 2.6)\cdot 10^{-44}\ \text{cm}^2 \tag{178}$$

for reaction of a proton with an anti-neutrino of the average energy of those given off in fission product decay; or, with 6.1 neutrinos per fission, an effective cross section per proton of

$$(6.7 \pm 1.5)\cdot 10^{-43}\ \text{cm}^2/\text{fission}\,. \tag{179}$$

---

(94) See A. R. RONZIO, C. L. COWAN jr. and F. REINES: *Rev. Sci. Instr.*, **29**, 146 (1958) for some of the recent developments in liquid scintillators; also *Methods of Experimental Physics*, vol. 5, edited by L. C. YUAN and C. S. WU, New York, in publication.

(95) F. REINES and C. L. COWAN jr.: *Phys. Rev.*, **92**, 830 (1953); C. L. COWAN jr. F. REINES, F. B. HARRISON, H. W. KRUSE and A. D. MCGUIRE: *Science*, **124**, 103 (1956); F. REINES and C. L. COWAN jr.: *Phys. Today*, **10**, 12 (1957); *Phys. Rev.*, **113**, 273 (1959).

The number expected in this experiment requires for its calculation only 1) a knowledge of the number of independent spin states open to the anti-neutrino, 2) the principle of microscopy reversibility, 3) the theory of the *relative* dependence of cross section upon energy, 4) the neutrino spectrum of the fission products—deducible from their β spectrum. CARTER, REINES, WAGNER and WYMAN ([96]) have measured this spectrum ([94]) and calculate

$$(6.1 \pm 1)\cdot 10^{-43}\ \text{cm}^2/\text{fission} \tag{180}$$

for anti-neutrinos which are described by two component wave functions and have only one spin state ([97]); and

$$(3.05 \pm 0.5)\cdot 10^{-43}\ \text{cm}^2/\text{fission} \tag{181}$$

TABLE X. – *Neutrino and anti-neutrino fluxes compared and contrasted.* Value of number flux from Savannah River reactor from REINES and COWAN ([95]). Value of number flux from sun from ALLEN ([98]), who also notes that neutrinos from the proton-proton reaction have energies below the threshold of the ^{37}Cl reaction, whereas in the carbon-nitrogen cycle the positive electron decays of ^{13}N and ^{15}O are associated with maximum neutrino energies of 1.24 MeV and 1.68 MeV. Values for cosmic ray-created neutrinos, based on the very rough figures of 1 primary/cm² min and 10 neutrinos per primary (5 of each kind). Value for distant stars based on known intensity of starlight and on assumption that roughly a tenth as much energy goes into neutrinos, as in the case of the sun. Value for URCA process based on assumption — only an assumption — that in the time of free fall (4 h) in the star an amount of mass is converted to energy of neutrinos and anti-neutrinos equal to 10^{-4} of the mass of the sun ($2\cdot 10^{33}$ g). R is the distance to the star in 10^6 light years (~ 2 for nearest galaxy, ~ 0.1 or less within Milky Way). The flux from an accelerator depends so greatly upon experimental conditions that it was not listed.

	Neutrinos		Anti-neutrinos	
	$\nu/\text{cm}^2\,\text{s}$	$\text{MeV}/\text{cm}^2\,\text{s}$	$\bar{\nu}/\text{cm}^2\,\text{s}$	$\text{MeV}/\text{cm}^2\,\text{s}$
Savannah River fission reactor	—	—	$1.3\cdot 10^{13}$	$\sim 2\cdot 10^{13}$
Sun	$6\cdot 10^{11}$	$\sim 6\cdot 10^{11}$	—	—
Cosmic rays	~ 10	$\sim 10^3$	~ 10	$\sim 10^3$
Stars other than the sun	$\sim 10^3$	$\sim 10^3$	—	—
URCA process	$\sim 10^2/R^2$	$10^3/R^2$	$\sim 10^2/R^2$	$4\cdot 10^3/R^2$
Detection mechanism	$^{37}\text{Cl}(\nu e^-)^{37}\text{A}$		$\text{p}(\bar{\nu}e^+)\text{n}$	
Its threshold	0.816 MeV		1.8 MeV	

([96]) R. E. CARTER, F. REINES, J. J. WAGNER and M. E. WYMAN: *Phys. Rev.*, **113**, 280 (1959).

([97]) T. D. LEE and C. N. YANG: *Phys. Rev.*, **105**, 1671 (1957).

([98]) J. S. ALLEN: *The Neutrino* (Princeton, 1958).

for neutrinos which resemble electrons in having two spin states and obeying the four component Dirac equation. For a four component Majorana theory the value

$$14.4\cdot 10^{-43}\ \text{cm}^2/\text{fission} \tag{182}$$

is predicted ([96]). The observations are therefore consistent with the principle of microscopic reversibility and the two-component, one-spin theory of the neutrino.

5. – Anti-neutrinos distinguished from neutrinos.

Attempts have been made to detect the absorption of neutrinos themselves using the reaction

$$^{37}\text{Cl}\,(\nu,\ e^-)\ ^{37}\text{A}\ \ (\text{radioactive})\,, \tag{183}$$

in an experiment proposed by PONTECORVO and assessed by ALVAREZ. DAVIS ([99])

TABLE XI. – *Euwema's predictions, many necessarily very uncertain, for certain neutrino reactions, evaluated in the domain of low energies, and on the assumption of a* 1 GeV *cut-off.* Only the starred results are strongly sensitive to the precise value of the cut-off energy. The cross sections are in cm²; the energies (e_0=initial energy, e=final energy, etc.) are in MeV.

Initial state	Final state	σ in cm²
$\bar{\nu}$, p	n, e^+	$\approx 6.5\cdot 10^{-44}\, ee_0$
ν, n	p, e	$\approx 6.5\cdot 10^{-44}\, ee_0$
ν_1, μ	ν_2, e	$\sim 6.5\cdot 10^{-44}\, \nu_{20}/e_0$
ν_1, e	ν_2, μ	$\sim 6.5\cdot 10^{-44}\, \nu_2^2$
ν, $\bar{\nu}$	μ^-, e^+	$\sim 1.3\cdot 10^{-44}\, ee_0$
ν, γ	ν, μ, e	$\sim 1.5\cdot 10^{-47}\, \nu_2^2 e^3/\omega$
ν in field of *Ze*	ν, μ, e	$\sim 3\ \cdot 10^{-49}\, Z^2\nu_2^2\mu^3 e^3/\omega^6$
ν, n	ν, n	$\sim 3\ \cdot 10^{-57}\, \nu_2^2$ *
$\bar{\nu}$, p	$\bar{\nu}$, p	$\sim 3\ \cdot 10^{-57}\, \nu_2^2$ *
ν, e	ν, e	$\sim 3\ \cdot 10^{-57}\, \nu_2^2$ *
ν	ν, ν, $\tilde{\nu}$	infinite half life
ν, $\bar{\nu}$	ν, ν	$\sim 6\ \cdot 10^{-57}\, \nu\bar{\nu}$ *
ν, $\bar{\nu}$	e, $\bar{e}$	$\sim 1.4\cdot 10^{-57}\, \nu\bar{\nu}$ *
e, $\bar{e}$	ν, $\bar{\nu}$	$\sim 4\ \cdot 10^{-58}\, \nu\bar{\nu}$ *
ν, γ	ν, ν, $\bar{\nu}$	$\sim 2\ \cdot 10^{-72}\, \nu_3\nu_2\omega\nu_4^3$ *
ν in field of *Ze*	ν in field of *Ze*	$\sim 5\ \cdot 10^{-61}\, Z^2\nu_1\nu_2$ *
ν, γ	ν, γ	$\sim 5\ \cdot 10^{-65}\, \nu^3/\omega$ *

([99]) R. DAVIS jr.: *Phys. Rev.*, **97**, 766 (1955); *Bull. Am. Phys. Soc.*, no. 4 (1956). paper UA5.

carried out such an experiment with 1000 gallons of CCl_4 at Savannah River, measured $\sigma = (0.3 \pm 0.4)\cdot 10^{-45}\ \text{cm}^2$, and concluded

$$\sigma < 0.09\cdot 10^{-44}\ \text{cm}^2\,, \tag{184}$$

as consistent with a real difference between neutrinos and anti-neutrinos (Table X).

EUWEMA [90] has investigated the neutrino processes listed in the following Table XI. The calculated cross sections in a number of cases depend strongly upon assumptions about the form factor for the Fermi interaction. He adopts for this form factor the assumption that it is equivalent to a cut-off of intermediate states above 1 GeV.

6. – Production of pairs out of the vacuum by gravitons.

Elementary processes have been studied which involve the interaction of gravitational fields with elementary particles [100]—particularly with neutrinos [101]. The cross section for two gravitons to interact and produce a pair of neutrinos or electrons can be determined (Table XII) along the lines used by BOHR to describe the production of a pair of electrons by two γ-rays. The cross section thus estimated,

$$\sigma \sim (GE/c^4)^2 \sim (1.6\cdot 10^{-33}\ \text{cm})^4/\lambda\!\!\!^{-2}\,, \tag{185}$$

in agreement with the calculation of IVANENKO, attains the order of magnitude of $\lambda\!\!\!^{-2}$ itself only at wave lengths comparable to the scale of gravitational field fluctuations,

$$L^* \sim 1.6\cdot 10^{-33}\ \text{cm}$$

and at mass-energies of the order of 10^{-5} g or 10^{28} eV.

The calculated cross section for the reverse reaction follows the same formula (185), and has the same energy dependence as the cross section for the

(100) D. IVANENKO and A. SOKOLOV: *Vestnik Moscovskogo Universiteta*, no. 8 (1947); A. SOKOLOV: *Vestnik Moscovskogo Universiteta*, no. 9 (1952); D. IVANENKO and A. BRODSKI: *Compt. Rend.* (*Dokl.*) *Acad. Sci. USSR*, **92**, 731 (1953); D. IVANENKO and A. SOKOLOV: *Klassische Feldtheorie* (Berlin, 1953), especially Sect. **56**, p. 320; D. IVANENKO: *Max Planck Festschrift* (Berlin, 1958), p. 353; D. IVANENKO and A. SOKOLOV: *Quantum Theory of Fields* (in Russian), part II (Moscow, 1952), Sect. **5**; I. PIIR: Theoretical Papers of the Institute of Physics and Astronomy of the Esthonian Academy of Sciences (Tartu, 1957).

(101) D. R. BRILL and J. A. WHEELER: *Rev. Mod. Phys.*, **29**, 465 (1957).

TABLE XII. – *Order-of-magnitude estimate of cross section for creation of a pair by the collision of two quanta of equal but opposite momenta* (from BRILL and WHEELER [69]).

Process	$\gamma+\gamma\to e^{+}+e^{-}$	$G+G\to\nu+\bar{\nu}$ or $e+\bar{e}$
Energy of one quantum	$E=\hbar c/\lambda\!\!\!^{-}$	$E=\hbar c/\lambda\!\!\!^{-}$
Localization volume	$\sim\lambda\!\!\!^{-3}$	$\sim\lambda\!\!\!^{-3}$
Energy density	$\sim\hbar c/\lambda\!\!\!^{-4}$	$\sim\hbar c/\lambda\!\!\!^{-4}$
Relevant field	electric	gravitational
Square of field	$\sim(\hbar c)^{\frac{1}{2}}/\lambda\!\!\!^{-2}$	$\sim(\hbar cG)^{\frac{1}{2}}/\lambda\!\!\!^{-2}$
Available potential in region of energy concentration	$\delta A\sim(\hbar c)^{\frac{1}{2}}/\lambda\!\!\!^{-}$	$\delta g\sim(\hbar G/c^{3})^{\frac{1}{2}}/\lambda\!\!\!^{-}$
Potential required to produce transition from $E_1=-\hbar c/\lambda\!\!\!^{-2}$ to $E_2=+\hbar c/\lambda\!\!\!^{-2}$ with nearly 100% probability	$\delta A\sim\hbar c/\lambda\!\!\!^{-}e$	$\delta g\sim 1$
Available disturbance/required disturbance	$\sim e/(\hbar c)^{\frac{1}{2}}$	$\sim(\hbar G/c^{3})^{\frac{1}{2}}/\lambda\!\!\!^{-}$
Number of times this factor enters into matrix element	2	2
Number of times matrix elements occur in transition probability	2	2
Pair creation cross section for 100% creation probability	$\sim\lambda\!\!\!^{-2}$	$\sim\lambda\!\!\!^{-2}$
Resulting estimate for cross section for pair creation	$\sigma\sim(e^{2}/\hbar c)^{2}\lambda\!\!\!^{-2}$ $\sim(e^{2}/mc^{2})^{2}(mc^{2}/E)^{2}$	$\sigma\sim(\hbar G/c^{3})^{2}/\lambda\!\!\!^{-2}$ $\sim(1.6\cdot10^{-33}\text{ cm})^{4}/\lambda\!\!\!^{-2}$ $\sim(GE/c^{4})^{2}$
Asymptotic behavior of accurate formula for cross section, high energy, unpolarized radiation	$\sigma\sim 2\pi(e^{2}/mc^{2})^{2}(mc^{2}/E)^{2}\cdot$ $\cdot\ln[2E/e^{\frac{1}{2}}mc^{2}]$	Not yet calculated

production of μ^{+} and e^{-}. The ratio of the two cross sections is

$$\text{(186)}\qquad \frac{\sigma(\nu+\bar{\nu}\to\mu^{+}+e^{-})}{\sigma(\nu+\bar{\nu}\to G+G)}\sim\frac{(g^{2}/\hbar^{2}c^{4})\,(E/\hbar)^{2}}{(GE/c^{4})^{2}}\sim(gc^{2}/G\hbar^{2})^{2}\sim 10^{34}\,,$$

in conformity with the well known great ratio between β and gravitational couplings.

7. – Response of neutrinos to gravitational fields of larger scale.

Neutrinos have been discussed generally in the context of emission and absorption processes describable by cross sections ([102]). If knowledge about electrons were equally limited, one would know the rate at which electrons are emitted in β decay or absorbed in K-capture processes, but nothing about the motion of electrons in electric and magnetic fields, nothing about the binding of electrons in atoms, and very little about the stress energy tensor of the electron. Yet the neutrino does not respond directly to electric and magnetic fields. Therefore any study of its motion through space centers about its response to gravitational fields. Calculations to date in this direction ([101]) have treated 1) the motion and 2) the energy levels of a neutrino in a gravitational field and 3) the properties of a geon which derives it mass-energy from neutrinos.

8. – Reason for weakness of gravitational radiation.

In turning from neutrinos and their interaction with gravitation to pure gravitational radiation, it is appropriate to recall the analogies with electromagnetic radiation (Table XIII) and the reason for the smallness of the radiation in the one case as compared to the other. For the case of an electron circulating about a nucleus, the dipole moment of the system dominates in determining the radiative field. In the cases of two masses circulating about each other, however, the mass dipole moment relative to the center of gravity is necessarily zero. In analysing the radiation in this case it is therefore necessary to go to the next order of approximation and allow for the difference in travel cotime, r_1 *vs.* r_2, for the disturbances from the two centers. The contributions to the radiation field no longer compensate each other exactly when allowance is made of the resulting phase corrections, $\omega r_1/c$ and $\omega r_2/c$. The estimated rate of energy loss, in agreement with Einstein's early calculations, is proportional to the square of the mass quadrupole moment and the sixth power of its frequency of rotation.

([10]) For two good surveys, see ALLEN, ref. ([98]) and the chapter *The Neutrino* by C. S. WU in *Theoretical Physics in the Twentieth Century; a Memorial Volume to Wolfgang Pauli*, ed. by M. FIERZ and V. WEISSKOPF (New York, 1960).

TABLE XIII. – *Fields produced by accelerated charges and by accelerated masses (1) at distances small compared to the cotime of acceleration, $T = c\,\Delta t$ and (2) distances large compared to this cotime. In both cases a represents the component of the acceleration perpendicular to the line of sight.*

	Electromagnetism	Gravitation
Near Far	e/r^2 $ea/c^2 r$	Gm/r^2 $Gma/c^2 r$
Effect of pair of centers revolving around center of gravity	$(e_1 a_1 + e_2 a_2)/c^2 r$	$G(m_1 a_1 + m_2 a_2)/c^2 r$
Value of sum when account is taken of law of action and reaction	Same	Zero
Effect of allowing for difference in time of arrival from the two centers	Unimportant	$\sim \sum_{k=1}^{2} (\omega r_k/c) \cdot (G m_k r_k \omega^2/c^2 r)$
Factor by which square of field strength should be multiplied to obtain outward energy flux	$4\pi r^2/8\pi$	$\sim (c^2/G) r^2$
Resultant values of $-\mathrm{d}E/\mathrm{d}t$	$\sim e^2 a^2/c^3$ $\sim (\omega^2 p)^2/c^3$	$\sim G(\omega^3 I)^2/c^5$
Moment relevant for radiation in periodic motion	$p = e_1 x_1 + e_2 x_2$	$I = m_1 r_1^2 + m_2 r_2^2$

9. – Impulsive sources of gravitational radiation.

These considerations refer to a steady rate of radiation. The opposite extreme is also of interest, when the source experiences a sudden disturbance lasting for a time Δt and gives out a pulse of radiation with length of the order $\Delta T = c\,\Delta t$ (Table XIV). The analysis towards the end of the table is a little simplified in that the relevant quantity is not the total kinetic energy but the off-center part, or the quadrupole part, of the kinetic energy. For example, in case a star explodes, what counts is not the total energy release, but the product of this quantity by the eccentricity carried over into the expansion as a consequence of rotation or any other causes.

Energy outputs from a few impulsive sources are estimated in very rough order of magnitude in Table XV. Little consideration has so far been given

TABLE XIV. – *Analysis of impulsive radiation.*
(Appreciation is expressed to Professor V. TELEGDI for stimulating discussions leading to the preparation of this table.)

	Electromagnetism	Gravitation
Typical moment relevant for radiation	$p_x(t)$	$I_{xx}(t)$
Its Fourier transform	$(2\pi)^{-\frac{1}{2}}\int p_x \exp[i\omega t]\,\mathrm{d}t$	$(2\pi)^{-\frac{1}{2}}\int I_{xx} \exp[i\omega t]\,\mathrm{d}t$
Name for this quantity	$p_x(\omega)$	$I_{xx}(\omega)$
Time decomposition of total radiative energy loss ΔE	$c^{-3}\int \ddot{p}(t)^2\,\mathrm{d}t$	$Gc^{-5}\int \dddot{I}(t)^2\,\mathrm{d}t$
Decomposition of ΔE according to circular frequency	$c^{-3}\int \ddot{p}^2(\omega)\,\mathrm{d}\omega$	$Gc^{-5}\int \dddot{I}^2(\omega)\,\mathrm{d}\omega$
Integrand nearly constant with respect to ω from $\omega=0$ up to a critical value of ω, beyond which radiation falls off very fast	$\omega_{\text{crit}} \sim 1/\Delta t$	$\omega_{\text{crit}} \sim 1/\Delta t$
$-\,\mathrm{d}\,\Delta E/\mathrm{d}\omega$ for $\omega < \omega_{\text{crit}}$	$\sim c^{-3}\ddot{p}^2(0)$	$\sim Gc^{-5}\dddot{I}^2(0)$
Zero frequency moment that enters this formula	$\sim (e_1\,\Delta v_{x1} + e_2\,\Delta v_{x2})$	Δ(« Kinetic Energy »)$_{xx}$
Rewrite of $-\,\mathrm{d}\,\Delta E/\mathrm{d}\omega$	$\sim (e\,\Delta v)^2/c^3$	$\sim G[\Delta(\text{« K.E. »})_{xx}]^2/c^5$
Total energy of pulse	$\sim$ This/Δt	$\sim$ This/Δt

to detecting effects of this kind by their influence on the geometry of a system of test particles, originally disposed in a circle normal to the direction of arrival of the radiation, and impulsively set into motion into an elliptical pattern by the passage of the pulse. However, considerations have been presented by WEBER on the production and detection of *continuous* gravitational radiation ([103]). Whichever one uses—a detector of continuous radiation or a detector of a pulse of radiation—it is clear that one will hope in the first instance for a fortunate accident of nature that will supply one free of charge with an adequate source of radiation—such as the radio stars supplied for electromagnetic radiation. If this line fails it will still be possible, according to Weber's estimates, to build artificial sources of gravitational radiation of sufficient intensity to render them detectable.

([103]) J. WEBER: *Phys. Rev.*, **117**, 306 (1960).

TABLE XV. – *Energy released in gravitational impulse radiation for four kinds of event.* Preparation of this table was stimulated by hearing at the Royaumont conference Professor SCHUCKING's interesting considerations on gravitational radiation associated with fission.

Event	One fission of 180 MeV	Fission bomb yield 17 kilotons at 10% efficiency	Meteorite striking earth at escape velocity	Explosion of star when 10^{-4} of mass is released
Mass	$4\cdot10^{-22}$ g	10^4 g	10^9 g (*)	$2\cdot10^{33}$ g
Velocity	$1.2\cdot10^9$ cm/s	$4\cdot10^8$ cm/s	$11\cdot10^5$ cm/s	$4\cdot10^8$ cm/s
Energy	$2.9\cdot10^{-4}$ erg	$7\cdot10^{20}$ erg	$6\cdot10^{20}$ erg	$1.8\cdot10^{50}$ erg
Fraction assumed relevant to radiative moment	1	0.1	1	0.1
Time integral of this moment = = « K.E. »$_{xx}$	$2.9\cdot10^{-4}$ erg	$7\cdot10^{19}$ erg	$6\cdot10^{20}$ erg	$1.8\cdot10^{49}$ erg
« K.E. »$_{xx}/c^2$	$3.2\cdot10^{-25}$ g	0.08 g	0.67 g	$2\cdot10^{28}$ g
$\dfrac{dE}{d\omega}\sim\dfrac{G}{c}\left(\dfrac{KE_{xx}}{c^2}\right)^2$	$2.3\cdot10^{-67}\,\dfrac{\text{erg}}{\text{rad/s}}$	$1.4\cdot10^{-20}\,\dfrac{\text{erg}}{\text{rad/s}}$	$1.0\cdot10^{-18}\,\dfrac{\text{erg}}{\text{rad/s}}$	$9\cdot10^{38}\,\dfrac{\text{erg}}{\text{rad/s}}$
Δt	10^{-21} s	10^{-8} s	10^{-3} s	10^4 s
$\Delta\omega\sim1/\Delta t$	10^{21} rad/s	10^8 rad/s	10^3 rad/s	10^{-4} rad/s
$\Delta E_{\text{radiated}}$	10^{-46} erg	10^{-12} erg	10^{-15} erg	10^{35} erg
Assumed distance to detector	10^3 cm	10^3 cm	10^9 cm	10^{23} cm
$\Delta E/4\pi r^2$	10^{-53} erg/cm²	10^{-19} erg/cm²	10^{-34} erg/cm²	10^{-12} erg/cm²

(*) 1961 Note: For evidence for a fall of mass $\sim 10^{16}$ g, see R. S. DIETZ, *Scientific American* **205**, No. 2, p. 50 (1961).

10. – Long wave-length gravitational radiation; if intense, can cause distant galaxies to show in multiple.

It is not necessary to limit consideration to gravitational radiation being produced at the present time. Great amounts of such radiation must be created automatically by the act of implosion and re-explosion of the universe if that process follows anything like the pattern of undersea bubbles, turning inside out one prong and spike at a time. The large scale irregularities produced in the metric in such an event will propagate about as gravitational radiation. It is not obvious that this radiation will be limited in content of effective mass-energy to anything of the same order as the mass in the form of « material particles ». Therefore it is of interest to ask what is the effective amount of energy carried in such disturbances. Wave lengths of centimeters to kilometers may be studied by detecting equipment of the kind that the next decade or two will bring forth. However, it is quite possible to believe that gravitational radiation—if there is much of it—came into being with a scale of wave lengths comparable to the scale of separation of the large clusters of matter in the universe, the galaxies. The galactic separations will change with time during the expansion of the universe, but so will the wave lengths of the gravitational radiation, and in proportion. The separations today being of the order of $2 \cdot 10^6$ light years, it will be of interest to ask about gravitational waves and irregularities in the metric with the same characteristic distance [104]. Fig. 19 gives a schematic representation of a closed space endowed with a metric of varying curvature. Two nearby points can be connected in a natural way by only one geodesic. Points at greater separation, however, can sometimes be connected by two or more geodesics of comparable length. The analogous situation in the case of sound is well known. An explosion at one point may give rise some distance away to one or three or five « booms », the number of acoustical images of the source depending upon the inhomogeneities in the refractive index of the atmosphere. So in the case of curved space, the $g_{\mu\nu}$ play in a generalized sense the role of the refractive index in acoustics. *The number of optical images of a distant star*—or of a star explosion—*will therefore provide a measure of the large scale fluctuations in the metric and, if not observed, will set an upper limit to the effective energy content of gravitational radiation.*

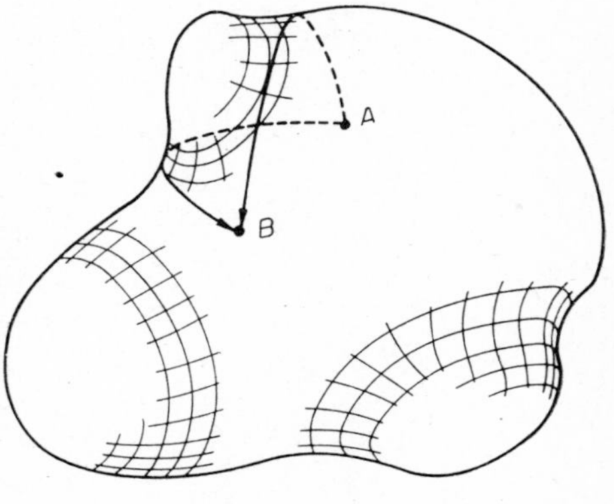

Fig. 19. – There is more than one geodesic of reasonable length that connects two sufficiently distant points, A and B, in an irregularly curved space.

---

(104) Appreciation is expressed to Professor M. Schwarzschild for discussions of the astrophysical implications of gravitational radiation, the question of the most important wave lengths, and the problem whether anything about the dynamics internal to a galaxy can be used as a means to test for the presence of gravitational radiation. Appreciation is expressed to Dr. B. Bertotti and Mr. F. Gross for a number of discussions on the question of multiple images in a space of irregular curvature, and to Professor U. Ingard and Professor C. Harris for references to the related literature in the field of sound, and to Professor S. Chandrasekhar for discussions of his work on the related problem of scintillations.

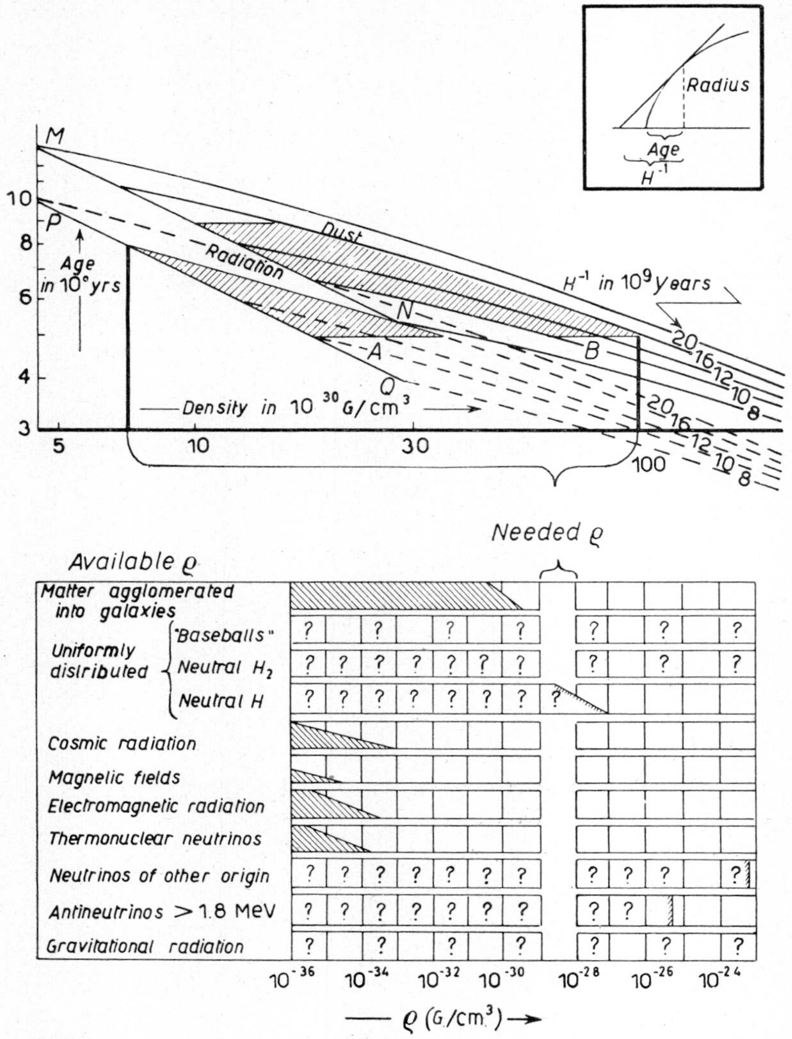

Fig. 20. – Density of mass-energy required to hold the universe together according to Einstein's general relativity (above) compared to individual sources of mass-energy (below), the values of some of which are known reasonably well, others not at all, as indicated by question marks. The curves in the upper diagram tell how much present density is required for any specified value of the present age of the universe and for any present value of the rate of expansion, H, or of the extrapolated time back to the start of expansion — the « inverse Hubble constant », H^{-1}. If for example H^{-1} is taken to be $12 \cdot 10^9$ years, and the age is taken to be $5 \cdot 10^9$ years, then two lines are determined which intersect at A. Thereby the required density is determined. The calculated density differs appreciably according as the source of the density is primarily inert matter (dust; smooth curves) or radiation (dashed curves). The cross-hatched regions assume 5 and $9 \cdot 10^9$ years as lower and upper limits on the age and 10 and $16 \cdot 10^9$ years as lower and upper limits on the inverse Hubble constant. The

By way of illustration, it may be noted that the effective overall radius of curvature of space, R, which can be produced by ripples in the metric of scale L and magnitude δg, is given in order of magnitude by the formula

$$\frac{1}{R^2} \sim \frac{(\delta g)^2}{L^2}\,; \tag{187}$$

so that with $R \sim 10^{10}$ light years, $L \sim 10^6$ light years, and no *other* sources of curvature, one would have $\delta g \sim 10^{-4}$. Comparison with the Einstein field equations,

$$R_{\mu\nu} - \tfrac{1}{2} g_{\mu\nu} R = (8\pi G/c^4) T_{\mu\nu}\,, \tag{188}$$

shows that the right hand side of (187) can be regarded for rough purposes of estimation as equivalent to an effective energy density, though of course according to first principles there is really zero energy density in a source free gravitational field.

11. – Enough mass-energy to curve up space into closure?

Gravitational radiation, neutrinos, photons, « ordinary matter », and all other sources of mass-energy come to a common standard of comparison (Fig. 20) when the question is asked: Is the total large enough to curve up space into closure? Available observational evidence ([105]) is insufficient to make more than a challenging beginning towards answering this important question.

---

density deduced from these limits lies between 7 and $100 \cdot 10^{-30}$ g/cm^3 as indicated by the cross hatched region in the lower diagram. There the hatching indicates known sources of mass-energy and approximate uncertainty limits on present values. Among the potential sources of mass-energy for which no present estimates are available are two (neutral H and anti-neutrinos) where approximate upper limits can be given. In view of present day ignorance about several potential sources of mass-energy it is impossible to say that there is any contradiction between the facts and the predictions of Einstein's general relativity. Diagram modified from KLAUDER, WILLEY, WHEELER.

([105]) A summary of the evidence, and an earlier version of Fig. 20 appears in the section by L. KLAUDER jr., R. WILLEY and J. A. WHEELER: *La structure et l'évolution de l'univers* (Brussels, 1958). See G. B. FIELD: *Astrophys. Journ.*, **129**, 536 (1959) for recent considerations on the abundance of hydrogen. A. W. SUNYAR and M. GOLDHABER, in a kind personal communication, give a neutrino flux limit of $\leqslant 2.5 \cdot 10^{20}$ per cm^2/s from the reaction ^{87}Rb $\rightarrow$ ^{87}Sr^m.

12. – Minimum angular effective size for distant galaxies a new prediction from Einstein's theory.

Questions have of course always been raised whether it is really known that the universe is closed and expanding at a diminishing rate as demanded by Einstein's general relativity when the idealization of uniform curvature is accepted. On this account it is interesting to see that a very striking prediction ([106]) comes out of this theory, which should be subject to experimental test. A sequence of galaxies, all of approximately the same physical dimensions, but more and more remote from the observer, should not decrease in-

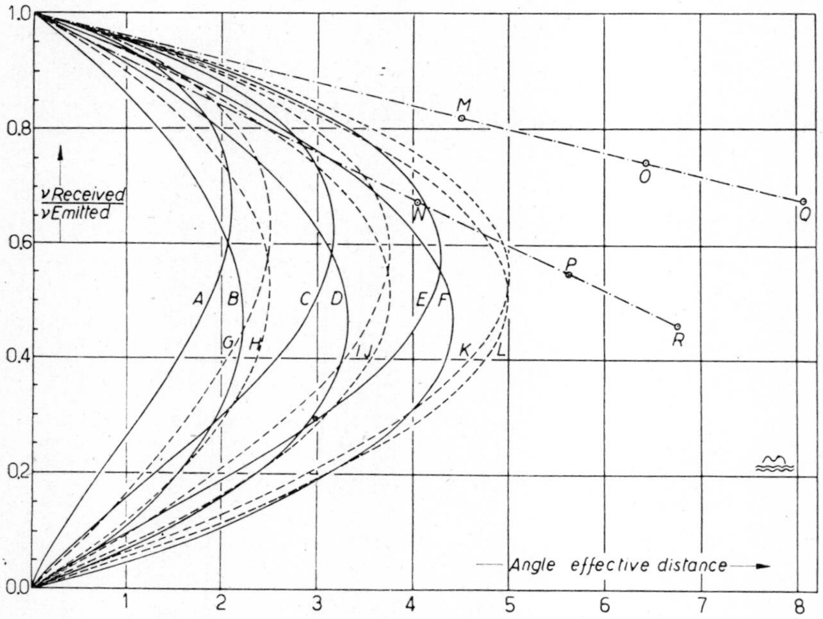

Fig. 21. – Apparent distance of distant galaxy plotted horizontally, frequency of lines in its spectrum relative to standard frequencies plotted vertically. The curves apply to a variety of values of H^{-1} and of the age of the universe in the interesting portion of Fig. 19. Smooth curves refer to the case of a universe where the sources of mass-energy give negligible pressure (« dust »); and dashed curves refer to the case where the pressure has the maximum possible value, one third of the energy density (« radiation »). The dot-dash curve refers to the completely different and non-Einsteinian theory of Bondi, Gold and Hoyle. The frequency scale at the left provides the most unambiguous physical scale related to true distance. The angle effective distance is to be identified with the true diameter of the galaxy (assumed the same as for typical nearby galaxies) divided by the apparent angular diameter of the nearby galaxy. Diagram from Wakano and Wheeler ([106]).

([106]) M. Wakano and J. A. Wheeler in the book cited in ref. ([105]).

definitely in apparent size. Instead, those which are receding at about $v/c = 0.5$ should show a minimum angular dimension, and both those more remote and those nearer at hand should look larger (Fig. 21). The effect is most easily visualized by imagining 1) a spherical shell of good clear glass in which here and there a few pennies are imbedded, 2) a hole drilled in this shell near the north pole, 3) a means of observing light which comes through the glass to this hole. Then nearby pennies will look large, those at the equator will look smaller, but those near the south pole will again look large to the observer at the north pole. Optical telescopes do well only to distances a little short of $v/c = 0.2$, so that it would appear that radiotelescopes alone could test this prediction, and thereby further test Einstein's theory.

13. – Change of particle masses with time? Or with curvature of space-time? Or not at all?

Elementary particles contribute to the density of mass energy and thereby affect the curvature of the universe, according to general relativity. Does the curvature of the universe conversely act back on elementary particles? As it changes, does it affect their characteristic masses and other properties? Not having any such effect of curvature in mind, DIRAC nevertheless long ago suggested on quite other grounds that the dimensionless physical constants might change with time during the expansion of the universe ([107]). He noted the coincidence in order of magnitude of three very large numbers,

$$(189)\quad \left\{\begin{aligned} N_1 &\sim \frac{e^2}{Gm_e m_p} \sim 2\cdot 10^{39}, \\ N_2 &\sim \frac{ct_{\text{universe}}}{e^2/m_e c^2} \sim 4\cdot 10^{40}, \\ N_3 &\sim \left(\frac{4\pi}{3}\,\frac{\varrho R^3_{\text{universe}}}{M_p}\right)^{\frac{1}{2}} \sim 2\cdot 10^{39}, \end{aligned}\right.$$

and argued that the coincidence is not reasonably interpreted as due to chance.

([107]) P. A. M. DIRAC: *Proc. Roy. Soc. London*, A **165**, 199 (1938). For further discussion of Dirac's considerations, see E. TELLER: *Phys. Rev.*, **73**, 801 (1948) and R. H. DICKE: *Rev. Mod. Phys.*, **29**, 363 (1957).

If the three quantities maintain the same ratios one to another as the expansion proceeds, then the physical constants will have to change. If the viewpoint of geometrodynamics is useful, then the set of units introduced long ago by PLANCK have to be considered as the fundamental and constant quantities,

$$(190)\qquad \begin{cases} L^* = (\hbar G/c^3)^{\frac{1}{2}} = 1.6\cdot 10^{-33}\ \text{cm}\,, \\ \text{Time} = L^*/c\,, \\ m_1 = (\hbar c/G)^{\frac{1}{2}} = 2.2\cdot 10^{-5}\ \text{g}\,, \end{cases}$$

and the other physical constants have to be regarded as changing with respect to these standards. DICKE has analysed a number of the possibilities for testing for such a change with time ([107]). It is not clear that such an effect, if observed, would be inconsistent with general relativity. Indeed, if the properties of the particles do change as the expansion proceeds, it would seem that the influence of the curvature tensor on the particle would be the most natural covariant and local quantity to which to ascribe this effect.

V. – Neutrino Equilibrium and the Law of Conservation of Nucleons.

1. – No equilibrium for supercritical mass.

Space curvature of large scale may or may not have an appreciable effect on particle masses; but there is one context in which an influence of the metric upon the stability of elementary particles appears inescapable. *There is a limit of mass of the order of* 0.7 *of the mass of the sun, above which there is no equilibrium configuration for a mass of cold matter catalyzed to the end point of thermonuclear evolution.* The pressure at the center goes to infinity as the mass is increased towards this finite limit, and also at the center the separation between positive and negative energy states goes to zero. The details of the transition depend upon the equation of state assumed, but the existence of the effects does not [108]. Fig. 22 describes a configuration short of the critical mass, and also the critical configuration itself, for the model in which the

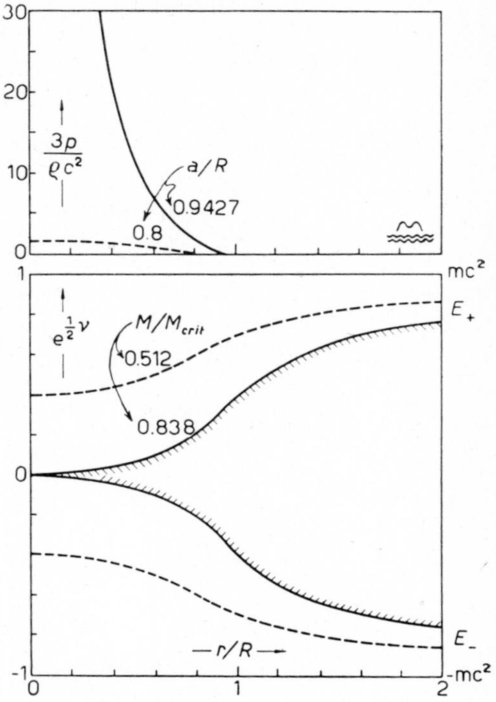

Fig. 22. – Pressure (above) and metric, or equivalent gravitational potential (below) as functions of distance for two configurations of an ideal incompressible liquid, one (dashed curves) for a mass which is $0.512/0.838 = 0.611$ of the critical mass, the other (smooth curves) for the critical mass itself. In Newtonian theory the gravitational potential due to a fluid mass varies as $1/r$ outside, and inside as a harmonic oscillator potential with value and slope which match at the boundary, $r = a$. The corresponding quantity in general relativity is the square root of the time component of the metric, $[-g_{TT}(r)]^{\frac{1}{2}} = (\text{Schwarzschild's } \exp[\nu(r)])^{\frac{1}{2}}$. When multiplied by the rest mass of the electron, this quantity gives the lower boundary of the sea of available energy levels. The shaded region therefore shows how the separation between positive and negative energy states goes to zero as the center of the critical configuration is approached. The pressure at the center goes to infinity (upper diagram). A formal — but singular — solution of the field equations can be given for still greater masses; then the point at which the metric goes to zero — and the pressure becomes infinite — moves outward. When this point coincides with the radius of the fluid mass itself (case $a = R$, $M = M_{\text{crit}}$; not shown in diagram) the mass all lies within the so-called Schwarzschild radius. On this account the question is sometimes raised, does not the mass cut itself off from the rest of the universe? However, all solutions are physically unacceptable already as soon as M reaches 0.838 times the M_{crit} defined — not very happily — in terms of this « cut-off » configuration; or as soon as a reaches $0.9427R$. The problem of equilibrium is already without a solution as soon as the pressure goes to infinity *at the center*. The question of a « cut-off » never has opportunity to arise. To allow for a compressibility of the fluid only makes the density go up at the center, makes gravitational pressures higher, and therefore causes the pressure to go to infinity at the center at a *lower* critical mass.

---

[108] The following account is based on the article by B. K. Harrison, M. Wakano and J. A. Wheeler in the book cited in note [105], pag. 117, and Figs. 22, 23 and 24 are taken from it. See that article for an account of the important contributions made to the problem of the critical mass by Landau, Oppenheimer, Serber, Volkoff, Snyder, Chandrasekhar, Rudkjobing, Tauber and J. W. Weinberg.

matter of the star is assumed to be an incompressible fluid. Fig. 23 shows a more realistic equation of state (B. K. HARRISON) used in a re-analysis of the problem.

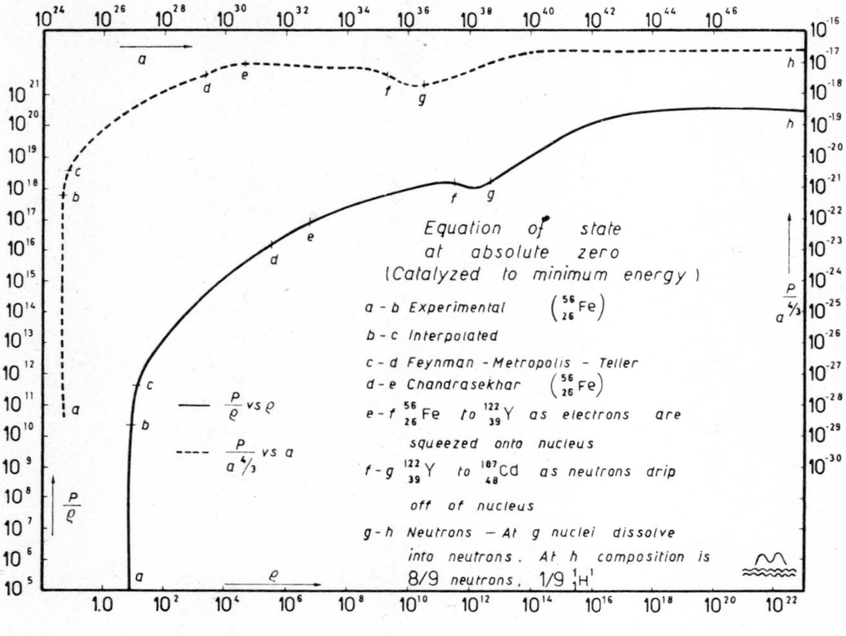

Fig. 23. – Harrison's equation of state for cold matter catalyzed to the end point of thermonuclear evolution. The smooth curve gives P/ϱ in cm²/s² as a function of the density ϱ in g/cm³. The dashed curve gives the ratio $P/a^{4/3}$ in g cm³/s² as a function of the number of nucleons/cm³, a. Until the density arrives at a value of the order of 10^6 g/cm³ the pressure is insufficient to squeeze electrons onto the nucleus or to alter the position of the minimum on the packing fraction curve. The composition is therefore 100% ^{56}Fe. Higher pressures alter the composition of minimum energy in the direction of heavier nuclei with a higher ratio of neutrons to protons. Eventually a point f is reached where the nucleus can hold no more neutrons. The equilibrium composition is a mixture of free neutrons, degenerate electrons with high Fermi energy, and the nuclear species appropriate to the given pressure. The equilibrium was calculated by use of the familiar semi-empirical mass formula. At a density of the order of 10^{14} g/cm³ the medium becomes as compact as nuclear matter. The further course of the pressure density relation becomes more uncertain. If a hard core repulsion begins to dominate, it might be conceivable to use as idealized representation of the equation of state an incompressible fluid, as assumed in the derivation of Fig. 22. In the present curves the opposite idealized limiting behavior was assumed, a perfect Fermi gas at high pressures. In the relativistic limit the equilibrium goes asymptotically to a mixture of neutrons, protons and electrons in the ratio 8 : 1 : 1.

2. – Equation of state.

Harrison's equation of state assumes cold matter ideally catalyzed to the end point of thermonuclear evolution. This end point at ordinary pressures is ^{56}Fe. At higher pressures the nuclear composition of minimum energy is altered. This region was treated by making use of the usual semiempirical formula for nuclear binding energies, plus the standard principle of statistical equilibrium. At very high densities nuclear forces were overlooked and all particles were treated as belonging to ideal Fermi gases. To allow in a more drastic way for a hard core repulsion could not bring back into being a stable state of affairs for arbitrarily high masses because a critical condition already develops in the ideal case of an incompressible fluid.

3. – Relativistic hydrostatic equilibrium.

Harrison's equation was inserted into the same general relativistic equations of hydrostatic equilibrium which had previously been used by OPPENHEIMER and VOLKOFF (109) to treat the case of a neutron gas:

$$\left\{\begin{aligned} &\mathrm{d}M(r)/\mathrm{d}r = 4\pi\varrho(p)\,r^2\,, \\ &\mathrm{d}p(r)/\mathrm{d}r = -\frac{[\varrho(p)+c^{-2}p]\,G[M(r)+4\pi c^{-2}p(r)\,r^3]}{r[r-2GM(r)/c^2]}\,. \end{aligned}\right. \tag{191}$$

These equations of equilibrium were integrated numerically on the MANIAC computer of the Institute for Advanced Study by M. WAKANO with the advice and support of Dr. HANS J. MAEHLY and the collaboration of Mrs. BARBARA WEYMANN. The integration proceeds in this way, that a value is picked arbitrarily for the central density, ϱ_0. The equation of state then gives an associated value of the central pressure, p_0. The value of the mass function $M(r)$ at the center is of course zero. The first order equations then uniquely determine the progress of the functions $M(r)$, $\varrho(r)$ and $p(r)$ from the center to the outside. The outside is defined as that point where the pressure goes to zero: $r = R$. The mass $M = M$ (at $r = R$) is then determinate. In other words a problem is first solved, and then one finds out what problem it is that he has solved. The results of the hydrodynamic analysis of WAKANO are summarized in Fig. 24 (relation between total mass and central density) and Fig. 25 (relation between radius and central density).

The work of HARRISON and WAKANO like the earlier work of LANDAU (110) and of OPPENHEIMER and VOLKOFF, emphasizes that one simply does not

(109) J. R. OPPENHEIMER and G. VOLKOFF: *Phys. Rev.*, **55**, 374 (1939).

(110) L. D. LANDAU: *Phys. Zeits. Sow.*, **1**, 285 (1932).

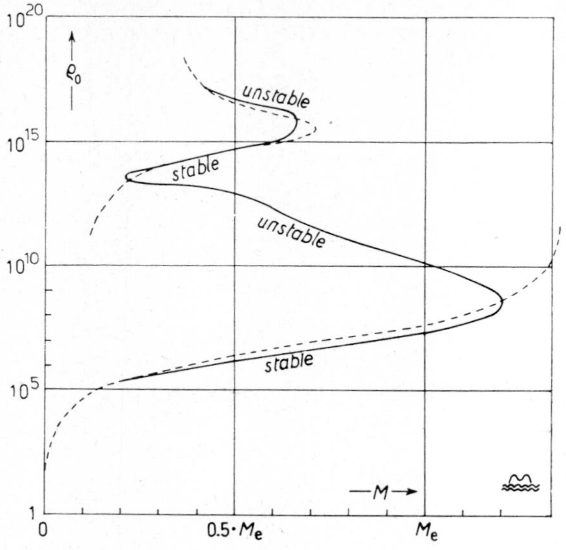

Fig. 24. – Mass of a star made out of cold matter, catalyzed to the end point of thermonuclear evolution, in units of the mass of the sun, $M_\odot = 1.987 \cdot 10^{33}$ g, as a function of the central density, ϱ_0 in g/cm³, as deduced by the relativistic hydrostatic analysis of WAKANO (45 integrations on the MANIAC computer of the Institute for Advanced Study with the kind collaboration of Dr. H. J. MAEHLY and Mrs. B. WEYMANN) The lower dashed curve shows the connection between mass and central density which was deduced by CHANDRASEKHAR: (1) without allowance for the corrections due to general relativity; (2) without allowance for the crushing of electrons into combination with protons to make neutrons. In other words, CHANDRASEKHAR deals with an effective mass per electron and assumes for this quantity a constant value ($\mu = 56/27 = 2.07$ in the figure; the value $\mu = 56/26 = 2.15$, corresponding to $^{56}_{26}Fe$, would have been more reasonable. It can be obtained from the dashed curve in the diagram by a small change in the M scale, proportional to μ^2, and in the ϱ scale proportional to μ). The upper dashed curve represents the results of OPPENHEIMER and VOLKOFF derived by integrating the general relativity equation of hydrostatic equilibrium for an idealized pure and relativistic Fermi neutron gas. So far as is known a curve has never before been available to connect the region where the pressure is mainly of atomic origin with the region where the pressure is mainly of nuclear origin. The two transitions on this curve from stable equilibrium to unstable equilibrium mark what might be called two « crushing points ». The lower curve marked « stable » is of course — where it runs under the upper curve marked stable — actual metastable with respect to contraction to a higher density; however, a potential hill has to be surmounted to pass from the less compact condition of equilibrium to the more compact one. The present considerations refer exclusively to cold stars. Hot stars have thermal pressure to help sustain them against gravitational pull and can have much higher masses than the Landau-Oppenheimer-Volkoff limit, $0.7 M_\odot$, without instability. But for a cold compact star there is no condition of equilibrium for a mass greater than about $0.7 M_\odot$.

know the fate of a compact assembly of cold matter, catalyzed to the end point of thermonuclear evolution, when the mass of that assembly exceeds about 0.7 times the mass of the sun.

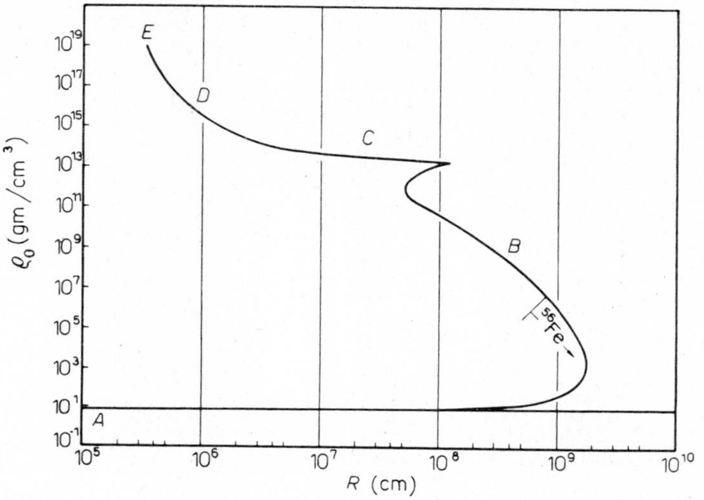

Fig. 25. – Radius versus central density for cold matter catalyzed to the end point of thermonuclear evolution, as found in the general relativistic hydrostatic analysis of WAKANO, based on the equation of state of HARRISON. The horizontal line near the bottom of the diagram shows how the curve would run if iron were incompressible. Some sections of the curve B C D are associated with unstable configurations (cf. Fig. 24).

4. – Independent of course of evolution.

It should be emphasized that the point under consideration is a point of principle, and has nothing at all directly to do with the actual course of thermonuclear evolution. One knows the lowest energy state of a system of A nucleons when A is 20 (^{20}Ne), when A is 56 (one ^{56}Fe) when A is 112 (two ^{56}Fe), when A is 560 (ten ^{56}Fe), when A is $56\cdot2\cdot10^{54}$ (corresponding to a little less than 0.1 the mass of the sun) (equilibrium configuration: $2\cdot10^{54}$ atoms of ^{56}Fe compacted as indicated in Figs. 24 and 25) but one has every reason to believe that there is *not* a lowest energy state of any ordinary character for a compact system of $A=56\cdot2\cdot10^{55}$ nucleons (mass before assembly about $0.9M_\odot$) It is of no interest in the present context how long it takes to arrive in the normal course of nuclear burning to arrive at such a situation, or how many different regimes of burning the star goes through—proton-proton reaction; carbon-nitrogen cycle; α particle reactions; etc. It may even be that the star always explodes before it approaches the conditions in question. In this case let the ejected matter be caught and let its kinetic energy be extracted, also the energy of fall back onto the star. Then as a result of the explosion the system is in a lower energy state than before, but the number of nucleons is unchanged. Let evolution continue, as well catalyzed as possible, with means for the removal of heat as efficient as possible. Ultimately the star gets tired. It can't eject matter. It can't radiate photons. It can't emit neutrinos. It comes into the absolutely lowest state possible for a system of A nucleons under the dual action of nuclear and gravitational forces. However long the time may be to get to this final state, this is the state of interest as a matter of principle.

Until the nature of this final state is established, the whole theory of thermonuclear reactions in stars will be open-ended. The situation will continue to be in nuclear-gravitational physics as it would have been in physical chemistry if one knew some details of the mechanism and rate of the fantastically complicated reaction

$$2\,H_2 + O_2 \rightleftarrows 2\,H_2O$$

but one did not know so elementary a quantity as the difference in free energy between the initial and final state of the reactants! Therefore one is compelled to ask again: *What is the final equilibrium state of an A-nucleon system under gravitational forces when A is large?* (« The big A problem »).

The big A problem involves elementary particle physics and gravitation physics together in the most inextricable way because 1) the pressure at the center goes towards infinity and 2) the separation of positive and negative energy states goes to zero. The conditions are severe for the central nucleons, but not for the rest of the system. What then happens when one more kilo of matter beyond the critical mass is added to the outside? The final mass —after the system has again settled down—must not exceed the critical mass. Therefore the added mass must be radiated away.

If the added mass were to escape in the form of particles, their kinetic energy could be abstracted from them, also the gravitational energy of fall back onto the massive object. The build up of these particles on the system would then ultimately lead back to the paradoxical situation from which an escape is sought.

After the added mass has all been radiated away, the number of nucleons 1) is the same as before the 1 kilo was added or 2) has been increased by the number of nucleons contained in 1 kilo or 3) is undefined. If 1) applies, then an indefinitely large number of nucleons can be confined into a finite amount of space—and indeed in the limited region of space near the center of the star, since conditions in the rest of the system are unaltered. To assume this possibility is almost the same as assuming that nucleons can be destroyed or that the number of nucleons has no meaning.

5. – Critical mass as catalyzer of nucleon creation and destruction.

It appears therefore that there is no escape from regarding a system of critical mass as a catalyzer, which can attract nucleons in from outside and dissolve away an equivalent number of nucleons at the center into radiation —electromagnetic, gravitational, or neutrinos—at such a rate or in such numbers as to keep the total number of nucleons in the system from exceeding a certain critical number.

The process now under consideration, of dissolution of nucleons into neutrinos and other radiation at high pressures, is fully compatible with the laws of conservation of momentum and energy. It violates the law of conservation of nucleons but upholds most other conservation laws. It does not contradict the observation (111) that nucleons have a half life against spontaneous breakup greater than $4\cdot10^{23}$ years because the pressure at the center of the critical mass is presumably greater by orders of magnitude than the pressure in the nucleus. A motion picture of a large mass of nucleons dissolving away under high pressure into free neutrinos presents an odd sight when run backwards. Sufficiently many neutrinos of the right helicity coming together from all directions into the high pressure catalytic region of space over a short time interval form themselves into nuclear matter. Or in other words, *the nucleon equilibrium should be controlled by the Fermi energy* μ_ν *of the neutrino field.*

If it is reasonable to assume that the number of nucleons in the universe has not had for all time some magic and inexplicable value, then it would seem reasonable to consider the number of nucleons as a dynamical variable with its own laws of change. If this variable is to change at all, then the conditions most favorable to change would seem to be high density and small separation of positive and negative energy states; that is, greatly reduced difference in mass between nucleons and neutrinos. Moreover, no explanation of the « big A paradox » is evident which does not demand in effect just such a renunciation of the law of conservation of nucleons.

6. – Opacity to neutrinos.

It is not necessary to deal with the paradox of supercritical masses, nor needful to analyse any process of dissolution of nucleons into neutrinos, in order to encounter interesting astrophysical situations where neutrinos can be produced copiously. The URCA process of GAMOW and SCHOENBERG (4) can dominate over all other mechanisms of release of energy under appropriate conditions. Neutrinos encounter no such obstacle as light does in trying to

(111) F. REINES, C. L. COWAN jr. and H. W. KRUSE: *Phys. Rev.*, **109**, 609 (L) (1958).

escape from the hot interior of a star. But how much opacity does the star present to neutrinos? This question has been analyzed by EUWEMA [See pag. 104, note (90)]. For the mean free path of 1 MeV neutrinos in the sun ($\varrho \sim 1.4$ g/cm^3) he calculated $\sim 10^{19}$cm, a number in comparison with which the radius of the sun, $7 \cdot 10^{10}$ cm, is quite negligible. However, observed densities of white dwarfs go up to 10^8 g/cm^3, with a corresponding radius of 10^8 cm; and the highly compressed configurations analysed by OPPENHEIMER and VOLKOFF, and HARRISON and WAKANO, go up to 10^{14} g/cm^3. Therefore it is of interest to know whether neutrinos can penetrate freely even through such stars.

TABLE XVI. – *Mean free path λ at* 10^{15} g/cm^3 *on the assumption that the reaction* $\nu + e \to \mu + \nu$ *is dominating; values due to* EUWEMA.

E_ν (MeV)	21.3	23.4	27.7	36.2	45	128
λ (cm)	∞	$7.3 \cdot 10^6$	$5.7 \cdot 10^5$	$1.55 \cdot 10^4$	$1.3 \cdot 10^2$	1.9

EUWEMA treats separately the cases of high and low densities. At high densities, $\sim 10^{15}$ g/cm^3, the electrons in the Fermi sea have high energies, the neutrino energies of interest are also high, and the reaction $\nu + e \to \mu + \nu$ dominates in Euwema's analysis (Table XVI). It is apparent from his numbers ($\lambda = \infty$ below 21 MeV) that further processes will have to be considered before one has a reliable limit on the rate of transfer of energy out of very dense stars by neutrinos. For stars of lesser density the dominating mechanisms are

$$(192) \qquad \left\{ \begin{array}{l} \nu + n \to p + e^- , \\ \bar{\nu} + p + e^- \to n , \\ \bar{\nu} + p \to n + e^+ . \end{array} \right.$$

EUWEMA gives tables and graphs from which the opacity can be calculated for white dwarf densities. It will be interesting to see if these opacities have enough importance for astrophysical calculations of stellar evolution to give some direct check on neutrino absorption processes, over and above the Reines-Cowan experiments.

VI. – Weakness of Neutrino Interactions.

No explanation is apparent today why neutrino interactions are as weak as they are compared to electric interactions, nor as strong as they are compared to gravitational interactions.

VII. - The Central Position of the Neutrino in Elementary Particle Physics.

In conclusion, the vision of RIEMANN, CLIFFORD and EINSTEIN, of a purely geometrical basis for physics, today has come to a higher state of development, and offers richer prospects—and presents deeper problems—than ever before. The quantum of action adds to this geometrodynamics new features, of which the most striking is the presence of fluctuations of the wormhole type throughout all space. If there is any correspondence at all between this virtual foam-like structure and the physical vacuum as it has come to be known through quantum electrodynamics, then there seems to be no escape from identifying these wormholes with « undressed electrons. » Completely different from these « undressed electrons », according to all available evidence, are the electrons and other particles of experimental physics. For these particles the geometrodynamical picture suggests the model of collective disturbances in a virtual foam-like vacuum, analogous to different kinds of phonons or excitons in a solid.

The enormous factor from nuclear densities $\sim 10^{14}$ g/cm^3 to the density of field fluctuation energy in the vacuum, $\sim 10^{94}$ g/cm^3, argues that elementary particles represent a percentage-wise almost completely negligible change in the locally violent conditions that characterize the vacuum. In other words elementary particles do not form a really basic starting point for the description of nature. Instead, they represent a first order correction to vacuum physics. That vacuum, that zero order state of affairs, with its enormous densities of virtual photons and virtual positive-negative pairs and virtual wormholes, has to be described properly before one has a fundamental starting point for a proper perturbation theoretic analysis.

These conclusions about the energy density of the vacuum, its complicated topological character, and the richness of the physics which goes on in the vacuum, stand in no evident contradiction with what quantum electrodynamics has to say about the vacuum. Instead the conclusions from the « small distance » analysis (10^{-33} cm)—sketchy as it is—and from « larger distance analysis » (10^{-11} cm) would seem to have the possibility to reinforce each other in a most natural way.

The most evident shortcoming of the geometrodynamical model as it stands is this, that 1) *it fails to supply any completely natural place* for spin $\frac{1}{2}$ in general and *for the neutrino* in particular.

This is not the only outstanding problem. It may well have a deep inner connection with four other issues: 2) Can the ideas of Riemannian geometry and geometrodynamics be rephrased in such terms that the concept of relative complexion of two distant points will acquire a new simplicity? 3) Why do elementary particles have charges of a single complexion only? 4) What is the mechanism that ties together charge reversal and parity inversion? 5) Is there any escape from a breakdown of the law of conservation of nucleons at the center of a star of critical mass?

Not only problems, but also predictions flow out of neutrino theory and geometrodynamics, many of them already the subject of experiment test. Among the more interesting predictions not yet tested are 1) a minimum apparent angular diameter for typical galaxies a certain distance away—more distant galaxies as well as closer galaxies being predicted to have larger angular diameters; and 2) multiple images of sufficiently distant luminous objects, the minimum distance for observation of this effect with significant probability providing a measure of the energy carried by gravitational radiation of long wave length.

In speaking of his long-term hopes to see atomic structure explained in terms of field theory, EINSTEIN concluded ([112]) with the words: « All of these endeavors are based on the belief that existence should have a completely harmonious structure. Today we have less ground than ever before for allowing ourselves to be forced away from this wonderful belief. »

* * *

Appreciation is expressed to Professor G. POLVANI and Professor L. RADICATI and to members of the Villa Monastero School of Physics for very stimulating meetings on the subject of weak interactions; to Dr. S. GLASHOW Mr. THOMAS PHILIPS and Mr. DAVID SHARP for their assistance with the notes; to many collaborators and colleagues for their discussion of the subject matter; to the United States Air Force Office of Scientific Research for transportation to and from the meeting; and to the Friends of Elementary Particle Research for their assistance.

([112]) A. EINSTEIN: *Essays in Science*, translated by A. HARPIS (New York, 1934).

I. Geons (*).

J. A. Wheeler

Palmer Physical Laboratory, Princeton University - Princeton, N. J.

(Reprinted from *Phys. Rev.*, **97**, 511-536 (1955))

1. – Introduction and summary.

The position of the concept of « body » (¹) in the general theory of relativity (²) has always been interesting. A planet moving as a body along a

---

(*) The word « geon » is used here as an abbreviation for the phrase « gravitational-electromagnetic entity » and in place of the name kugelblitz or ball of light previously used in a survey of the problems of fields and particles: *Richtmyer Memorial Lecture, 29 Jan. 1954*; see also the point of view ascribed by the author to Sugawara-no-Michizane in *Proc. Phys. Soc. Japan*, **9**, 36 (1954). The present article is part V of a study of classical field theory. I is unwritten. In parts II, J. A. Wheeler and R. P. Feynman: *Rev. Mod. Phys.*, **17**, 157 (1945); III, J. A. Wheeler and R. P. Feynman: *Rev. Mod. Phys.*, **21**, 425 (1949), and IV, in preparation in collaboration with Prof. G. N. Plass, the emphasis is upon action at a distance, not as a way of understanding charged bodies, but as a way of understanding the fields that act between them. In the present paper the emphasis is on the fields interior to a *classical* body.

(¹) The noun « body » is used here to connote an object possessed of a mass and of three position co-ordinates, and subject both externally and internally to a classical description, in contrast to the notion of a particle, with at least the interior of which quantum properties are associated.

(²) By « general theory of relativity » is meant here that battle-tested system of ideas and equations which Einstein developed in 1915 to describe gravitation and electromagnetism. I am indebted to Prof. Einstein for several interesting discussions of the evolution of his ideas and of their relation to Newtonian concepts. Excluded here from the phrase « general theory » is the cosmological term, absent with good reason from the original formulation, introduced only when it was found that the original theory could not account for a static universe, and disowned when the universe was found not to be static. Excluded also are varied modifications of general relativity which attempt to « unify » gravitation and electricity, the latest of which has been shown by J. Callaway: *Phys. Rev.*, **92**, 1567 (1953) to predict that a test particle will move as if uncharged, no matter how much charge is loaded upon it. In the accepted

geodesic is the idealization behind one of the most important predictions of the general theory, and certainly the one that has received the most thorough

---

formulation of general relativity — to use the metric conventions of Pauli's treatise — the proper distance, ds, or proper interval of cotime (c times time), $d\tau$, between two neighboring events is given by

$$(ds)^2 = -(d\tau)^2 = g_{\alpha\beta}dx^\alpha dx^\beta .$$

The state of the space time continuum is specified by giving in addition to the ten gravitational potentials, $g_{ik}=g_{ki}$, the four electromagnetic potentials, A_i. The electromagnetic field, $F_{ik}=\partial A_k/\partial x^i - \partial A_i/\partial x^k$, has six distinct components, whereas gravitational effects are expressed in a covariant way by the twenty distinct components of the curvature tensor R_{abcd}; or by the mixed components of the same tensor,

$$R^h{}_{ikj} = \partial \Gamma_{ij}{}^h/\partial x^k - \partial \Gamma_{ik}{}^h/\partial x^j + \Gamma_{kd}{}^h \Gamma_{ij}{}^d - \Gamma_{jd}{}^h \Gamma_{ik}{}^d ,$$

where the typical Γ is an abbreviation for

$$\Gamma_{ij,k} = \tfrac{1}{2}(\partial g_{jk}/\partial x^i + \partial g_{ik}/\partial x^j - \partial g_{ij}/\partial x^k) .$$

Of the twenty distinct components of R_{abcd}, ten remain in the contracted curvature tensor $R_{ik}=R_{i\alpha k}{}^\alpha$; and of these one remains in the curvature invariant $R=g_{\alpha\beta}R^{\alpha\beta}$. The Einstein tensor $G_{ik}=R_{ik}-\frac{1}{2}g_{ik}R$ may be considered to be the translation into the language of general relativity of the notion of d'Alembertian of the gravitational potentials, g_{ik}. The gravitational field equations thus have the form

$$G_{ik} = (8\pi G/c^4)\, T_{ik} ,$$

where $G=6.67\cdot 10^{-8}$ cm^3/g s^2 is the Newtonian constant of gravitation, $c=3.00\cdot 10^{10}$ cm/s is the speed of light, and T_{ik} is the symmetric stress-momentum-energy tensor of the electromagnetic field,

$$T_{ik} = (\partial/\partial g^{ik})(1/8\pi) F_{\alpha\beta}F^{\alpha\beta} .$$

Of the equations for the electromagnetic field itself, half are already automatically satisfied by virtue of the way the fields are expressed in terms of the potentials, A_i. The other half are usually written as inhomogeneous equations,

$$(-g)^{-\frac{1}{2}}(\partial/\partial x^\alpha)(-g)^{\frac{1}{2}}F^{i\alpha} = 4\pi s^i ,$$

where g is the determinant of the g_{ik}, or where $(-g)^{\frac{1}{2}}$ is the ratio of an element of four-volume to the product $dx^1\, dx^2\, dx^3\, dx^4$, and where the four-vector s^i describes the density and flow of free electricity. We omit this source term (a) because we do not need it in the considerations of this article, (b) because there is no self-consistent classical theory for the existence of electric charge, (c) because the considerations of Sect. **1** and Sect. **7** suggest that the appearance of free electricity is a quantum phenomenon. Thus limited to charge-free space, general relativity constitutes a well defined, self-consistent, self-contained whole.

observational confirmation (3). In recent years a great advance has been made in the theory. The geodesic equation that determines the motion of the object in a known field, and the field equations that find the metric from the motions of the masses, have been shown not both to be necessary, as they have been in every other formulation of physics. Instead, the equation of motion of the body has been shown to follow as a *consequence* of the field equations (4). This circumstance, the fact that relativity is the first description of nature that makes geometry a part of physics, the absence of any acceptable alternative of comparable scope, and the battle-tested internal consistency of the theory, all make it necessary to take seriously general relativity and explore further its consequences and concepts. Of these concepts the notion of body is in an unhappy state. Either one sticks to general relativity as it is, and treats the object as a singularity in the metric, or one postulates that the field is regular everywhere, and counts on quantum theory somehow to explain how this can be so even in the region of the body. Both approaches lead for the time being to an impasse. For this reason it is interesting to discover that there exists a third possibility. On the basis of classical general relativity as it already exists, and without any call on quantum theory, it turns out to be possible to construct an entity that we call geon. This object serves as a classical, singularity free, exemplar of the «bodies» of classical physics. Of such entities there exist in principle a great variety, distinguished from one another by mass, intrinsic angular momentum, and other properties. The simplest variety (Fig. 1) is most easily visualized as a standing electromagnetic wave, or beam of light, bent into a closed circular toroid of high energy concentration. It is held in this form by the gravitational attraction of the mass

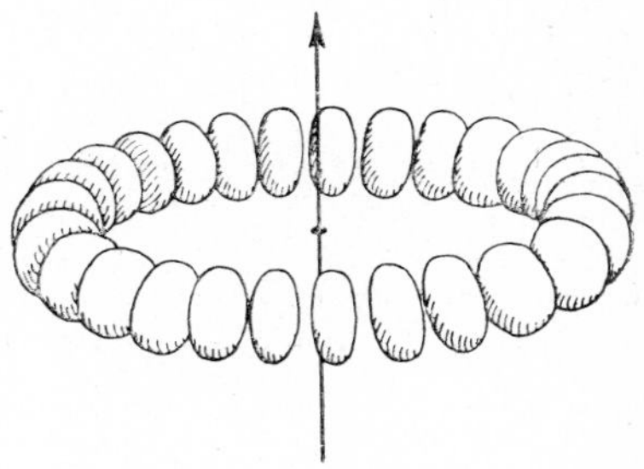

Fig. 1. – Regions of strong electric field strength in a simple toroidal geon of zero angular momentum. Two waves of equal strength run around the torus in opposite directions to produce a standing wave, with electric fields strong in the regions indicated, and magnetic fields strong in the region between. The gravitational field created by this disturbance, and required to hold the disturbance together, is representable to a good approximation as static and independent of azimuth.

(3) G. M. Clemence: *Rev. Mod. Phys.*, **19**, 361 (1947); *Proc. Am. Phil. Soc.*, **93**, 532 (1949).

(4) L. Infeld and A. Schild: *Rev. Mod. Phys.*, **21**, 408 (1949); see also A. Einstein, L. Infeld and B. Hoffmann: *Ann. Math.*, **39**, 65 (1938); D. M. Chase: *Phys. Rev.*, **95**, 243 (1954); and L. Infeld and J. Plebanski: *Motion and Relativity*, (New York, 1960).

associated with the field energy itself. It is a self-consistent solution of the problem of coupled electromagnetic and gravitational fields, as defined by the system of equations,

(1) $$G_{ik} = (8\pi G/c^4) T_{ik} \, ,$$

(2) $$T_i^{\ k} = (1/4\pi)(F_{i\alpha} F^{k\alpha} - \tfrac{1}{4} F_{\alpha\beta} F^{\alpha\beta} \delta_i^{\ k}) \, ,$$

and

(3) $$(-g)^{-\frac{1}{2}} (\partial / \partial x^\alpha)(-g)^{\frac{1}{2}} F^{i\alpha} = 0 \, ,$$

all derivable from the action principle:

(4) $$\delta \iiiint \{(1/16\pi c) F_{\alpha\beta} F^{\alpha\beta} - (c^3/16\pi G) R\} \, \mathrm{d}(\text{four-volume}) = 0 \, .$$

An order-of-magnitude discussion of the properties of these entities appears in Section **2**. Section **3** presents theory and results of electronic machine solutions of the self-consistent field equations for the particularly simple but rather idealized case of a spherical geon. The existence of geons would seem to impart to classical general relativity theory a comprehensiveness for which one had not dared to hope. This theory turns out not only to account for the fields produced by bodies, and the motions of bodies, but even to explain why there should be bodies. In this sense classical relativity theory would seem to be revealed as a logically self-consistent and completed whole of unexpected comprehensiveness.

Having geons as model for the bodies of classical physics, we can put into a new perspective some parts of general relativity. First, the geodesic equation of motion of a body displays itself clearly as an idealization. To be able to give any meaning to the metric that appears in this equation, we have to be able to speak of the « background field »—the gravitational and electromagnetic magnitudes that would be present in the absence of the geon. This will only be possible when the total fields at some distance from the object vary slowly over a distance comparable to the linear extension of the geon. In this case the object will accelerate coherently under the action of external forces. The happenings fit into the scheme of physics envisaged by NEWTON and MAXWELL: preexisting bodies generating forces and being acted upon by forces. The appropriate modifications to pre-Einsteinian physics associated with special and general relativity of course add themselves automatically. On the other hand, when the fields outside the geon approach non-uniform values, then this entity does not react as a unit. Its internal degrees of freedom are disturbed. When the external inhomogeneities are strong, the system will break into two or more parts. There is nothing in what we know today of physics that makes unreasonable the failure under such conditions of the idealization of body. Evidently there exist conditions where the idealization of « body » loses all significance, and where there comes into play a new kind of physics of geons—but a physics that is still entirely classical (Section **4**).

The existence of geon transformation processes makes clear a second point about classical relativity physics, that there exists in principle no sharp distinction between geons as concentrations of electromagnetic energy, capable of break-up and integration processes, and the « free » electromagnetic waves that pass through the space between geons, and experience scattering, absorption, or emission by geons. Legalistically speaking, the state of the universe of classical physics is described by the singularity-free electromagnetic and gravitational magnitudes at every point, and by nothing more.

Finally, physics as rounded out by the geon concept forms the only fully comprehensive and self-consistent system of classical physics that we possess. This picture of bodies and fields leaves as little place for free electric charges as for isolated magnetic poles: none at all. The electromagnetic field is as free of singularity as the gravitational field. Lines of forces never begin and never end. At most they form loops that shrink to zero and disappear, or reappear as time goes on and field strengths change. No natural way is evident to escape the conclusion that the quantum of electricity has to do with the quantum of action and does not belong within the framework of a *completely* classical physics. Considering that our physical world extends at least from 10^{-13} cm to 10^{27} cm, and that in the face of these forty decades or more e^2 differs from $\hbar c$ by only two powers of ten, it would also seem that one has some independent reason to believe that free electricity is a quantum phenomenon. Therefore it appears reasonable to accept as a description of a *classical* body the always electrically neutral geon.

What is the range of sizes of classical geons? These objects obey a simple scaling law. From one self-consistent solution of the coupled equations of gravitation and electromagnetism there follows another solution of $(1/n)$th the mass, by decreasing all distances by a factor n, increasing all electromagnetic field strengths by a factor n, and leaving all the gravitational potentials g_{ik} unaltered in strength. In this change the classical action integral, J, associated with the field disturbance falls to $1/n^2$ of its original value. Such a scaling law must exist because the field equations contain only the gravitation constant and the velocity of light, out of which one can form no quantity with the dimensions either of a length or a mass or a field strength or an action. Consistent with the scaling law, but even more specific, are the order-of-magnitude formulas of Section **2** for the simplest circular toroidal geons, with a number of standing waves around the circumference equal to an integer or azimuthal index number, a:

$$
(5)\quad \left\{
\begin{aligned}
&\text{mass} \sim a^{\frac{1}{2}}\ (\text{action}\cdot c/G)^{\frac{1}{2}}\,,\\
&\text{major radius} \sim a^{\frac{1}{2}}\ (\text{action}\cdot G/c^3)^{\frac{1}{2}}\,,\\
&\text{minor radius} \sim \text{small multiple of } \lambda\!\!\!^{-}\,,\\
&\lambda\!\!\!^{-} = (\text{wavelength}/2\pi) \sim a^{-\frac{1}{2}}\ (\text{action}\cdot G/c^3)^{\frac{1}{2}}\,,\\
&\text{frequency} \sim a^{\frac{1}{2}}\ (c^5/G\cdot\text{action})^{\frac{1}{2}}\,,\\
&(\text{mass density in active region}) \sim (\text{reasonable fraction of } (ac^5/G^2\cdot\text{action}))\,,\\
&(\text{peak field values in electrostatic V/cm or gauss}) \sim\\
&\qquad \sim (\text{reasonable fraction of } (ac^7/G^2\cdot\text{action})^{\frac{1}{2}})\,.
\end{aligned}
\right.
$$

The upper limit to the size of geons is the linear extension of the universe itself. This limit shows itself in the following way. The self-consistent field equations of the geon possess solutions, the properties of which depend upon the boundary conditions. In simple geon theory we impose the requirement that g_{ik}'s are asymptotic to a flat metric at distances large in comparison with the extension of the geon. This boundary condition has to be modified when the size of the geon is comparable to the radius of curvature of a closed universe. Then the relations (5) undergo characteristic corrections, such that the mass of the geon can never exceed the mass of the universe.

Incidentally it is interesting to notice that a purely classical closed universe consisting of a large number, N, of geons of comparable size must consist mostly of empty space. This conclusion follows from the fact that the proportionality factor between radius and mass,

$$\text{radius} \sim (G/c^2)\ \text{mass} = (0.74\cdot 10^{28}\ \text{cm/g})\ \text{mass}$$

is the same in order of magnitude for geons as for the universe itself. Consequently a ratio $1/N$ between the mass of the parts and the mass of the whole implies a ratio $\sim N(1/N)^3 = 1/N^2$ between the volume of the parts and the volume of the whole.

To find the lower limit to the size of classical geons, we have to investigate in turn the several physical magnitudes that characterize this object, and see which of these magnitudes, with decreasing geon size, first passes out of the domain of application of classical theory.

1) Is action the critical magnitude? Certainly one will be in the quantum domain when the action is comparable to the quantum of angular momentum,

$\hbar = 1.054 \cdot 10^{-27}$ g cm²/s. Inserting this value into the formulas (5), we find

$$\text{mass} \sim a^{\frac{1}{2}}\, 2.18 \cdot 10^{-5} \text{ g} ,$$

$$\text{major radius} \sim a^{\frac{1}{2}}\, 1.63 \cdot 10^{-33} \text{ cm} .$$

We can stop here with the evaluation. We are evidently far below the limit where it might have been right to use classical theory, and *quite outside the domain of application* of eq. (5). Electron theory allows no possibility to deal with distances smaller than the reduced Compton wavelength, $\hbar/mc = 3.87 \cdot 10^{-11}$cm without taking into account complex and specifically quantum mechanical fluctuations in the distribution of pairs and in the electromagnetic field. What about fluctuations in the gravitational field? They appear to be negligible on any ordinary scale of distances, as one sees from the following reasoning. In a region with space and cotime extensions of the order of L the relevant fluctuations in the electromagnetic field [5] are of the order $\Delta\mathscr{E} \sim (\hbar c)^{\frac{1}{2}}/L^2$, and $\Delta A \sim (\hbar c)^{\frac{1}{2}}/L$ in the potentials. The similarity in character of the gravitational and electromagnetic field equations, and the difference in the way they contain the various fundamental constants, indicate that the corresponding formula for the fluctuation in a typical gravitational potential is

$$\Delta g \sim (\hbar G/c^3)^{\frac{1}{2}}/L . \tag{6}$$

These fluctuations will be inappreciable in comparison to typical average values of the metric, $g \sim 1$, so long as the distances, L, under consideration are substantial in comparison with the characteristic length,

$$L^* = (\hbar G/c^3)^{\frac{1}{2}} = 1.63 \cdot 10^{-33} \text{ cm} . \tag{7}$$

This is exactly the distance in comparison with which we have just concluded that classical geons must be enormous.

2) Is distance the critical magnitude? We set the reduced wavelength in eq. (5) equal to $\hbar/mc$ and solve for the action and other physical magnitudes, finding

$$\text{action} \sim a(\hbar c/m^2 G)\hbar = a\, 5.72 \cdot 10^{44} \hbar ,$$

$$\text{mass} \sim a(5.72 \cdot 10^{44})^{\frac{1}{2}}\, 2.15 \cdot 10^{-5} \text{ g} = a\, 5.1 \cdot 10^{17} \text{ g} ,$$

$$\text{major radius} \sim a\, 3.87 \cdot 10^{-11} \text{ cm} ,$$

---

(5) N. Bohr and L. Rosenfeld: *Kgl. Danske Videnskab. Selskab., Mat.-fys. Medd.* **12**, no. 8 (1933); *Phys. Rev.*, **78**, 794 (1950).

$$\text{minor radius} \sim \text{small multiple of } 3.87 \cdot 10^{-11}\ \text{cm}\,,$$

$$(\text{wavelength}/2\pi) \sim 3.87 \cdot 10^{-11}\ \text{cm}\,,$$

$$\text{frequency} \sim mc^2/\hbar\,,$$

all of which is so far acceptable; but the mass density in the active region,

$$\text{geon density} \sim \text{a reasonable fraction of } (c^2/G)(mc/\hbar)^2 = 0.90 \cdot 10^{49}\ \text{g/cm}^3$$

is obviously fantastically in excess of the density of nuclear matter,

$$\text{nuclear density} \sim 1836\,m/[(4\pi/3)(e^2/2mc^2)^3] = 1.4 \cdot 10^{14}\ \text{g/cm}^3\,. \tag{8}$$

Consequently we still find ourselves in a domain where the classical geon relations (5) *cannot be applied.*

3) Is density the limiting magnitude? Taking this time nuclear densities, (8), as the reference point, we find from (5) values of the action, mass, radius, and frequency of the geon which are safely outside the obvious quantum limits; but the field strength in the active region,

$$(c^2\, 1.4 \cdot 10^{14}\ \text{g/cm}^3)^{\frac{1}{2}} = 3.6 \cdot 10^{17}\ (\text{gauss or electrostatic volt-cm})\,,$$

is then 8 000 times greater than the critical value met in the quantum electrodynamics of the vacuum,

$$\mathscr{E}_{\text{crit}} = m^2c^3/e\hbar = 4.42 \cdot 10^{13}\ (\text{gauss or electrostatic volt cm})\,. \tag{9}$$

Thus, when an electric field $\mathscr{E}$, working on an elementary charge e over the localizability distance $\hbar/mc$, can impart to an electron an energy of the order mc^2, then this electric field will bring forth from empty space pairs of positive and negative electrons. Under such conditions the geon requires for its description the specification of the state of the pairs as well as the statement of the electromagnetic and gravitational field strengths. Again we find ourselves outside the range of validity of the classical geon eq. (5).

4) We conclude that the *critical field strength,* $\mathscr{E}_{\text{crit}}$, *of pair theory marks the lower limit of classical geons.* Thus, simple *toroidal* electromagnetic geons are only then purely classical entities, when their magnitudes are on the large

geon side of the following limits:

$$
(10)\quad
\left\{
\begin{aligned}
\text{action} &\sim \text{reasonable fraction of } ac^7/G^2\mathscr{E}^2_{\text{crit}} \\
&= a\hbar(e^2/Gm^2)^2(\hbar e/e^2) \\
&= 2.38\cdot 10^{87} a\hbar\,, \\
\text{mass} &\sim \text{reasonable fraction of } ac^4/G^{\frac{1}{2}}\mathscr{E}_{\text{crit}} \\
&= a\,1.065\cdot 10^{39}\ \text{g}\,, \\
\text{major radius} &\sim \text{reasonable fraction of } ac^2/G^{\frac{1}{2}}\mathscr{E}_{\text{crit}} \\
&= a\,0.791\cdot 10^{11}\ \text{cm}\,, \\
\text{minor radius} &\sim 0.791\cdot 10^{11}\ \text{cm}\,, \\
(\text{wavelength}/2\pi) &\sim 0.791\cdot 10^{11}\ \text{cm}\,, \\
\text{frequency} &\sim 1\ \text{vibration}/16.6\ \text{s}\,, \\
\text{mass density} &\sim \mathscr{E}^2_{\text{crit}}/c^2 = 2.16\cdot 10^{6}\ \text{g/cm}^3\,, \\
\text{peak electric field} &\sim \mathscr{E}_{\text{crit}} \text{ of eq. (9)}\,.
\end{aligned}
\right.
$$

One has only to compare these critical dimensions with the properties of the sun, mass $= 1.97\cdot 10^{33}$ g, radius $= 6.95\cdot 10^{10}$ cm, to conclude that even the lightest *classical* geons form entities enormous in comparison to the objects studied in the laboratory. But the critical dimensions are still small compared to the scale of the universe. There is ample room between 10^{11} cm and 10^{28} cm to talk of classical geons and their motions, interactions and transformations. In this sense we continue to regard classical general relativity as a completed self-contained subject with a well-defined scope of its own.

Having surveyed the boundaries of the classical theory of geons, we can touch on a few of the implications of quantum theory for these objects. First as to the general situation, it is clear that the critical magnitudes of eq. (10) prevent us in no way whatever from considering geons of lower mass. It is only required that we take quantum effects properly into account. It is also clear that these effects will be of various kinds. As we move down in mass, first one effect, previously unimportant, will become decisive, then another effect, and so on. In each region certain idealizations will be appropriate. In each region the formulas connecting mass and other geon properties with the quantity of action will have characteristic forms of their own. Presumably the investigation of each region will present successively greater difficulties. Second, the quantum region earliest encountered (Section **5**) will lie between the realm of classical electrodynamics and the domain where fields are so strong that substantial numbers of pairs appear. In this intermediate « Region II », the fields vary in space and time fantastically slowly in comparison with the characteristic distances and times of electron theory. Moreover, they are strong enough to produce only virtual pairs. These pairs give rise to charges and currents that make a substantial contribution to the total field, as first analyzed in detail by EULER and KOCKEL and HEISENBERG (6). In quantum language, if two opposed photons of high frequency can produce a pair, then two opposed photons of low frequency can produce a virtual pair. With the reannihilation of the pair the photons go off in altered directions; hence a scattering of light by light (7) and an effectively non-linear electrodynamics. The consequence of this non-linearity for a simple toroidal electromagnetic geon is most simply envisaged as an increase of refractive index in the region of concentration of electromagnetic energy. The effective value of the speed of light is reduced. Geon mass no longer scales in proportion to the square root of the action variable. Instead, as the action of the system diminishes, the mass appears to fall faster than linearly (eq. (81)). However, soon we are into Region III, where real pairs first appear in large numbers. Here new studies must be made before any results can be stated.

As third circumstance in the relation of the quantum to the geon, there exist neutrinos: entities apparently co-ordinate with photons in the description of nature. Their Fermi-Dirac statistics, unlike those of photons, makes it impossible for more than one to be accommodated in a state of definite wave number and polarization. From them no disturbance can be built up of a classical magnitude, describable in correspondence principle terms. They have an inescapably quantum character. Apart from this circumstance they can be used in the construction of geons just as well as photons. In addition to purely electromagnetic geons there consequently also exist in principle (Section **6**) purely neutrino geons, and geons of mixed type. Thus half integral as well as integral spins are permitted to geons.

As last implication of the quantum for geon physics, the fluctuations in the gravitational metric are inescapable, little as one can say (Section **7**) about their consequences for the validity of Gausses theorem and for the existence of free electric charge.

Details of the discussion follow.

---

(6) H. EULER and B. KOCKEL: *Naturwiss.*, **23**, 246 (1935); W. HEISENBERG and H. EULER: *Physik*, **98**, 714 (1936).

(7) Low-frequency cross section in ref. (6); high-frequency cross section in A. ACHIESER: *Physik Z. Sowjetunion*, **11**, 263 (1937); forward scattering at all frequencies calculated by R. KARPLUS and M. NEUMAN: *Phys. Rev.*, **83**, 776 (1951); derived from dispersion relation by J. TOLL: *The Dispersion Relation for Light and Its Application to Problems Involving Electron Pairs*, Ph. D. thesis (Princeton, 1952); also J. TOLL and J. A. WHEELER: *Phys. Rev.*, **81**, 654 (A) (1951).

2. – Orders of magnitude for simple toroidal electromagnetic geons.

The gravitational deflection of a pencil of light into a torus is no different in principle from the deflection of light by the sun. Apart from factors of the order of two [8] one can estimate the deflection by equating a kinematic acceleration to a gravitational acceleration:

$$c^2/R \sim GM/R^2 .$$

Thus the radius R of the torus and the mass M are connected by the relation

$$R \sim (G/c^2)M = (0.741\cdot 10^{-28}\ \text{cm/g})M , \tag{11}$$

This formula is familiar in another connection, for it supplies the well known relation between the mass of an object and its so called gravitational radius, a measure of the distances at which the gravitational potential depart significantly from the values appropriate to flat space. This circumstance makes it evident that any accurate treatment of geon properties has to be carried out within the framework of general relativity.

Near a section of the torus the gravitational field will resemble approximately the field due to an infinitely long cylindrically-symmetrical distribution of mass. It will increase inversely as the first power of the distance, ϱ, from the center of the cylinder, until the point of observation moves into the region of strong energy concentration. There the gravitational potential will no longer continue its logarithmic increase.

The narrowness of the pencil of light, or of the region of strong energy concentration, will depend upon the wavelength. Define by a large integer a an azimuthal index number, and let the wavelength constitute the small fraction, $1/a$, of the circumference:

$$(\text{wavelength}/2\pi) \equiv \lambdabar \sim R/a .$$

The pencil of light cannot be concentrated into a region smaller in lateral extension than the order of magnitude of $\lambdabar$ by any type of variation of refractive index with distance. Owing to the logarithmic variation of gravitational potential and effective refractive index near the cylinder, the lateral extension of the disturbance in the case of the torus will be a small multiple

---

([8]) See for example R. C. Tolman: *Relativity, Thermodynamics, and Cosmology* (Oxford, 1934).

of λ, say $F\lambda$, where the dimensionless factor F will be approximately represented by a simple power of $\ln(R/\lambda) = \ln a$. Even if a equals 10^{10}, this logarithm is only 23.

The circumstance that the minor radius of the torus is significantly larger than λ implies that the gravitation field can be taken to be static in a reasonable approximation. Thus the source of the gravitation field, in accordance with the principle of equivalence of mass and energy, is the electromagnetic stress-energy tensor. This tensor varies rapidly over a distance of the order of λ. But the elementary contribution to the gravitation field is essentially a $1/r^2$, or long-range, field. The field, even in the most active part of the geon, comes mostly from distances of the order of the minor radius, $F\lambda$. Consequently local variations in gravitational source strength are relatively unimportant. What does count is the source strength averaged over a wavelength. In other words, the gravitational field may be regarded as depending upon ϱ and z, to use cylindrical polar co-ordinates, but not on φ and t.

Of course nothing prevents consideration of toroidal geons of small azimuthal index, a, but then it is no longer such a good approximation to treat the gravitational field as static, and the situation is much more complicated to discuss. Moreover, such geons disintegrate rapidly.

Even for the case of large azimuthal index number there is a difference in simplicity between those toroidal geons that carry equal electromagnetic waves going in the positive and negative senses around the ring, and those where the disturbance runs all one way, or there are two disturbances of different magnitudes. In the first case we have to do with a system of zero angular momentum. The electromagnetic disturbance is a simple standing wave. Many components of the metric tensor vanish when expressed in cylindrical polar co-ordinates ([9]). Significantly more distinct components of g_{ik} have to be considered when the system has angular momentum ([10]). Particularly interesting is the case when the disturbance is unidirectional. Then the angular momentum of the system is of the order

$$\text{angular momentum} \sim McR \sim (c^3/G)R^2 . \tag{13}$$

In the active region of a simple classical toroidal electromagnetic geon the field strengths will be of the order of magnitude $\mathscr{E}$, where

$$\mathscr{E}^2 R(\Delta R)^2 \sim Mc^2 . \tag{14}$$

([9]) F. J. Ernst jr.: *Cylindrically Symmetric Fields in General Relativity*, Junior Independent Paper, Princeton, 5 May 1954 (unpublished); *Phys. Rev.*, **105**, 1662, 1665 (1957).

([10]) For examples of gravitational sources endowed with angular momentum, see for example, G. E. Tauber: *Ph. D. Thesis*, University of Minnesota (1952), unpublished.

Consequently $\mathscr{E}\Delta R$, the order of magnitude of the typical difference of potential between two sides of the pencil of radiation, will have a universal value,

$$(15) \qquad \text{potential difference} \sim (Mc^2/R)^{\frac{1}{2}} \sim c^2/G^{\frac{1}{2}} = $$
$$= 3.49 \cdot 10^{24} \text{ (gauss cm or electrostatic volt)},$$

enough to impart to a particle of electronic charge and mass an energy greater than its rest energy by a factor $(e^2/Gm^2)^{\frac{1}{2}}$. This factor is the root of the ratio of the electric and gravitational forces between two electrons, and has the value $(4.17 \cdot 10^{42})^{\frac{1}{2}} = 2.04 \cdot 10^{21}$.

Through the symmetry axis of the torus passes a typical meridian plane and note the point in this plane where it intersects the region of maximum field strength in the torus. Then over a circle of radius $\sim \Delta R$ centered on this point the field strength has values smaller than the peak magnitude by a factor of only one or two powers of two. At distances from the most active point several times the magnitude ΔR, the field strengths fall off exponentially with a characteristic decay length of the order of magnitude of $\lambda\!\!\!^{-}$. This type of decay is familiar from the study of the propagation of light along the length of a long thin solid glass rod. The disturbance in the space surrounding the rod also has a characteristic decrement length of the order of $\lambda\!\!\!^{-}$. In the case of the geon we deal with a medium whose effective refractive index is non-uniform. The gravitational field has fallen off substantially at distances, from the symmetry center of the geon of the order of magnitude of $2R$ and greater. Consequently the electromagnetic disturbance sufficiently far from the geon finds itself once again in an allowed region, where it can propagate normally. The strength of the electromagnetic field outside is an exceedingly small fraction of the strength inside, the approximate value of this fraction being given by an algebraic function of the large number $R/\lambda\!\!\!^{-} = a$ multiplied by an approximately exponential factor of the form $\exp[-\text{constant} \cdot a]$.

The geon is thus not in principle an isolated entity. The object in question, and every other classical geon in a classical universe, are nothing but manifestations of the same all pervading electromagnetic field. But the field outside is so extremely small in comparison with the field inside that for most purposes the geon has the character of a well-defined body.

Whether the field outside the geon is an outgoing wave or an incoming wave or a standing wave depends upon the initial conditions. It will be most relevant to consider here, as in most problems of physics, an irreversible dissipation of energy. The external wave then has no incoming component It describes a continual transport of energy—and mass—out of the geon. We are faced with a purely classical analog to the Gamow-Condon-Gurney theory of radioactive α-decay. It seems appropriate to give the same name of radioactive decay to the geon process, though for our present purposes this process is to be regarded as having absolutely no quantum character. Of course, were we temporarily to abandon the ground of classical physics, we would describe the emission process in the language of quanta.

As a model showing the slow decay characteristic of a relatively stable geon, one can consider a sphere of highly transparent glass with a radius of the order of ten wavelengths of light. A high-speed electron which enters the sphere produces ions and excites electromagnetic disturbances including modes of vibration of visible wavelength. Of many of these modes the energy will leak out of the refractive index barrier quickly because of the nearly normal incidence of the equivalent ray system upon the air interface; but those described by spherical harmonics of the highest order, and therefore represented by the most nearly tangential rays, will be endowed with lives as long as 10^{-6} s. The exponential fall of the relevant modes in the air just outside the sphere « phosphor » will be similar to the behavior in the air above a totally internally reflecting prism. In that case the decay continues indefinitely with distance; but in the spherical case the decay ceases, and free oscillation commences, at a distance comparable to the radius of curvature of the surface.

As the geon slowly loses mass, it shrinks in accordance with the similarity law for these bodies. At the same time the circular frequency, ω, of the emerging electromagnetic disturbances goes up in inverse proportion to the radius and mass. Consequently the ratio of the loss per unit time to what remains at that time is not a constant, as in the usual theory of radioactive decay, but is proportional to the current frequency scale of geon processes:

$$\mathrm{d}M/M = \mathrm{d}R/R = -\,\mathrm{d}\omega/\omega = -\,\alpha\omega\,\mathrm{d}t\,. \tag{16}$$

Here α is a dimensionless constant, the « attrition », or fractional loss of mass per radian of the electromagnetic vibration. Integration of (16) gives

$$-\,t = 1/\alpha\omega\,; \tag{17}$$

the mass of the geon decreases linearly with time. The negative sign distinguishes the time at which the geon is observed to have the frequency ω from the time at which it collapses (quantum modifications in the later stages of the decay process being overlooked). Thus the reciprocal of the attrition measures the time to collapse in units of the present time per radian.

What has been said here refers to a geon energized by only a single mode of electromagnetic vibration. When several disturbances are present of different frequencies, they will in general leak out at different rates. Moreover, non-static components of the gravitational field will furnish a weak non-linear coupling between the modes, so that relative amplitudes and frequencies on this account also will change gradually with time. The evolution of the system in time is no longer describable as a simple scale transformation. Now it is appropriate to divide up the output of energy, or mass, $\mathrm{d}M$, in the elementary time interval $\mathrm{d}t$, into elementary parts $\delta \mathrm{d}M$, each of which refers to that part of the loss which occurs in a specific interval of circular frequency, $\delta\omega$:

$$(\delta \mathrm{d}M)/M \simeq -\beta\, \delta\omega\, \mathrm{d}t\,. \tag{18}$$

Here β is again a dimensionless quantity, the « attritivity » (attrition constant) of the geon. The attritivity is of course a function of the frequency in question; or more conveniently, it depends on the dimensionless measure of frequency $\omega^* = MG\omega/c^3$. The fact that a general geon changes the form of its spectral output as time advances prevents us in no way from considering two geons of quite distinct sizes, one of which can be obtained from the other by a simple scale transformation. Both geons then have the same dimensionless attritivity function, $\beta = \beta(\omega^*)$.

The frequency of the outgoing radiation, even in the case of a simple unimodal geon, can only be defined within a latitude of the order $\Delta\omega \sim \alpha\omega$. An analysis of the external electromagnetic field in time, and an analysis in terms of frequency, stand to each other in principle in a mutually exclusive relation. It is only the smallness of α that allows us to speak approximately of the frequency as a function of time. This we do when we go beyond simple transliteration of the function $\mathscr{E} = \text{constant}\cdot\cos[-\alpha^{-1}\ln(-t)]$ to the form $\mathscr{E} = \text{constant}\cdot\cos\int\omega\,\mathrm{d}t$, and give $\omega(t) = -1/\alpha t$ the name of « frequency ». On this account it is really optional whether the emission spectrum is regarded to be a sharp line of slowly changing frequency, or to be a continuous spectrum concentrated within a region of the order α about a center of gravity of gradually shifting location. In this sense we have a choice whether to describe the decay of a unimodal geon by way of a single number, the attrition, α, or by way of an attritivity function, $\beta(\omega^*)$:

$$\alpha = (\omega^*)^{-1} \int_{\text{neighborhood of } \omega^*} \beta(\omega^*)\,\mathrm{d}\omega^*\,. \tag{19}$$

In the case of a geon energized by several modes of electromagnetic vibration, the frequencies and amplitudes of which are continually changing by reason of their mutual interaction, the relevant quantity for the description of the slow leakage of energy out of the system is the attritivity.

When a simple monochromatic toroidal geon leaks an amount of radiation energy $\mathrm{d}E$, then its reduced action, $\mathscr{J} = \text{action}/2\pi$, decreases by an amount that satisfies the general relation

$$c^2\,\mathrm{d}M = \mathrm{d}E = \omega\,\mathrm{d}\mathscr{J}\,. \tag{20}$$

When the decrease becomes substantial in comparison with the original values then the frequency ω changes substantially. On this account we cannot apply to a geon the special relation, $E = \mathscr{J}\omega$, valid for a harmonic oscillator. Instead, we can note that the circular frequency of the electromagnetic disturbance rises in inverse proportion, $\omega \sim c/\lambda\!\!\!^{-} \sim c/(R/a)$, as the mass and radius of the system diminish:

$$GM/c^2 \sim R \sim ac/\omega \,. \tag{21}$$

Multiplying together from (20) and (21) the left- and right-hand sides, respectively, we find

$$\left\{\begin{array}{l} G\,\mathrm{d}(M^2) \sim ac\,\mathrm{d}\mathscr{J}\,, \\ \quad\text{or} \\ M \sim a^{\frac{1}{2}}(c\mathscr{J}/G)^{\frac{1}{2}}\,. \end{array}\right. \tag{22}$$

Thus it is not the mass values themselves, but the squares of the mass values, that are separated in proportion to the intervals of action.

From the mass value (22) follow at once the eqs. (5) of the introduction for the other physical quantities of the geon as a function of action.

3. – The idealized spherical geon.

The simple toroidal geon forms the most elementary object of geon theory much as a simple circular orbit constitutes the first concept of planetary theory. But the simplest physics does not go in the geon case with the simplest mathematics. Toroidal geometry and general relativistic field equations each have their complications, and the mixture requires some time for its analysis ([9]). On this account it is natural to look for a geon with spherical symmetry: a rotation-invariant gravitational field, and spherically symmetric distribution of gravitational source strength, or of stress-energy. Temporarily to adopt a photon point of view, we recognize that each photon orbit is a great circle. Therefore spherical symmetry in the density and flux of photons requires spherical symmetry in the distribution of their angular momentum vectors.

The different elementary disturbances must have different frequencies. If all had the same frequency, they would add coherently to form a single mode of distribution of electromagnetic field strength. But there is no such thing as a non-zero source-free spherically symmetrical electromagnetic field disturbance. Incoherence is essential for sphericity. Let the distribution of field strength be symbolized by the expression

$$\mathscr{E} = \sum E_i(x) \sin(\omega_i t + \delta_i)\,,$$

and the distribution of stress-energy by

$$\mathscr{E}^2 = \sum_{i,k} \mathscr{E}_i(x)\,\mathscr{E}_k(x)\,\sin(\omega_i t + \delta_i)\,\sin(\omega_k t + \delta_k)\,.$$

Then distinction of frequencies and randomness of phases is essential to justify the approximation

$$\mathscr{E}^2 = \tfrac{1}{2}\sum_i \mathscr{E}_i^2(x)\,.$$

The distribution of stress-energy being thus approximately static, it can also be made spherically symmetrical by properly co-ordinated choices of the elementary solutions $\mathscr{E}_i(x)$.

A geon spherically symmetric in the sense just described is in principle unstable with respect to transformation into a toroidal geon. TOLMAN showed long ago ([8]) that two nearly parallel pencils of light attract gravitationally with twice the strength one might have thought when their propagation vectors are oppositely directed, and when similarly directed attract not at all. Consequently a system of randomly oriented circular rays of light will drop to a state of greater stability when half of the angular momentum vectors orient themselves parallel, half antiparallel, to a certain direction in space. Then the number of attractive bonds between orbits will be maximized, and the nullity of the angular momentum will be conserved. Simultaneously there will occur a readjustment in the orbital radii.

The spherical geon, though thus unstable, is in unstable *equilibrium*. We can compare it to a pendulum standing the wrong way up. To envisage such a situation would not be of much use if one had it in mind to discuss the oscillations of the pendulum about its point of support, but is quite acceptable if our aim is to discuss the rigidity of the pendulum rod. Likewise the period of the various electromagnetic modes of vibration of the geon must be judged very short in comparison with the time of turnover of the system into a toroidal system. In this sense we can talk of the properties of the spherical geon in a reasonably well defined way. It is not necessary to treat all questions for geon stability in order to undertake the problem of the structure of a spherical geon.

The assumed sphericity of the system might appear to be a self-contradictory notion. Spherical symmetry of the static gravitational field, or of the effective refractive index, implies degeneracy of the modes of electromagnetic field oscillation. However, identity of frequency of the various modes, $\mathscr{E}_i(x)$, will rule out the incoherence of the various disturbances so necessary for a spherically uniform mass distribution. Two factors allow us to avoid this degeneracy: slight differences in the scale of the excited modes, and slight departures from spherical symmetry. We consider a disturbance with no radial modes, and characterize it by the order, l, of the relevant spherical harmonic, and by the azimuthal index number a, of this spherical harmonic. The mode of azimuthal index $a=l$ is concentrated in a toroidal region of major radius $R\sim l\lambda$ and minor radius $\Delta R\sim l^{\frac{1}{2}}\lambda$. The angular dependence of the intensity, for example, shows itself simply in the expression

$$\text{constant}\,|P_l^{(l)}(\theta)\exp[il\varphi]|^2=\sin^{2l}\theta=(1-\cos^2\theta)^l\doteq[1-(\Delta\theta)^2]^l\doteq\exp[-(l^{\frac{1}{2}}\Delta\theta)^2],$$

which falls to $\sim(1/e)$-th of its value in a distance $\Delta R=R\,\Delta\theta\sim R/l^{\frac{1}{2}}$, measured angularwise. Radialwise let us consider a fixed and pre-existing metric (Fig. 2). Then for each angular order of l there exists a minimum circular frequency,

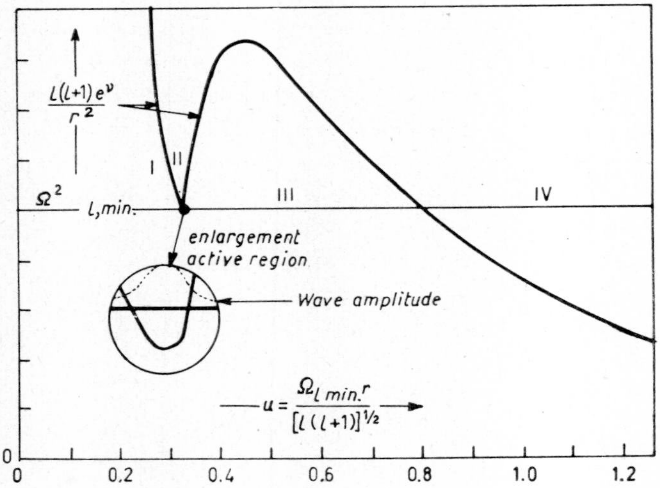

Fig. 2. – Case of simple idealized spherical geon; distance dependence of factors in the differential equation for the electromagnetic vector potential,

$$\mathrm{d}^2R/\mathrm{d}r^{*2}+[\Omega^2-l(l+1)e^{\nu}/r^2]R=0\,.$$

The proper solution, R, of lowest circular frequency, Ω/c, for a given high order of spherical harmonic, l, has the qualitative behavior indicated by the dotted line in the diagram. This solution rises exponentially with r in region I, has a single maximum in region II, falls off exponentially in region III, and in region IV oscillates with a very small amplitude (leakage wave). There exist also solutions of the same order, l, but of higher frequency, Ω, corresponding to a higher position for the horizontal line in the figure. The square of the wave number is represented by the distance measured positively upwards from the curve to the horizontal line. An increase of $l^*=[l(l+1)]^{\frac{1}{2}}$ and of Ω by the same factor leaves all turning points unchanged. However, the height of the barrier against leakage is increased as l^{*2}, so that the exponent of the penetration factor is proportional to l^*. The size of the active region is very small on the scale of the diagram, being proportional only to $l^{*\frac{1}{3}}$; hence the enlargement of this region, presented more in detail in Fig. 3. In the present figure the left-hand section of the curve up to $u=b\doteq\frac{1}{3}$ is given by the expression b^2/u^2; and the right-hand region by $(1/u^2)[1-b(1-b^2/u)]$.

$\omega = c\Omega_{l,\min}$, such that the corresponding mode shows only a single radial maximum in the active region. For different l's the maxima overlap one another. Relative to the co-ordinate, $r = R$, of this maximum, the quantity $1/\Omega \equiv \lambda\!\!\!^{-}$ has a value of the order of R/l. The width of the region of maximum activity is of the order of $R^{\frac{1}{3}}\lambda\!\!\!^{-\frac{2}{3}} \sim l^{\frac{1}{3}}\lambda\!\!\!^{-} \sim R/l^{\frac{2}{3}}$, as follows by simple JWKB analysis from the circumstance that the square of the wave number changes linearly with departure from the point of maximum wave number with a slope, d(wave number)^2/dr, of the order of $\Omega^2/R \sim l^2/R^3$. Thus a sequence of l-values yields a family of modes, of which the stress-energy is all concentrated in the same region, $r = R$. To have the spatial spread of energy also nearly the same for all modes, we have only to ask that the range, Δl, of the orders of the activated modes should not exceed some reasonable fraction of l itself. As the other factor freeing the oscillations from degeneracy we must admit some departure of the average gravitational field from exact spherical symmetry. A slight ellipticity will split up into $l+1$ separate frequencies the otherwise $(2l+1)$-fold degenerate vibrations of order l. Counting together both possibilities at our disposal we have of the order of l^2 modes with distinct frequencies. On the other hand, to obtain a distribution of energy that is completely symmetric in angle it is sufficient to add the squares of the $(2l+1)$ normalized spherical harmonics of order l, according to the well-known completeness theorem of spherical harmonics. Moreover, we do not demand for the geon a completely smooth distribution of the energy over the surface, for the long-range character of the law of gravitation smooths out in the field the minor irregularities that were present in the mass density. Consequently we can actually do with disturbances having considerably fewer than $2l+1$ values of the azimuthal index, a. Comparing $2l+1$ with $\sim l^2$, we conclude that we have more than adequate margin to obtain the postulated uniformity of energy distribution with non-degenerate modes.

For the purposes of calculations it is justifiable to idealize the picture we have just formed. The radial distribution of energy does not differ importantly from one of the excited modes to another; consequently we treat the radial factors in all the distributions as identical to that calculated for a single fixed value of l. The total angular distribution is nearly uniform, so we take it to be exactly uniform; *i.e.*, we take the oscillations of the $2l+1$ values of a belonging to the given order, l, as normalized to identical energy contents. The only consequence of exact spherical symmetry that we do not accept is *coherence* of the $2l+1$ modes. In the actual « spherical » geon, we know that the frequencies are distinct; so in the idealized spherical geon, where legalistically the frequencies come out identical, we disregard this circumstance, and add energy densities according to the law for incoherent disturbances.

To proceed to details, we make Schwarzschild's choice of polar co-ordinate system, r, θ, φ, such that elementary distances at right angles to the radius vector are represented by the usual geometrical formula. Then dr gives proper distances, ds, in the radial direction only after correction by a certain r-dependent factor. Likewise dt, or rather the cotime, d$T = c\,$dt, gives correctly intervals of proper cotime, dτ, only after multiplication by another r-dependent factor. Both correction factors are independent of T because the gravitational field is static. One factor is the reciprocal of the other in the well-known Schwarzschild solution for the metric about a point mass, but no such simple relation holds in the interior of an object with the distributed mass of a geon:

$$(23)\qquad (\mathrm{d}s)^2 = -(\mathrm{d}\tau)^2 = g_{\alpha\beta}\,\mathrm{d}x^\alpha\,\mathrm{d}x^\beta = \exp[\lambda(r)]\,(\mathrm{d}r)^2 + r^2[(\mathrm{d}\theta)^2 + (\sin\theta\,\mathrm{d}\varphi)^2] - \exp[\nu(r)]\,(\mathrm{d}T)^2\,.$$

As solution of the electromagnetic field equations it is reasonable to look for a periodic function of time, multiplied by a function of r, multiplied by a function of angle generated from the spherical harmonic $(\sin\theta)^l \exp[il\varphi]$ Such a disturbance is easily visualized in terms of a toroidal concentration of electromagnetic energy. The other elementary disturbances that we need to give a spherically symmetric distribution of energy are readily generated from this mode of vibration by the operations of the rotation group. This circumstance means that we can consider as starting point one mode as well as another. Mathematically simplest is not the choice just named, with $a = l$, but the spherical harmonic of azimuthal index $a = 0$, for in this case the dependence upon φ disappears. Thus we look for a solution of the form

$$(24)\qquad \begin{cases} A_r = A_\theta = A_T = 0\,; \\ A_\varphi = (\sin\Omega T)\,R(r)\,\sin\theta(\mathrm{d}/\mathrm{d}\theta)\,P_l(\cos\theta)\,, \end{cases}$$

where either group theory or the relevant differential equation tells us at once the form of the angular factor. The electric field points always in the φ direction and the magnetic field and the Poynting vector lie always in the meridian plane:

$$(25)\qquad \begin{cases} E_\varphi \sim F^{T\varphi} = -e^{-\nu}(r\sin\theta)^{-2}\,\partial A_\varphi/\partial T\,, \\ -H_\theta \sim F^{r\varphi} = e^{-\lambda}(r\sin\theta)^{-2}\,\partial A_\varphi/\partial r\,, \\ H_r \sim F^{\theta\varphi} = (r^2\sin\theta)^{-2}\,\partial A_\varphi/\partial\theta\,. \end{cases}$$

In principle we should consider modes which differ from (25) by the interchange of the role of electric and magnetic vectors. To do so would make no difference in the final averaged energy and stress densities, for divergence-free relativity is, despite its appearance, completely symmetric between electricity and magnetism. Consequently we do not need to sum over polarizations. We deal with a standing wave with flow of energy back and forth from north to south pole of the sphere, concentrated in the present case in an active region between R and $R+\Delta R$. We have the superposition of a number of toroidal disturbances, each passing through the north and south poles, with all azimuths of orientation of the tori weighted equally. In line with this picture, A_φ is stronger in the region of overlap near the poles than it is at the equator.

Of the electromagnetic field eq. (3), three components unite in saying that A_φ should be independent of φ, and in saying only this; while the remaining, or φ, component, makes the statement

$$(\partial/\partial r)\exp[(\nu-\lambda)/2](\sin\theta)^{-1}\partial A_\varphi/\partial r+(\partial/\partial\theta)\exp[(\nu+\lambda)/2](r^2\sin\theta)^{-1}\partial A_\varphi/\partial\theta-$$
$$-\exp[-(\nu-\lambda)/2](\sin\theta)^{-1}\partial^2A_\varphi/\partial T^2=0\,,$$

whence the radial wave equation

$$\mathrm{d}^2R/\mathrm{d}r^{*2}+[\Omega^2-l(l+1)e^\nu/r^2]R=0\,. \tag{26}$$

Here $\mathrm{d}r^*$ is an abbreviation for

$$\mathrm{d}r^*=[\exp(\lambda-\nu)/2]\,\mathrm{d}r\,.$$

Let us imagine that we have calculated the time-average value, $\langle T_{i\ (\mathrm{I})}^{\,k}\rangle$, of the electromagnetic stress-momentum-energy tensor of the disturbance under discussion: mode number I. This tensor depends only on r and θ. Let there be altogether N modes of different frequencies excited, all of about the same strength and properties as mode I, but differing from it in orientation. Let the distribution of stress, momentum, and energy in a typical one of these disturbances be visualized by mapping out on a rigid sphere the distribution of mode I, and then rotating the north pole of this sphere to an angle α with respect to its original position, and to an azimuth β. Thus $\langle T_{i\ (D)}^{\,k}\rangle$, for a typical disturbance, D, is a tensor function of r, θ, and φ, the functional dependence being completely known in principle as soon as we know the angles α and β associated with the mode D. Let us sum the values at a typical point, θ, φ, of the energy density over all N modes, obtaining.

$$\langle T_T^{\,T}\rangle=(N/4\pi)\iint\langle T_{T\ (D)}^{\,T}\rangle\sin\alpha\,\mathrm{d}\alpha\,\mathrm{d}\beta\,. \tag{27}$$

This result cannot depend upon θ and φ, because of the spherical symmetry. Consequently the point of evaluation can be taken to lie at the original location of the north pole, $\theta=0$. Here the energy density of disturbance D is the same as was the energy density of disturbance I at the polar angle $\theta = \alpha$ Consequently (27) reduces to the form

$$\langle T_T{}^T \rangle = (N/2) \int \langle T_T{}^T{}_{(I)} \rangle \sin\theta \, d\theta \, . \tag{28}$$

Similarly we obtain for the radial tension

$$\langle T_r{}^r \rangle = (N/2) \int \langle T_r{}^r{}_{(I)} \rangle \sin\theta \, d\theta \, . \tag{29}$$

In evaluating the tangential components of the tension we have to proceed more carefully, for the definition of the relevant directions differs between the original mode and the rotated modes. Consequently we have to employ the standard rules for transformation of the components of a tensor. Fortunately all the transformations are carried out in the local tangent space, and the rules for Cartesian tensors apply:

$$\begin{aligned} \langle T_\theta{}^\theta \rangle = (N/4\pi) \int [\langle T_\theta{}^\theta{}_{(I)} \rangle \cos\beta \cos\beta + \langle T_\theta{}^\varphi{}_{(I)} + T_\varphi{}^\theta{}_{(I)} \rangle \sin\beta \cos\beta \, + \\ + \langle T_\varphi{}^\varphi{}_{(I)} \rangle \sin\beta \sin\beta] \sin\alpha \, d\alpha \, d\beta = (N/4) \int \langle T_\theta{}^\theta{}_{(I)} + T_\varphi{}^\varphi{}_{(I)} \rangle \sin\theta \, d\theta \, . \end{aligned} \tag{30}$$

The expression for $\langle T_\varphi{}^\varphi \rangle$ is identical to this. All other components of the total stress-energy tensor have mixed indices and must vanish on account of one or another symmetry argument. Thus $\langle T_\theta{}^T \rangle$ and $\langle T_\varphi{}^T \rangle$ describe the tangential flow of energy, which has to vanish; the shears $\langle T_r{}^\theta \rangle$, $\langle T_r{}^\varphi \rangle$, $\langle T_\theta{}^\varphi \rangle$ must be null; and the component $\langle T_r{}^T \rangle$ represents the net radial flow of energy, which in a static situation must also be zero. Whether the geon leaks no energy at all, or only a very little energy, depends upon whether we impose upon the electromagnetic field at large distances the requirement that it be a standing wave, or a pure outgoing wave. Which choice we make has negligible effect upon the structure of the geon. We already made our choice when we took the circular frequency, $c\Omega$, to be real and assumed the product representation (24) of the vector potential. From the radial eq. (26) it then follows automatically that $R(r)$ must represent a standing wave, and that the radial flux must vanish. In summary, we have for the non-zero components of the average value of the total electromagnetic stress-energy tensor (2) the following values:

$$\left\{ \begin{aligned} &\langle T_r{}^r \rangle = (N/2) \int \sin\theta \, d\theta (8\pi)^{-1} (\{r\varphi\} - \{T\varphi\} - \{\theta\varphi\}) = [r\varphi] - [T\varphi] - [\theta\varphi] \, , \\ &\langle T_\theta{}^\theta \rangle = \langle T_\varphi{}^\varphi \rangle = (N/2) \int \sin\theta \, d\theta (8\pi)^{-1} \{\theta\varphi\} = [\theta\varphi] \, , \\ &\langle T_T{}^T \rangle = (N/2) \int \sin\theta \, d\theta (8\pi)^{-1} (\{T\varphi\} - \{r\varphi\} - \{\theta\varphi\}) = [T\varphi] - [r\varphi] - [\theta\varphi] \, . \end{aligned} \right. \tag{31a}$$

Here we used as abbreviations:

$$\{r\varphi\} \equiv \langle F_{r\varphi} F^{r\varphi} \rangle = e^{-\lambda}(r \sin\theta)^{-2} \langle (\partial A_\varphi/\partial r)^2 \rangle \sim \langle H_\theta^2 \rangle \,;$$

$$\{\theta\varphi\} \equiv \langle F_{\theta\varphi} F^{\theta\varphi} \rangle = (r^2 \sin\theta)^{-2} \langle (\partial A_\varphi/\partial\theta)^2 \rangle \sim \langle H_r^2 \rangle \,;$$

$$\{T\varphi\} \equiv \langle F_{T\varphi} F^{T\varphi} \rangle = - e^{-\nu}(r \sin\theta)^{-2} \langle (\partial A_\varphi/\partial T)^2 \rangle \sim - \langle E_\varphi^2 \rangle \,,$$

and

$$[\;] = (N/16\pi)\int \{\}\sin\theta\, \mathrm{d}\theta \,;$$

thus

$$(31b) \qquad \begin{cases} [r\varphi] = (N/16\pi)\, l(l+1)(2l+1)^{-1} e^{-\lambda} (\mathrm{d}R/r\,\mathrm{d}r)^2_\bullet \,; \\ [\theta\varphi] = (N/16\pi)\, l^2(l+1)^2(2l+1)^{-1}(R/r^2)^2; \\ [T\varphi] = -(N/16\pi)\, l(l+1)(2l+1)^{-1} e^{-\nu} (\Omega R/r)^2 \,. \end{cases}$$

Having an equation for the influence of gravitation upon the electromagnetic disturbance (26), and expressions (31) for the stress-energy density of this disturbance, we can now complete the circle of the self-consistent system and write down the equations

$$(32) \qquad G_{ik} = (8\pi G/c^4) T_{ik}$$

for the determination of the gravitational potentials. In the mixed covariant-contravariant notation (which gives $T_4{}^4$ a sign opposite to T_{44}), we have [11]

$$(33) \qquad \begin{cases} G_r{}^r = e^{-\lambda}(r^{-1}\,\mathrm{d}\nu/\mathrm{d}r + r^{-2}) - r^{-2} \,, \\ G_\theta{}^\theta = G_\varphi{}^\varphi = \frac{1}{2} e^{-\lambda}[\mathrm{d}^2\nu/\mathrm{d}r^2 + \frac{1}{2}(\mathrm{d}\nu/\mathrm{d}r)^2 + r^{-1}\mathrm{d}\nu/\mathrm{d}r - r^{-1}\mathrm{d}\lambda/\mathrm{d}r - \frac{1}{2}(\mathrm{d}\nu/\mathrm{d}r)(\mathrm{d}\lambda/\mathrm{d}r)], \\ G_T{}^T = e^{-\lambda}(r^{-2} - r^{-1}\,\mathrm{d}\lambda/\mathrm{d}r) - r^{-2} \,. \end{cases}$$

The field equation $G_\theta{}^\theta = (8\pi G/c^4) T_\theta{}^\theta$ is identical with the equation for $G_\varphi{}^\varphi$ and can be disregarded, for it says nothing in addition to the equations for $G_T{}^T$ and $G_r{}^r$. One has only to differentiate with respect to r the equation for $G_r{}^r$, add to it a proper linear combination of the equations for $G_r{}^r$ and $G_T{}^T$, and employ the wave eq. (26) to get the content of the equation for $G_\theta{}^\theta$. This result only says that the tangential tensions in a spherical shell have to be balanced by the radial pressure gradient. We therefore end up with two equations of the

(11) See for example L. Landau and E. Lifschitz: *The Classical Theory of Fields*, translated by M. Hamermesh (Cambridge, Mass., 1951).

first order for the two unknown functions λ (= twice the number of napiers of change of scale in radial distances) and ν (= twice the number of napiers of change of scale in time measurements):

$$(34)\qquad e^{-\lambda}(r^{-1}\,\mathrm{d}\nu/\mathrm{d}r + r^{-2}) - r^{-2} = [l(l+1)GN/2(2l+1)c^4]\cdot \cdot[e^{-\lambda}(\mathrm{d}R/r\,\mathrm{d}r)^2 + e^{-\nu}(\Omega R/r)^2 - l(l+1)(R/r^2)^2]\ ;$$

$$(35)\qquad e^{-\lambda}(r^{-2} - r^{-1}\,\mathrm{d}\lambda/\mathrm{d}r) - r^{-2} = [l(l+1)GN/2(2l+1)c^4]\cdot \cdot[-e^{-\lambda}(\mathrm{d}R/r\,\mathrm{d}r)^2 - e^{-\nu}(\Omega R/r)^2 - l(l+1)(R/r^2)^2]\ .$$

The scale invariance of classical geon theory shows itself at once. For geons of the same index l, but different sizes and masses and therefore different circular frequencies $c\Omega$, we introduce the same dimensionless measure of radial co-ordinate, $\varrho = \Omega r$. Also we define the dimensionless measure of potential

$$(36)\qquad f(\varrho) = [l(l+1)GN/2(2l+1)c^4]^{\frac{1}{2}}\,\Omega R(r)\ .$$

Furthermore we recall that the Schwarzschild solution for the field of a point mass has the form $e^{-\lambda} = e^{\nu} = 1 - 2r^{-1}L_0$, where $L_0 = GM/c^2$ is a measure of the mass of the object. We have to expect a similar result for the metric around the geon at distances where the electromagnetic field has fallen exponentially to negligible values, but where the gravitational field may be still quite strong. Consequently we shall write

$$(37)\qquad \begin{cases} e^{-\lambda} \equiv 1 - 2\varrho^{-1}L(\varrho)\ , \\ e^{\lambda+\nu} \equiv Q^2(\varrho)\ , \\ e^{\nu} = [1 - 2\varrho^{-1}L(\varrho)]\,Q^2(\varrho)\ . \end{cases}$$

Here the dimensionless measure, $L(\varrho)$, of mass inside the radius r is nearly zero from $\varrho = 0$ to a value of ϱ close to the inner surface of the active region of the geon, a value of the order of

$$\varrho \sim l^* \equiv [l(l+1)]^{\frac{1}{2}}\ ;$$

then $L(\varrho)$ rises quickly over a range of ϱ of the order $\Delta\varrho \sim l^{*\frac{1}{3}}$; and then $L(\varrho)$ stays essentially constant from this point to very large distances. The correction factor, Q, is likewise essentially constant inside and outside the geon, and only makes a sudden rise in the active region. In these notations the geon is described by the self-consistent solution of three equations: the wave equation

(38) $$\mathrm{d}^2 f/\mathrm{d}\varrho^{*2} + [1 - (l^* Q/\varrho)^2 (1 - 2L/\varrho)] f = 0 ,$$

where $\mathrm{d}\varrho^*$ is an abbreviation for

(39) $$\mathrm{d}\varrho^* = Q^{-1}(1 - 2L/\varrho)^{-1}\,\mathrm{d}\varrho ;$$

and the two field equations, of which the first gives the change of mass with distance:

(40) $$\mathrm{d}L/\mathrm{d}\varrho^* = (1/2Q)[f^2 + (\mathrm{d}f/\mathrm{d}\varrho^*)^2 - (l^* Q f/\varrho)^2 (1 - 2L/\varrho)] ,$$

and the second gives the variation of the factor Q:

(41) $$\mathrm{d}Q/\mathrm{d}\varrho^* = (\varrho - 2L)^{-1}[f^2 + (\mathrm{d}f/\mathrm{d}\varrho^*)^2] .$$

It is an interesting feature of the system of eq. (38), (40), (41) that they still permit the possibility of a change of scale of distance without a change of form:

(42) $$\left\{\begin{aligned} \varrho &= b\varrho_1 , \\ Q &= bQ_1 , \\ \varrho^* &= \varrho_1^* , \\ L &= bL_1 , \\ f &= b^{\frac{1}{2}} f_1 . \end{aligned}\right.$$

Now $g_{rr} = e^{\lambda}$ is already so normalized, according to eq. (37), that it goes over to the Euclidean value of 1 at very large distances. Consequently we wish the corresponding cotime factor, e^{ν}, also to go to unity. Another value is perfectly possible, but it would correspond to an unhappy choice for the value of the speed of light. Thus, according to (37), we want the factor Q to go to unity at large distances. This normalization means, according to the law (41) of increase of Q, that Q must start off at the origin with a value less than 1. But how much less we do not know until we have integrated the differential equation. Accordingly, we distinguish between the solution Q, L, f that we want and the solution Q_1, L_1, f_1 that we get from our numerical integration of the equations of the self-consistent field. In both solutions the mass factor, L or L_1, and the field factor, f or f_1, start at zero and are well behaved at large distances. In the former Q starts at a value less than one and rises to unity; in the latter we start, for convenience, at $Q_1 = 1$ and arrive at large distances at a value greater than one. This value then defines the scale factor required in (42) to go from the preliminary solution to the desired solution:

$$b = 1/Q_1(\infty)\ ; \qquad Q_1(0) = 1\ . \tag{43}$$

In preparing for the numerical integration of the geon equations we note that the behavior of the solutions near the origin is obvious and not very interesting

$$\begin{cases} f_1 = F\varrho_1^{l+1} + \dots, \\ L_1 = 2^{-1}(l+1)F^2\varrho_1^{2l+1} + \dots, \\ Q_1 = 1 + (2l)^{-1}(l+1)^2F^2\varrho_2^{2l} + \dots\ . \end{cases} \tag{44}$$

What is important is the circumstance that there is no adjustable constant except the starting value of the field strength. This field strength, or the constant F, must be so chosen as to give the geon stability. We have to do with an eigenvalue, but an eigenvalue of a non-linear system of equations.

The key to the eigenvalue problem is the wave eq. (38). Where the expression in square brackets is positive, there the solution is oscillatory; where it is negative, there the solutions rises or falls approximately exponentially. This expression has the following behavior when the factor F in the field strength has been chosen to give the geon stability. 1) At distances less than those that characterize the active region of the geon, $L_1 \doteqdot 0$, $Q_1 \doteqdot 1$, and the bracket has the approximate form $[1-(l^*/\varrho_1)^2]$. Thus, in moving out from $\varrho_1 = 0$ to ϱ_1 near l^*, we have until the very end a strongly negative bracket, and therefore a solution that rises approximately exponentially. Consequently we have yet to arrive at the zone of maximum activity. 2) In the active zone near $\varrho_1 = l^*$ there occurs a quick rise in Q_1 and L_1, with very little change in the radial co-ordinate. When the field strength is properly chosen, these changes that follow from (40) and (41) are such that the square bracket is positive over a limited range of ϱ. Thus f rises to a maximum and starts to fall off exponentially as ϱ_1 passes out of the region of oscillation, provided that the field strength is great enough to give the geon the requisite mass for stability in a single wave zone. 3) For values of ϱ_1 just slightly larger than l^*, the mass factor L_1 and the quantity Q_1 have attained essentially constant values. These values are such that $(1-2L_1/l^*)$ is much less than unity, but Q_1^2 is much greater than unity, and the product of these two factors also exceeds unity by a considerable margin. Moreover, as ϱ_1 increases, the factor $(1-2L_1/\varrho_1)$ evidently rises rapidly percentagewise at first, then levels off to a saturation value. The factor $(Q_1 l^*/\varrho_1)^2$, on the other hand, falls off in a more nearly uniform way. Consequently the product of these two factors rises as we leave the active zone behind, reaches a maximum when the increase, $\varrho_1 - l^*$, of the radial co-ordinate is some substantial fraction of l^*, then falls off and passes through the value unity for $\varrho_1 - l^*$ of the order of l^* (Fig. 2). The product of factors under discussion in the present classical problem evidently plays the part of the potential in a typical problem of quantum mechanics. The analogy with the theory of α-decay is complete even to topological identity of the two forms of barrier to be penetrated. In the barrier in the present problem the field factor f of an eigenfunction falls off exponentially by a number of napiers of the order of l^*. 4) With further increase of the radial co-ordinate beyond the point of emergence from the barrier, oscillation sets in. The amplitude is of course exceedingly small compared to the amplitude inside the geon. The wavelength is at first long but eventually settles down to the value appropriate to a disturbance of the given frequency in free space:

$$(45)\quad f/\text{constant} \doteqdot \sin(\varrho^* + \delta) = \sin\big(Q_1(\infty)\varrho_1 + \delta\big) = \sin(\varrho + \delta) = \sin(\Omega r + \delta)\,.$$

To go further, we seem to have to obtain for each conceivable value of the index number l a self-consistent numerical solution of three non-linear equations. However, there exists in addition to the exact scaling law already exploited another and distinct scaling law, valid asymptotically for large l^*, which reduces all these problems to a single one. Similar scaling laws are familiar from other parts of mathematical physics. In quantum mechanics one reduces all hydrogenic atoms to one problem by appropriate choice of scale of length. However, then the radial wave function for the lowest state for each value of l has a different mathematical expression, $\{[(l+1)/2]^{2l+3}(2l+2)!\}^{-\frac{1}{2}}\varrho^l \cdot \exp[-\varrho/(l+1)]$. Yet simple analysis of the behavior of this function in the neighborhood of its maximum, $\varrho = l(l+1)$, shows that it has a form,

$$\simeq [\pi l(l+1)^2]^{-\frac{1}{4}} \exp[-(\Delta\varrho)^2/2l(l+1)^2]\,,$$

which is the same up to a scale change for all values of l. A similar scaling principle applies to the geon, with two differences: the reduced field factor, f, does not have the form of a harmonic oscillator wave function; and the relevant length variable is not $x = \Delta\varrho/l^{\frac{1}{2}}(l+1)$, as in the hydrogenic problem, but

$$(46)\qquad x = (\varrho^* - l^*)l^{*-\frac{1}{3}}\,.$$

The whole of the active region of the geon will be described by a range of x of the order of unity.

To bring this similarity transformation into evidence, we consider large values of l^*, and expand the relevant quantities in inverse powers of $l^{*\frac{1}{3}}$:

$$(47)\quad \begin{cases} \mathrm{d}\varrho^* \equiv l^{*\frac{1}{3}}\,\mathrm{d}x\,, \\ \varrho_1 = l^* + l^{*\frac{1}{3}} r_0(x) + \dots\,, \\ L_1 = l^*\lambda_0(x) + l^{*\frac{2}{3}}\lambda_1(x) + l^{*\frac{1}{3}}\lambda_2(x) + \dots\,, \\ Q_1 = [1/k(x)] + l^{*-\frac{1}{3}} q_1(x) + l^{*-\frac{2}{3}} q_2(x) + \dots\,, \\ f_1 = l^{*\frac{1}{3}}\varphi(x) + \varphi_1(x) + l^{*-\frac{1}{3}}\varphi_2(x) + \dots\,, \\ [1-(Q_1 l^*/\varrho_1)^2(1-2L_1/\varrho_1)] = l^{*-\frac{2}{3}}\, j(x)\,k(x) + \dots\,. \end{cases}$$

Inserting these expression into the system of eq. (38), (4), (41), and identifying coefficients of like powers of l^*, we find from the lowest relevant terms the wave equation

$$(48)\qquad \mathrm{d}^2\varphi/\mathrm{d}x^2 + j(x)\,k(x)\,\varphi(x) = 0\,,$$

and the two field equations:

$$(49)\qquad \mathrm{d}k/\mathrm{d}x + \varphi^2 = 0\,,$$

$$(50)\qquad \mathrm{d}j/\mathrm{d}x = 3 - [1 + (\mathrm{d}\varphi/\mathrm{d}x)^2]/k^2\,.$$

If we can find by integration of these three equations the reduced field factor $\varphi(x)$ and the supplementary time scale correction factor $k(x)$ and the reduced oscillation factor $j(x)k(x)$, then we can determine the other leading terms in expressions (47) by simple calculation:

$$(51)\quad \begin{cases} \mathrm{d}r_0/\mathrm{d}x = k(x)\,, \\ \lambda_0 = (1-k^2)/2\,. \end{cases}$$

We seek a solution of (48), (49), and (50) with the following properties. The field factor $\varphi(x)$ tends to zero both for large positive x and for large negative x. The contraction factor $k(x)$ is unity for large negative x, and falls in the active region near $x = 0$, and for large positive x approaches a value which is less than $(1/3)^{\frac{1}{2}} = 0.577$ but still positive. The quantity $j(x)$ is very large and negative for large negative x. It rises with increasing x with a positive slope of two until x reaches the vicinity of the active region. There j succeeds in becoming positive for a limited range of x in the neighborhood of $x = 0$. For larger x, the slope $\mathrm{d}j/\mathrm{d}x$ approaches the negative value $3 - k^{-2}(\infty)$. Thus j falls off again to $-\infty$. The oscillation factor, the product $j(x)k(x)$, is positive in only a limited range of x.

There exist a number of solutions having the desired behavior, distinguished from one another by an integer, s, which represents the sum of the number of maxima and minima in the field factor, $\varphi(x)$, in the active region. This integer has the value one for the simplest type of idealized spherical geon. Higher values of s also represent physically acceptable geons. We make the choice between one solution and another when in the integration of the equation we pick one starting magnitude of $\varphi(x)$ or another. The solution $s=1$ is characterized by the largest field strength, for in one-half wave enough energy and mass has to accumulate to hold the geon together. A comparable amount of mass belongs to a geon of higher s, but the energy is distributed over a larger number of half waves and on this account the concentration of energy and the field strength are weaker.

We can summarize the eigenvalue characteristics of our system of equations as follows. We accept that for large negative x, the factors j and k have the form $k(x) \doteqdot 1$ and $j(x) \doteqdot 2x$, and that $\varphi(x)$ is approximately the exponentially rising solution of

(52) $$d^2\varphi/dx^2 = 2x\varphi\ ;$$

thus,

(53) $$\varphi \doteqdot A(-2x)^{-\frac{1}{4}} \exp[-(-2x)^{\frac{3}{2}}/3]\ .$$

Here the constant A, the «amplitude factor», is the sole quantity at our disposal in selecting the character of the solution of (48), (49), 50). If A is chosen very small in comparison with unity, then (49) says that $k(x)$ stays close to 1 for a long range of x, and (50) says that $j(x)$ continues to behave nearly as $2x$ for a considerable range of positive values of x. There likewise (52) remains a good approximation, and the solution, essentially an Airy function, goes over from the exponential character (53) to the oscillatory form

(54) $$\varphi \doteqdot 2A(2x)^{-\frac{1}{4}} \sin[(2x)^{\frac{3}{2}}/3 + (\pi/4)]\ ,$$

passing through the value

$$\varphi \doteqdot 6^{5/6} 2^{-1} \pi^{-\frac{1}{2}} \Gamma(4/3) A$$

at $x=0$. Averaging over oscillations in this first part of the active region, we have

$$dk/dx \doteqdot -\langle\varphi^2\rangle \doteqdot -\sqrt{2}\, A^2/x^{\frac{1}{2}}\ ,$$

or

$$k \doteqdot 1 - 2^{\frac{3}{2}} A^2 x^{\frac{1}{2}}\ ;$$

and

$$\mathrm{d}j/\mathrm{d}x \doteqdot 2 - 2^{\frac{3}{2}} 3 A^2 x^{\frac{1}{2}} ,$$

or

$$j \doteqdot 2x - 2^{\frac{5}{2}} A^2 x^{\frac{3}{2}} . \tag{55}$$

These approximations begin to fail when x becomes of the order $1/A^4$. Thereafter we quickly come to the end of the active region. 1) If the amplitude factor has the value, A_s, appropriate to the s-th proper solution, then this field factor, $\varphi(x)$, falls off exponentially. 2) If the amplitude factor has a value so little greater than A_s that the difference, $A - A_s$, is small compared to the distance $A_{s-1} - A_s$, to the next eigenvalue, then there is not quite opportunity to finish the last oscillation in the active region. The field factor starts to fall off after what would have been the last maximum but instead of continuing to fall towards zero, reaches a minimum and then commences to rise exponentially (Fig. 3). The contribution to the mass therefore also rises exponentially. The scale factor k of eq. (49), instead of decreasing to a reasonable value between 0 and 0.577, continues to fall, and goes to zero at a certain critical value, x^*, as $(x^* - x)$ multiplied by a slowly varying function which has qualitatively the character of a power of $\ln 1/(x^* - x)$. The quantity j therefore becomes singular, and goes to negative infinity as $-(x^* - x)^{-3}$ multiplied again by a slowly vary-

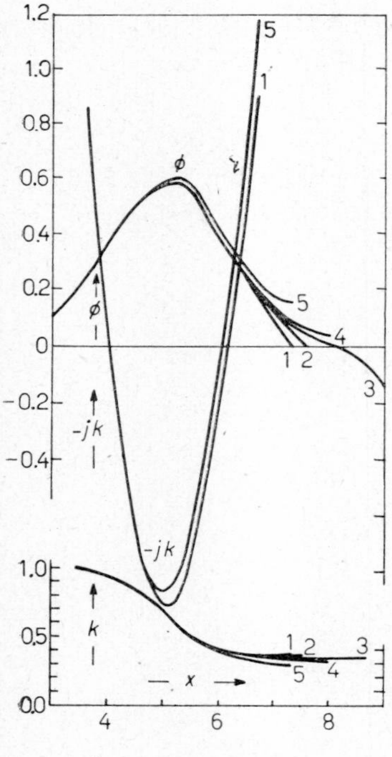

Fig. 3. – Results of numerical integration of the differential eq. (48), (49), (50) for the simple idealized self-consistent spherical geon, giving a more detailed account of the active region shown in the circle in Fig. 2. Here φ is the dimensionless measure of the radial factor in the electromagnetic potential, jk is the oscillation factor in the differential equation $\mathrm{d}^2\varphi/\mathrm{d}x^2 + jk\varphi = 0$, and k is a metric correction factor. The range of integration from start at $x = -4$ up to $x = 3$ is not shown owing to the inappreciable difference there between the curves with nearly identical starting values: $\varphi(-4) = \varphi_0$; $\varphi_0 \cdot 10^4 = 1.025$ (case 1); 1.028125 (2); 1.03 (3); 1.03125 (4); 1.0375 (5). The eigenvalue evidently lies between cases (3) and (4). For any given geon mass in the classical range, the curves permit one in principle to find field strengths, metric, and all other relevant physical quantities in the active region of the geon.

ing factor of logarithmic character. Finally, the field factor $\varphi(x)$ goes to infinity qualitatively with much the slowly varying behavior of a power of a logarithm of $[1/(x^*-x)]$. Thus the integration stops at x^*. This limit will be the further beyond the active region, the closer the amplitude factor lies to A_s. 3) As the difference $A-A_s$ becomes larger, the singular point of the integration moves inwards towards what one might still appropriately call the active zone. For a certain A the point x^* has come in to its maximum extent. With further increase in A this critical point moves out again. At or near the value of A for which this turnabout occurs, the sign of φ at the singularity also changes; *i.e.*, the singularity swallows up the last node of the wave function. Thus, for A just less than the critical value, $\varphi(x)$ is described by a quasi-logarithmic function that goes to infinity with one sign; for A just above the critical value, by a singular quasi-logarithmic function of the opposite sign; and for A just right to annihilate a node, by (x^*-x) times a quasi-logarithmic function of (x^*-x). In this particular case the scale factor $k(x)$ goes as $(x^*-x)^3$ times a pseudo-logarithmic function, and the oscillation factor jk goes as $-(x^*-x)^{-2}$ times a pseudo-logarithmic function. 4) As A approaches the proper amplitude factor, A_{s-1}, of the next solution, the singularity moves out towards $x^*=+\infty$ and finally disappears. 5) With further increase in A the sequence (1), (2), (3), (4) repeats itself until finally there are no more nodes in the wave function to be swallowed. At this stage we have passed the last eigenvalue, A_1.

It is appropriate to notice that the system of eq. (48), (49), (50) does not contain explicitly the argument x. Hence, if $\varphi(x)$, $k(x)$, $j(x)$ is a solution, so is $\varphi(x+a)$, $k(x+a)$, $j(x+a)$. Consequently there is a certain indeterminacy in the start of the integration process. We remove this ambiguity and completely—though indirectly—define the origin of x when we adopt as convention the asymptotic formula $j(x)=-2x$ and the corresponding asymptotic eq. (52) and (53).

With this convention for origin of x, the reduced equations of the spherical geon were integrated numerically to determine approximately the first proper function and first proper value. Thanks are due to Mr. ARTHUR KOMAR for checking the algebra and to Mr. ROBERT GOERSS for carrying out the computations on an International Business Machines card-programmed electronic calculator. The logical scheme of the integration is outlined in Fig. 4, where each line symbolizes a successive stage in the calculation, and where Δ represents the size, 0.05, of the interval of x used between one step and the next. The integration was started at $x=-4$ with values derived from the asymptotic formula (53):

$$(56)\qquad \begin{cases} \varphi_0 \;\; = \varphi(-4) = \text{arbitrary}\,, \\ \delta\varphi_{\frac{1}{2}} = 8^{\frac{1}{2}}\varphi_0\Delta\,, \\ k_0 \;\; = 1\,, \\ j_0 \;\; = -8\,. \end{cases}$$

Fig. 3 presents the results of the integrations. The first eigenvalue was found to lie between those amplitude factors, A, that correspond to initial values, at $x = -4$, between $\varphi_0 = 1.030\,00 \cdot 10^{-4}$ and $\varphi_0 = 1.031\,25 \cdot 10^{-4}$. The active region ($jk > 0$) did not begin until $x = 4.05$ and reached only to $x = 6.12$. The field factor, $\varphi(x)$, reached a peak value of 0.59 for x about equal to 5.1. The scale factor, $k(x)$, approached an asymptotic value, $k(\infty)$, of approximately 0.33.

These curves and numbers give us essentially all the information we need to determine the structure of a simple idealized spherical geon with only one maximum, $s = 1$, in the electromagnetic potential and with number of nodes over the surface equal to any arbitrary large number l. Thus, having chosen an l, we calculate $l^* = [l(l+1)]^{\frac{1}{2}}$. This quantity represents the approximate radial co-ordinate, ϱ_1, of the active zone. Then, from our curves and eq. (47) and (51) we find the relation between the dimensionless measures of distance, ϱ_1; of mass out to a given distance, L_1; of metric correction factor, Q_1; and of potential, f_1. In particular we have for the asymptotic value of Q_1 the value $1/b \doteq 1/0.33$ and for the asymptotic value of L_1 the value $L_1 = l^*(1-b^2)/2 \doteq 0.45\,l^*$. Next, we make the scale change of eq. (42) and (43) in order to have a metric that approaches the Euclidean values at large distances. The scale factor is $b \doteq 0.33$. In the new dimensionless units the radial co-ordinate of the active zone is about $0.33\,l^*$. The metric correction factor Q has the value $b \doteq 0.33$ in the inner inactive part of the geon, rises in the active zone, and has outside a value 1.00. The corresponding new dimensionless measure of mass, L, essentially zero in the inner inactive region, and outside the active region has the value $L \doteq (b/2)(1-b^2)l^* = 0.15\,l^*$. Finally, we transform to cgs units of measure via (36) and (37) and the related discussion. A clock ticks at the center of the geon at only about 33 percent of the rate of an identical clock far away from the geon. In terms of the frequency, Ωc, of electromagnetic radiation observed to come from the geon, the radius of the active zone of the system is described by a co-ordinate

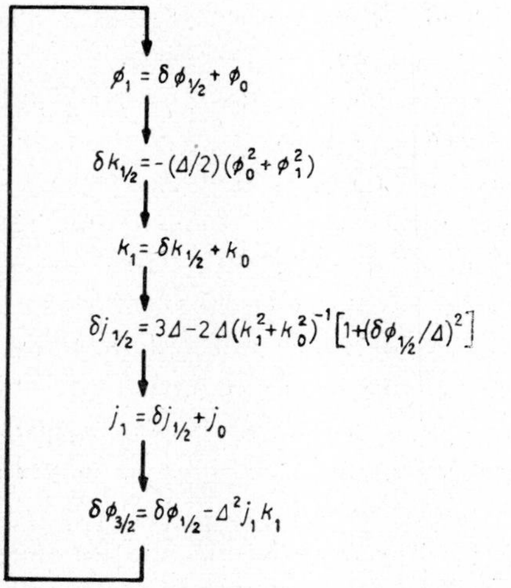

Fig. 4. – Flow diagram of numerical integration. In the last term in the last equation there should appear — and did appear in the numerical calculations — a factor φ_1.

$$(57) \qquad r = R \doteq 0.33\,l^*/\Omega \qquad \left(\textit{exactly } l^*/3\Omega;\ 1961 \text{ addendum } (^9)\right).$$

The mass is

$$M \doteqdot 0.15\, c^2 l^* / G\Omega \,. \tag{58}$$

Let an observer far from the geon have a clock that flashes every second, and let an identical clock be placed at the center of the geon. The flashes of light from this second clock will reach the observer, not every second, but about every $b^{-1} \doteqdot (0.33)^{-1} = 3$ s.

The mass, circular frequency, and radius of the spherical geon can be expressed in terms of the reduced action, $\mathscr{J}(=\text{action}/2\pi)$, by way of the relation

$$c^2\,\mathrm{d}M = c\Omega\,\mathrm{d}\mathscr{J}\,, \tag{59}$$

thus:

$$\begin{cases} M \doteqdot 0.54\,(l^*\mathscr{J}c/G)^{\frac{1}{2}}\,; \\ c\Omega \doteqdot 0.27\,(l^*c^5/G\mathscr{J})^{\frac{1}{2}}\,; \\ R \doteqdot 1.2\,(l^*G\mathscr{J}/c^3)^{\frac{1}{2}}\,. \end{cases} \tag{60}$$

The root-mean-square value of the electric field, averaged with respect to time and with respect to polar co-ordinates over a sphere of that radius r which goes with the dimensionless co-ordinate x is,

$$\begin{aligned} E_{\text{rms}} &= \{-8\pi[T\varphi]\}^{\frac{1}{2}} = \{c^4 f^2 e^{-\nu}/Gr^2\}^{\frac{1}{2}} \\ &= c^2\Omega G^{-\frac{1}{2}} b^{-\frac{2}{3}} l^{*-\frac{2}{3}} \varphi(x) \\ &= (c^7/\mathscr{J}G^2)^{\frac{1}{2}} l^{*-\frac{1}{6}} [(1-b^2)^{\frac{1}{2}}/2b]\,\varphi(x) \end{aligned}$$

with a peak value

$$E_{\text{peak rms}} = 0.46\, l^{*\frac{1}{3}} c^4 / G^{\frac{3}{2}} M \,.$$

4. – Transformations and interactions of pure electromagnetic geons.

Energy leaks out of a simple idealized spherical geon at a rate easily estimated by the methods of the theory of α-decay. Were the refractive index barrier removed, the energy would disappear from its present region of concentration in a time of the order of one vibration period. The attrition, α, in the equation of definition

$$\mathrm{d}M/M = -\alpha\omega\,\mathrm{d}t\,, \tag{61}$$

would have a value of the order of unity. Owing to the presence of the barrier, the attrition is cut down to a value of the order

$$\alpha \sim \exp[-2P], \tag{62}$$

where P is the barrier penetration integral determined by eq. (38):

$$P = \int [(\mathrm{d}^2 f/\mathrm{d}^*\varrho^2)/f]^{\frac{1}{2}}\,\mathrm{d}\varrho^* = \int [-1 + (l^* Q/\varrho)^2 (1 - 2L/\varrho)]^{\frac{1}{2}} Q^{-1} (1 - 2L/\varrho)^{-1}\,\mathrm{d}\varrho\,. \tag{63}$$

The integral extends from the outer odge of the active zone to the point of re-emergence from the barrier. The relevant range in ϱ is of the order of $l^* = [l(l+1)]^{\frac{1}{2}}$, whereas the thickness of the active zone is only of the order $\Delta\varrho \sim l^{*\frac{1}{3}}$. For this reason it is legitimate to use for Q and L in the evaluation of the integral (63) the constant values that apply outside the active zone. The error made in the penetration exponent by this approximation will be only of the order of $l^{*\frac{1}{3}}$, whereas the exponent itself will be of the order l^*. Thus in accordance with the results at the end of the last section we write

$$\begin{cases} Q = 1\,, \\ \Omega r_{\text{inner}} = \varrho_{\text{lower limit}} = bl^* = l^*/3\,, \\ L = (b/2)(1 - b^2)\, l^* \doteqdot 0.15\, l^*\,. \end{cases} \tag{64}$$

and find by algebraic examination of the roits of the bracket in (63) that the outer turning point is

$$\Omega r_{\text{outer}} = \varrho_{\text{upper limit}} = l^* \{-(b/2) + [1 - (3b^2/4)]^{\frac{1}{2}}\} \equiv Bl^* \doteqdot 0.79\, l^*\,. \tag{65}$$

The penetration integral has the value

$$P = l^* \int_b^B \{x^{-2}[1 - (1 - b^2)(b/x)] - 1\}^{\frac{1}{2}} [1 - (1 - b^2)(b/x)]^{-1}\,\mathrm{d}x = 0.76\, l^*, \tag{66}$$

where the variable of integration is $x = \varrho/l^* = \Omega r/l^*$; and the attrition has the rough value

$$\alpha \sim \exp[-4.56\, R/\lambda\!\!\!^{-}]\,. \tag{67}$$

As examples, consider two simple idealized spherical geons not very far—on a logarithmic scale—above the limit where quantum effects come in by way of pair production. Let both have masses of 10^{42} g and only one-half wave of disturbance in the radial direction in the active zone, but let the wavelength, and therefore the thickness of this zone, have quite different values in the two cases, as indicated in Table I. It is evident from the numbers given there that geons, even systems of the same mass and radius, can have fantastically different rates of radiation leakage.

TABLE I. – *Leakage of radiation from simple idealized spherical geons: illustrative examples.* The last column gives the factor of change of scale for a similarity transformation which leaves the geon a classical object.

	Geon I	Geon II	Scale factor
Mass	10^{42} g	10^{42} g	$\times n$
Radial co-ordinate of active zone (58)	$1.67\cdot10^{14}$ cm	$1.67\cdot10^{14}$ cm	$\times n$
Spherical harmonic index $l^*=[l(l+1)]^{\frac{1}{2}}$	10	$8.43\cdot10^{9}$	$\times 1$
Circular frequency of emergent radiation (57)	$6.00\cdot10^{-4}$ rad/s	$5.06\cdot10^{5}$ rad/s	$\times(1/n)$
Wavelength outside	$3.14\cdot10^{14}$ cm	$3.72\cdot10^{5}$ cm	$\times n$
Approximate attrition (67)	$2.5\ \cdot10^{-7}$	$10^{-5\,570\,000\,000}$	$\times 1$
Time to collapse assuming leakage only and classical behavior throughout	212 years	$\sim\infty$	$\times(1/n)$
Rms electric field in most active region [eq. (60) ff]	$4.66\cdot10^{10}$ esu/cm	$4.41\cdot10^{13}$ esu/cm	$\times(1/n)$
Critical field for pair production	$4.41\cdot10^{13}$ esu/cm	$4.41\cdot10^{13}$ esu/cm	a constant

$l-m$ nodes from N to S;
m nodes as φ increases by π
l nodes altogether

To switch to quantum language, we can speak of the leakage process as single photon emission. In addition to such processes there will occur what can temporarily describe as double photon processes (Fig. 5): two quanta moving tangentially collide and go off in two new directions, not far from parallel or antiparallel to the radius vector, and thus escape from the system simultaneously. To follow the terminology of light rays a little further, we can speak as is well known, of a critical angle required for escape. For rays whose angle of inclination, θ, to the radius vector is greater than this critical amount, there exists a maximum distance to which the ray can go before it falls back on the geon. This maximum distance is obtained by calculating the appropriate root of the equation

$$(68)\qquad \frac{l^{*2}\sin^2\theta}{\Omega^2 r^2}\left[1-\frac{l^* b(1-b^2)}{\Omega r}\right]-1=0\,.$$

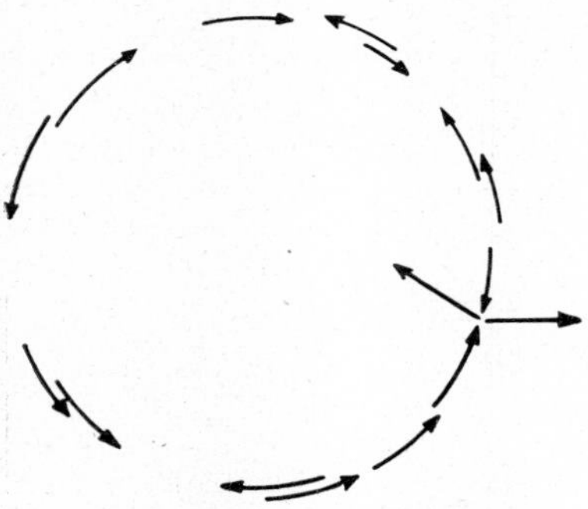

Fig. 5. – Photon-photon collisions provide one of the mechanisms for escape of energy from the active region of a geon. The same mechanism is describable from the wave point of view in terms of a coupling between otherwise independent modes of oscillation of the electromagnetic field. The two sources of the non-linear coupling are virtual pair phenomena and the non-static parts of the gravitational field.

The quantity on the left-hand side of this equation evaluated for the case $\sin\theta = 1$, came into the argument of the barrier penetration integral, another illustration of the close connection between the Hamilton-Jacobi analysis of rays and the differential equation for waves. It provides a simple interpretation of expression (68) to think of $l^*\sin\theta$ as a measure of the angular momentum of the ray: either a ray on the inside trying to get out; or a ray coming from infinity and trying to get in. The turning points for these two cases undergo merger when we have zero not only for the left-hand side of (68), but also for its derivative with respect to r. This happens when

$$(69)\qquad \sin\theta = (3^{\frac{3}{2}}/2)\, b(1-b^2) \doteqdot 0.77 = \sin 50.4^\circ\,.$$

and the double root then lies at

$$(70)\qquad r = (3l^*/2\Omega)\, b(1-b^2) \doteqdot 0.44\, l^*/\Omega\,,$$

that is, at the peak of the barrier in Fig. 2. This distance should be compared with the impact parameter, or distance of closest approach in the absence of gravitational forces, of a photon with the same energy and angular momentum:

$$(71)\qquad \text{impact parameter} = l^*\sin\theta/\Omega = 0.77\, l^*/\Omega\,.$$

In contrast, the rays that hold the geon together have in this sense an impact parameter equal to $1.00\, l^*/\Omega$, and have the inner and outer turning points,

$$(72)\qquad r = 0..3\, l^*/\Omega \quad \text{and} \quad r \doteqdot 0.79\, l^*/\Omega\,.$$

Rays with an impact parameter less than $0.77 l^*/\Omega$ have a component of motion in the radial direction sufficiently great to pass freely from the inner region to the outer region.

Everything just stated in ray language can be rephrased more appropriately in terms of waves. In the quasi-static gravitational field of force of the geon we have already found a solution of the wave equation for the electromagnetic potential which has only one maximum in the active region, varies with angle as a spherical harmonic of order $l \doteq l^* - \frac{1}{2}$, has a proper circular frequency $c\Omega$. In addition to waves of such a kind excited to a strength sufficient to hold the geon together, we can have proper solutions of weak amplitude with a great variety of values for the number, s, of radial maxima and minima in the active region and of values of the indices l and m of the spherical harmonic. A typical disturbance of this type will be characterized by a proper value, $\Omega_{s,l}$, and an amplitude factor as $A_{s,l,m}$. Let the wavelength of this mode be small compared to the dimensions of the geon. Then it is appropriate to characterize this mode, too, by an equivalent ray-optical impact parameter, $P \equiv \{(l/\Omega_{s,l})$ times a quantity having the significance of $\sin\theta$ and to be calculated via appropriate analysis from the relative values of s and $l\}$. The motion of the trapped ray will have an outer bound equal to the next to the largest solution of the equation

$$(P^2/r^2)[1 - (l^*b/\Omega r)(1 - b^2)] - 1 = 0\,. \tag{73}$$

Outside of this distance the strength of the mode in question falls off exponentially through a refractive index barrier. A standing wave of this kind is the proper transcription of the idea of photon with a radial component of motion too small to allow escape. Evidently the prohibition of escape is not absolute. There will be leakage through the barrier to an extent the greater, the closer P falls to the critical impact parameter for escape, $P = 0.77\, l^*/\Omega$. For smaller values of the impact parameter we have no proper solutions with an exponential region of fall off. Instead, we have solutions capable of transporting energy freely from the inside of the geon to outer space, and endowed with a continuum of frequency values. These waves correspond to the notion of photons able to escape from the system.

Instead of speaking of photon-photon collisions, we can talk of excitation of secondary waves by the waves that carry the primary energy supply of the geon. Such excitation is not envisaged in a linear wave equation, derived from a Lagrangian function that contains the fields to the second order. The differentiation of a quadratic Lagrangian gives a time rate of change of the field strength proportional only to the first power of field quantities. However, the Lagrangian actually contains correction terms of the fourth order and higher. They give in the expression for the time rate of change of a field quantity supplementary terms containing the product of three or more field quantities. These terms constitute a non-linear coupling that takes energy slowly out of the primary modes and redistributes it over secondary radiations. Some of this energy is picked up in characteristic modes. In any such mode the energy is reflected back and forth in a standing wave limited by two values of r. Other parts of the energy go into unbounded waves and are lost to infinity. The existence of the barrier leakage phenomenon means of course that the distinction between the stationary modes and the unbounded waves is only approximate. The stationary modes will themselves leak some of the energy that they get. Moreover these vibrations can transfer energy via non-linear couplings to still other modes, and also to still other waves that escape.

The relative importance of simple leakage, and of transfer of energy to free-running waves, depends upon the relative strength of excitation of the various modes of the geon. The detailed specification of the state of a general geon is so complicated that there exists the greatest variety of objects, showing amongst them the greatest extremes of behavior.

In a geon where non-linear terms make the more important contribution to the energy dissipation, we evidently face a problem so complicated that statistical arguments are needed to make any headway. We have to take into account the totality of the stationary modes of the geon in an approximately static gravitational field, and the distribution of energy among these modes. But their number is infinite, as in Rayleigh's paradox of blackbody radiation. No proper account of the distribution can be given without taking into account the quantum of action. We are therefore invited to assign to each mode of characteristic frequency ω an energy $\hbar\omega[\exp(\hbar\omega/\Theta-1]$, where Θ, expressed in energy units, has the significance of a temperature. We can also idealize the energy of each unbounded wave as zero in a first approximation, these waves being most easily distinguished by the criterion (73). The very number of the modes of vibration simplifies the problem. To find in each mode the radial distribution of field strength, and stress and energy, it is no longer necessary to integrate the wave equation numerically. The JWKB method gives the answer in terms of purely algebraic operations. Thus the system of three equations of the theory of spherical geons reduces to two differential equations of the first order for the metric quantities $\lambda(r)$ and $\nu(r)$, or $L(r)$ and $Q(r)$, with the temperature Θ as parameter of integration. No attempt is made here to solve this pair of equations for the « thermal geon ».

The thermal geon is obviously an idealization that suggests itself for following out the consequences of the non-linear interactions between different modes of vibration. In the next approximation one has to make further allowance for the effects of the intermodal couplings, by way of radiation losses through photon-photon collisions. Here the picture will be very different according as the mean free path of the most relevant photons is large or small in comparison with the dimensions of the system. In the second case it becomes necessary to analyse the effective opacity of the system, and to take account of the variation of temperature with radial co-ordinate in a fashion familiar from stellar theory—a problem again not investigated here.

The non-linear couplings arise from two sources: the electron pair field, and the gravitational field. The second is classical. The source of the gravitation field—the stress energy tensor—has a reasonably smoothly varying average value, but on top of this are superposed fluctuations due to the fact that the electromagnetic field does after all vary in space and in time. A typical constituent of the fluctuation will have a character qualitatively of the form $A_1 f_1(x, y, z) \sin(\omega_1 t + g_1) A_2 f_2(x, y, z) \sin(\omega_2 t + g_2)$. This term will give rise to a fluctuating component of the gravitational field. Consequently in the differential equation for the electromagnetic field the coefficients of metric origin will not be exactly static functions of position alone, but will have small alternating terms with circular frequencies, $(\omega_1 + \omega_2)$ and $(\omega_1 - \omega_2)$, and with amplitudes proportional to $A_1 A_2$. Let the uncorrected amplitude of the mode under consideration be $A_3 f_3(x, y, z) \sin(\omega_3 t + g_3)$. Then the wave equation for this oscillation has to be visualized as containing four supplementary source terms, with frequencies $\omega_1 \pm \omega_2 \pm \omega_3$, and with amplitudes proportional to the product $A_1 A_2 A_3$. Thus the primary disturbances in the geon inevitably generate secondary waves.

For an order-of-magnitude estimate of the strength of the effect, let $\lambda\!\!\!^{-}$ denote the general scale of the space variations in the relevant primary modes, and let $\mathscr{E}$ denote the order of magnitude of the associated electromagnetic fields. Then a typical inhomogeneity in the distribution of stress and energy will possess a mass of the order of $\mathscr{E}^2 \lambda\!\!\!^{-3} / c^2$. The fluctuations in the gravitational metric will have the general magnitude $\Delta g \sim G\, \Delta m / c^2 \lambda\!\!\!^{-} \sim (G/c^4) \lambda\!\!\!^{-2} \mathscr{E}^2$. The square of this dimensionless factor, multiplied by a dimensionless function of the geometry of the geon—depending upon ratio of typical wavelengths to the size of the system, and upon other details—will determine the fraction of the energy of the system lost per cycle via non-linear coupling processes of gravitational origin.

The correction effects due to virtual production of electron pairs by slowly varying but intense fields bring in a coupling which has the same qualitative consequences as that due to gravitational fields, except that the governing dimensionless factor, Δg, of the previous paragraph is to be replaced by $\sim (e^2/\hbar c)[\mathscr{E} e(\hbar/mc)/(mc^2)]^2$. Thus the pair effects depend upon the electric field itself, whereas the gravitational effects depend upon the electric potential, $A \sim \lambda\!\!\!^{-} \mathscr{E}$. The two effects become of the same order of magnitude for wavelengths of the order

$$\lambda\!\!\!^{-} \sim (e^2/Gm^2)(G\hbar/c^3)^{\frac{1}{2}} = (4.16 \cdot 10^{42})(1.60 \cdot 10^{-33}\ \text{cm}) = 0.67 \cdot 10^{10}\ \text{cm}\,. \tag{74}$$

To justify the classical analysis of geon structure, we already know that we have to deal with *radii* of the order of the limit (74) or greater. On the wave-lengths we have not previously had any limit, except inferiority to the radius. However, in dealing with geons in which many modes are excited, or especially with a thermal geon, it will ordinarily be reasonable to consider wavelengths quite small compared to the limit (74). Then for most purposes gravitational transfer of energy between modes can be neglected in comparison with the coupling due to the charges and current of virtual pairs.

In analysing the behavior of a geon classical in the sense of being large compared to the limit (74), we encounter both a large scale static gravitational field and small scale rapid variations in this average. There will exist in addition long scale periodic or secular changes in the configuration of the system, some of which will in certain cases describe significant mechanisms for the disintegration of a geon. It is easy to visualize a slow vibration in the case of a simple toroidal geon. The shape of the torus changes from circular to elliptical first in one sense and then in the other, with the elementary electromagnetic disturbances, or ray tracks if one will, adjusting themselves adiabatically to these slow readjustments in the distribution of refractive index. The gravitational interaction between the various elementary electromagnetic oscillations imposes upon their readjustments of shape a collective character. In these collective motions the coupling between the electromagnetic oscillators by way of gravitational interactions will exceed the coupling via virtual pair effects, so long as we are in the classical domain of geon sizes.

The same mode of vibration of a simple toroidal system, endowed with enough energy, will lead to deformations not far in form from a figure eight, and with still further excitation of this mode scission will occur. Whether the two separate rings then completely break their association depends upon the magnitude of the kinetic energy of recoil from the act of scission. When this energy exceeds the gravitation potential energy of attraction between the two objects, they fly apart to make two distinct systems, and we have a complete act of fission. When the recoil energy is less than the binding, the two rings separate to a limiting distance, reverse their motion, collide, pass through each other, again separate, and so on. At each act of collision some of the energy of relative motion will be redistributed. Some will go into excitation of the electromagnetic modes of the one ring, some into modes of the other ring, some into modes that owe their existence to the combined gravitational field of the pair of rings, some into collective vibrations and rotations of the individual rings, and some will escape into space as free radiation. Ultimately the relative motion of the two tori will be damped down and they will come together to form a single geon with a smaller mass, and a much more complicated distribution of energy among modes, than characterized the original system.

Fission can in principle take place spontaneously in any classical geon. The principal requirement is adequate time for the exchange of energy between the various modes of the system, so that ultimately, by a statistical fluctuation in the distribution of energy, enough becomes concentrated upon a collective mode of distortion to lead to a critical deformation followed by fission. As between the mechanisms of energy dissipation, and compared to radiation leakage and non-linear coupling to free running waves, the probability of fission will vary in a complicated way depending upon whether the distribution of energy among modes is finegrained or coarsegrained, whether the gravitational field is symmetric or has large scale irregularities, and whether the total angular momentum is small or large. These circumstances will also affect the distribution in size of the fragments from fission in those classes of cases where this process occurs with appreciable probability.

A geon is characterized not only by its internal structure and by the genetics of its radioactive decay processes, but also by its interaction with other geons. When the two systems pass by each other at a separation large compared with the size of either of them, they will act on each other like the bodies of classical physics. The interaction is the relativistic generalization of the simple Newtonian law of force, $F = -GM_1M_2/r_{12}^2$. The electromagnetic interaction between the two systems will give rise to an additional force which is enormously weaker than the gravitational force. Thus the flux of outgoing leakage radiation from one of the systems undergoes scattering by the other geon and gives rise to a radiation force of the order

$$(75)\qquad F \sim (-c^2\,\mathrm{d}M_1/c\,\mathrm{d}t)[\pi R_2^2/4\pi r_{12}^2] \sim (cM_1\alpha_1\omega_1)[R_2(GM_2/c^2)/r_{12}^2] \sim \sim (GM_1M_2/r_{12}^2)(\alpha_1 l_1 R_2/R_1)\,.$$

An additional force will arise from the pressure of the radiation emitted by the other body. In expression (75) the attrition, α_1, is an exponentially small function of the order, l_1; thus the dimensionless product $\alpha_1 l_1$ will be extremely small for all stable geons. Of course, if the two geons are exceedingly unlike in size, or one of them is decaying so fast as to constitute an explosion, then the radiation force between the objects can become comparable to the gravitational force.

When two geons have large intrinsic angular momenta, the forces depend upon orientation as well as upon distance. Let two simple toroidal geons be oriented with their principal planes perpendicular to the line that connects their centers. When the rays of light in one geon all go around one way, and those in the second go around the other way, then the attraction is stronger than it is in the case of parallel orientation of the two angular momentum vectors. This circumstance is a reminder that a gravitational field is described by quantities more complicated than a static potential. The supplementary orientation-dependent forces constitute in this case a fraction $\sim R_1 R_2/r_{12}^2$ of the total gravitational force.

As one geon flies by another at the minimum separation r_{12} and with a relative velocity v perpendicular to this line, it not only sets up in the other geon a bulk gravitational field of the order $G_1 M_1/r_{12}^2$, but also creates tide-producing forces of the order $GM_1 R_2^2/r_{12}^4$. Both forces have frequency components ranging from $\omega = 0$ to $\omega \sim v/r_{12}$. The first acts on the center of mass, a degree of freedom with zero natural frequency and produces a bulk motion in accord with the classical concept of « body ». The second acts on a mode of deformation with a natural frequency of the order c/R_2, very much higher than that of the driving force. Consequently the response will be adiabatic and a negligible part of the energy of motion will be left in internal degrees of freedom after the two geons have gone far apart.

When two geons pass by each other at a distance which brings the outer boundaries of their active regions to a separation, ΔR, small in comparison with geon radii, then the interaction between the two objects becomes more complicated. First, on account of the tidal deformations the gravitational forces will experience fractional increases of the order $R_2^2 r_{12}^2$ and R_1^2/r_{12}^2. Second there will come into being fluctuating forces of electromagnetic origin, of the order of magnitude of the product of typical field strengths, $\mathscr{E}_1$ and $\mathscr{E}_2$, in the active regions of the two geons, multiplied by an exponential decrement factor of the character $\exp[-\Delta R/\lambda\!\!\!^{-}]$, multiplied by an area-of-contact factor of the order $R\lambda\!\!\!^{-}$. Here we have assumed that the important wavelengths in the two geons are of the same general magnitude. Also we have used R to represent the radius of the smaller of the two geons; or better, R can be identified with the reduced radius, $R_1 R_2/(R_1+R_2)$. Let f_1 denote the fraction of the volume of the first geon occupied by its active region, so that

$$\mathscr{E}_1^2 f_1 R_1^3/c^2 \sim M_1 \sim c^2 R_1/G \,. \tag{76}$$

Then the electric field in the active region of this geon will be of the order

$$\mathscr{E}_1 \sim f_1^{-\frac{1}{3}} G^{\frac{1}{2}} M_1/R_1^2 \,, \tag{77}$$

and the expression for the electromagnetic force between the two system will have the character

$$F \sim (f_1^{-\frac{1}{2}} f_2^{-\frac{1}{2}} \lambda\!\!\!^{-}/R)(GM_1 M_2/r_{12}^2) \exp[-\Delta R/\lambda\!\!\!^{-}] \,. \tag{78}$$

As the first dimensionless combination of factors will be of the order of unity for many classes of geons, it follows that the interaction (78) is of the order of the gravitational force, multiplied by a characteristic exponential function of distance.

Two geons which almost touch as they pass will display not only an anomalous interaction but also energy exchanges and energy losses. Where the refractive index barrier between the two systems is thinnest, radiation will leak across from one body to the other. Some modes previously excited weakly or not at all will gain energy, and other important modes will lose energy. Thus the two bodies will part company with a relation of masses different from what they had when they met. Their total mass will be diminished at the same time, both via momentary stimulation of the leakage of radiation to the outside, and by way of local perturbations of the gravitational field that deflect some light rays to the outside from orbits that previously were relatively stable.

Let two geons collide still more directly, so that they pass through each other. It will be rare for the two systems to emerge from the encounter without much loss of mass or redistribution of mass. The frequency spectrum of the perturbations experienced by one of the geons during the encounter will range from tidal forces of frequency $\sim c/R$ at one end of the spectrum, through strong components of frequency $\sim c/$(thickness of active region), to fluctuations with the scale of wavelengths and frequencies associated with the individual electromagnetic modes themselves. As a result almost everything that can happen ordinarily will happen. There will be a substantial loss of energy in the form of free radiation. Collective modes of motion will be excited. Individual electromagnetic modes will have quite new amplitudes. Moreover, forces will be at work to induce fission of the original geons into smaller fragments. In view of all these circumstances, it is not appropriate to describe the close interaction of two classical geons in terms of an effective law of force, or potential curve. Instead, one has to use the much more complicated language of transmutation physics, and to try to describe the distribution in mass of the products of a geon reaction. Evidently the geon decay processes and interaction mechanisms form an extensive subject for a more detailed investigation, not undertaken here.

5. – Influence of virtual pairs on geon structure.

As we go down in the mass and size spectrum of geons, we eventually pass out of the purely classical realm (Region I) into conditions (Region II) where the field strengths are no longer negligible compared to the critical field, $\mathscr{E}_{\text{crit}} = m^2c^3/\hbar e$, of the theory of electron pairs; and from here it is but a short step to Region III, where the fields are strong enough to turn a problem of virtual pairs into one where real pairs are present in large numbers. About III we say nothing; and about II our considerations are very primitive. The induced charges and currents of the virtual pairs alter the electromagnetic properties of the medium, so that it acquires a refractive index, n. It will be reasonable to consider all the electromagnetic modes of the geons under consideration to have wavelengths very long in comparison with the Compton length, $\hbar/mc$. Under these conditions the refractive index will be independent of frequency but will be dependent upon field strength, $\mathscr{E}$:

$$n - 1 \sim (e^2/\hbar c)(\mathscr{E}/\mathscr{E}_{\text{crit}})^2 . \tag{79}$$

To be more specific, let the geon be a simple toroid of azimuthal index number a. Then the relevant field strength in (79) is some appropriate average over the active region. The speed of light around the torus is reduced to c/n. The connection between radius of the geon and frequency of its leakage radiation, will be altered to the form $\omega \sim nac/R$, where the integer, a, represents as before the azimuthal index number. The general relation between changes in energy and changes in reduced action, $\mathscr{J} = \text{action}/2\pi$, becomes

$$\mathrm{d}M = c^{-2}\omega\,\mathrm{d}\mathscr{J} \sim na\,\mathrm{d}\mathscr{J}/cR = [1 + a(\mathscr{J}_{\text{crit}}/\mathscr{J})]a\,\mathrm{d}\mathscr{J}/cR . \tag{80}$$

In the last line for convenience we have translated expression (79) for the refractive index correction from a field strength dependence to an action dependence, according to relation (5) between the two variables, the uncorrected formula (5) being legitimate in the evaluation of a first order correction. The deflection of the radiation in the gravitational field is more difficult to discuss. In lieu of an accurate analysis, for which only the bare formalistic bones are presented below, the following order of magnitude analysis is presented, which may well be in error through oversight of some significant factor. A photon which outside has a frequency ω has inside a mass of the order $\hbar\omega/c^2$, and experiences in the gravitational field of the geon a force of attraction of the order $(GM/R^2)(\hbar\omega/c^2)$. This expression should equal the time rate of change of the momentum of the photon: the product of its momentum, $n\hbar\omega/c$, by the angular rate of revolution in its orbit, c/nR; that is, $\hbar\omega/R$. Equating the gravitational and dynamic terms gives the same relation that we had in the absence of a refractive index correction:

$$M \sim (c^2R/G)(?) .$$

Multiplying this formula by (80), we have

$$M\,\mathrm{d}M \sim (ac\,\mathrm{d}\mathscr{J}/G)/1 + a(\mathscr{J}_{\text{crit}}/\mathscr{J})](?) . \tag{81}$$

Here the question mark indicates that the relation in question is subject to possible correction. If this relation is correct, it states that the square of the geon mass, though nearly a linear function of action for values of the action large in comparison with a certain characteristic value, nevertheless for lower values of the action curves towards a steeper dependence on $\mathscr{J}$. The region where (81) should apply is too small on the scale of Fig. 6 to allow showing this curvature there.

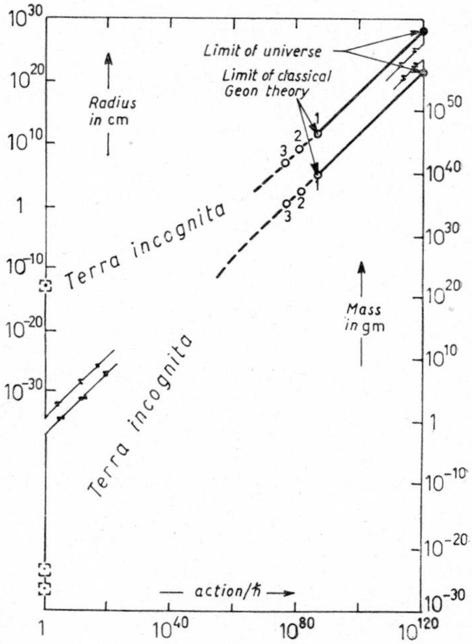

Fig. 6. – Mass and radius as functions of action for classical geons (slanting full lines in upper right hand portion of diagram). With diminishing mass and radius, the electric fields active in an electromagnetic geon increase to a point, 1, where electron pairs are produced, below which point a classical analysis of geons completely fails (dot-dash line in diagram). For pure neutrino geons it may be possible to carry a simple analysis down as far as point 2 in the diagram before pair effects appear (Sect. **6** of text). Point 3 indicates where densities of the nuclear order of magnitude would be attained in either electromagnetic or neutrino geons were extrapolation of simple geon theory justified, which it certainly is not. Neither is any further extrapolation of the curves for mass and radius at all allowed (*Terra Incognita*). Masses and radii of electron and proton are indicated on the diagram for orientation as to magnitudes. The representation of geon mass or radius by a single line, or the action variables of the system by a single number, gives a rather oversimplified picture, as is clear from eq. (5) for even the simplest variety of toroidal geons. The numbers in the present diagram may be thought of as applying to simple toroidal geons with azimuthal index number, a, equal to 10 or less.

The dependence of effective refractive index increment upon the square of the field strength lets itself be seen in two different ways ([12]). From the photon point of view the torus is a channel filled by two streams of quanta moving in opposite directions. The space density of photons going one way is of the order

$$n_1 \sim \mathscr{E}^2/\hbar\omega_1 . \tag{82}$$

([12]) J. S. Toll: *The Dispersion Relation for Light and Its Application to Problems Involving Electron Pairs, Ph. D. Thesis* (Princeton, 1952) (unpublished); J. S. Toll and J. A. Wheeler: *Phys. Rev.*, **81**, 654 (1951).

The photons travelling the other way are not able to make pairs by the process [13] $\hbar\omega_2+\hbar\omega_1 \to e^+ + e^-$ through want of energy: $\hbar\omega_1 = \hbar\omega_2 \ll mc^2$; but could do so were their quantum energies greater than $\hbar\omega^* = (mc^2)^2/\hbar\omega_1$. For this process the absorption cross-section starts at zero at the threshold $\hbar\omega_2 = \hbar\omega^*$, rises to a peak value $\sigma \sim (e^2/mc^2)^2$ at a small multiple of this frequency, and then falls off. The absorption presented by the medium at high frequencies implies a contribution to the refractive index, n, at low frequencies, according to the formula

$$(83) \qquad n(\omega_2) - 1 = (c/\pi)\int_{\omega^*}^{\infty} n_1\sigma(\omega_2')\,\mathrm{d}\omega_2'/(\omega_2'^2 - \omega_2^2) \sim (c\mathscr{E}^2/\hbar\omega_1)(e^2/mc^2)^2/\omega^* \sim$$
$$\sim (e^2/\hbar c)[\mathscr{E}e(\hbar/mc)/(mc^2)]^2 ,$$

in agreement with (79). Alternatively stated, there exists a process of scattering of light by light [6], for which the differential cross-section at low frequencies in the forward direction

$$(84) \qquad (\mathrm{d}\sigma/\mathrm{d}\Omega)_{\text{forward}} \sim (e^2/\hbar c^2)^2(e^2/mc^2)^2(\hbar\omega_2/mc^2)^4(\hbar\omega_1/mc^2)^2 ,$$

makes a contribution to the refractive index given by Rayleigh's formula

$$(85) \qquad n - 1 = n_1 2\pi(c/\omega_2)^2(\mathrm{d}\omega/\mathrm{d}\Omega)^{\frac{1}{2}}_{\text{forward}} ;$$

this contribution is in agreement with (79).

This analysis of the non-linear behavior of a strong electromagnetic field makes it clear that the corrections to be applied in Region II will be very different for a toroidal geon according as it has an angular momentum of zero, so that half the photons go each way, or has the maximum possible angular momentum, so that the photons meet no counterstream. In the second case the onset of strong pair corrections will evidently be postponed to higher field strengths and smaller bodies.

The picture of photon-photon collisions and a refractive index is not suitable for a precise evaluation of the pair corrections. For example, in a simple toroidal geon of zero angular momentum the standing electromagnetic wave with which we deal will, if strong, produce changes in the properties of the medium with twice the periodicity of the wave itself. This phase relation means that no simple averaging of the properties of the medium is appropriate. For a detailed treatment of the corrections it is therefore appropriate to go back to first principles, as typified by the variational principle (4) of classical relativity theory. HEISENBERG and EULER [14] have analysed the case

---

[13] G. BREIT and J. A. WHEELER: *Phys. Rev.*, **46**, 1087 (1934).

[14] W. HEISENBERG and H. EULER: *Zeits. Phys.*, **98**, 714 (1936); see also V. WEISSKOPF: *Kgl. Danske Videnskab. Selskab., Mat.-fys. Medd.*, **14**, no. 6 (1936-37).

of slowly varying but strong fields and have shown that the charges and currents of the virtual pairs have the same effect as if there were no pairs, but instead the Lagrangian of the variation principle of the electrodynamics of special relativity theory were corrected from $\mathscr{L}$, where

$$-\mathscr{L} = (\boldsymbol{E}^2 - \boldsymbol{B}^2)/8\pi = (1/8\pi)\mathscr{E}^2_{\text{crit}} S\,, \tag{86}$$

to $\mathscr{L}^*$, where

$$(-\mathscr{L}^*) - (-\mathscr{L}) = (1/8\pi^2)(e^2/\hbar c)\mathscr{E}^2_{\text{crit}}\int dx \exp[-x]x^{-3}\cdot \left(ix^2P\frac{\cos[x(S+2iP]^{\frac{1}{2}} + \text{conj.}}{\cos[x(S-2iP]^{\frac{1}{2}} - \text{conj.}} - (x^2S/3) + 1\right). \tag{87}$$

Here S represents the scalar, $(\boldsymbol{E}^2 - \boldsymbol{B}^2)/\mathscr{E}^2_{\text{crit}}$ and P represents the pseudoscalar, $(\boldsymbol{E}\cdot\boldsymbol{B})/\mathscr{E}^2_{\text{crit}}$. For small field strengths,

$$-8\pi\mathscr{L}^*/\mathscr{E}^2_{\text{crit}} = S + \pi^{-1}(e^2/\hbar c)\{(S^2 + 7P^2)/45 + (26P^2S + 4S^3)/315 + \ldots\}. \tag{88}$$

In general relativity the appropriate scalar and pseudoscalar quantities are

$$\begin{cases} \mathscr{E}^2_{\text{crit}}S = -\frac{1}{2}F_{\alpha\beta}g^{\alpha\gamma}g^{\beta\delta}F_{\gamma\delta}\,, \\ \mathscr{E}^2_{\text{crit}}P = \frac{1}{8}(-g)^{\frac{1}{2}}\varepsilon^{\alpha\beta\gamma\delta}F_{\alpha\beta}F_{\gamma\delta}\,. \end{cases} \tag{89}$$

Here g represents the determinant of the g_{ik}. The quantities ε^{1234} do not form a tensor. They are defined instead by the statement that $\varepsilon^{1234}=1$ and that ε changes sign on the interchange of any two indices. To correct for the effect of virtual pairs in geon theory we have only to replace $\mathscr{L}/c = (1/16\pi c)\,F_{\alpha\beta}F^{\alpha\beta}$ in the variational principle (4) of general relativity by $\mathscr{L}^*/c$, calculated as just defined. In taking the variation of the integral, which includes the volume factor $(-g)^{\frac{1}{2}}\,dx^1\,dx^2\,dx^3\,dx^4$, we regard as the quantities to be varied the 16 gravitational potentials g^{ik} and the four electromagnetic potentials A_i in $F_{ik} = (\partial A_k/\partial x^i) - (\partial A_i/\partial x^k)$. The coefficient of δg^{ik} contains two parts, of which one is the Einstein analog, $G_{ik} \equiv R_{ik} - \frac{1}{2}g_{ik}R$, of the d'Alembertian of the gravitational potential, and the other is the stress-energy tensor, T_{ik}:

$$\begin{aligned} T_{ik} &= 2(-g)^{-\frac{1}{2}}\,\delta[(-g)^{\frac{1}{2}}\mathscr{L}^*]/\delta g^{ik} = \\ &= 2(\partial\mathscr{L}^*/\partial S)(\delta S/\delta g^{ik}) + 2(\partial\mathscr{L}^*/\partial P)(\delta P/\delta g^{ik}) - g_{ik}\mathscr{L}^* = \\ &= -2F_{i\beta}\,g^{\beta\delta}\,F_{k\delta}\mathscr{E}^{-2}_{\text{crit}}(\partial\mathscr{L}^*/\partial S) - g_{ik}(P\,\partial\mathscr{L}^*/\partial P + \mathscr{L}^*)\,. \end{aligned} \tag{90}$$

Thus the gravitational field equations take their usual form, $G_{ki} = (8\pi G/c^4)T_{ik}$, witho nly the change (90) in the form of the stress-energy tensor. Similarly the coefficient of the variation, δA_i, of a typical electromagnetic potential, equated to zero, gives the i-th electromagnetic field equation,

$$(91)\qquad 0 = 4\pi(-g)^{-\frac{1}{2}}(\partial/\partial x^\alpha)[(-g)^{\frac{1}{2}}\,\partial\mathscr{L}^*/\partial(\partial A_i/\partial x^\alpha)] =$$

$$= 4\pi(-g)^{-\frac{1}{2}}(\partial/\partial x^\alpha)\{(-g)^{\frac{1}{2}}(\partial\mathscr{L}^*/\partial S)(2F^{i\alpha}/\mathscr{E}^2_{\text{crit}}) + (-g/2)(\mathscr{E}^{-2}_{\text{crit}}\,\partial\mathscr{L}^*/\partial P)\varepsilon^{\alpha i\gamma\delta}F_{\gamma\delta}\},$$

where the F's are considered to be expressed in terms of the A's. Eq. (90) and (91) define the theory of geons in Region II.

6. – Neutrino-containing geons.

There is little difference between the theory of a geon built out of neutrinos, and one built out of electromagnetic fields, apart from the fact that each neutrino state will accommodate only one quantum of energy. The general relativity version of Maxwell's equations is replaced by the general relativity form of Dirac's equation ([15]) for an entity of zero rest mass. The stress-energy tensor for Dirac particles of zero rest mass forms the source term in the gravitational field equations. The equation $GM/c^2R \sim 1$ still connects mass and radius of the object. The modes of dissipation of energy are still leakage through the refractive index barrier, coupling through non-linear effects if possible to waves that run freely to infinity, and various forms of fission. Consequently there is little point to reformulating in terms of neutrinos our discussion of the properties of electromagnetic geons.

One difference appears in the process of interpenetration of two geons. When both are made of neutrinos, the overlap of the active regions of the two objects will force a promotion of their constituent neutrinos to states of higher momentum and energy, in accordance with the Pauli principle. The uptake of energy implies a strong effective repulsion compared with the forces that would otherwise have been at work, as for example in the collision of an electromagnetic geon and a neutrino geon, or the impact of a neutrino geon on an antineutrino geon. Thus there is a certain interesting specificity about the interaction of geons.

A second and fundamental difference shows between pure neutrino geons and pure electromagnetic geons when one asks how small the object can be before quantum effects come in. In the neutrino case quantum effects are of course in principle present right from the start, in the action of the Pauli exclusion principle. But no other quantum effects are evident, and one does not at first sight see any reason why one should not be able to follow the properties of neutrino geons down to very small sizes, enormously less than

([15]) See for example M. Riesz: *L'équation de Dirac en relativité générale*, *Lund Univ. Math. Sem.*, **12**, (1954); also in *Comptes rendus du douzième congrès des mathématiciens Scandinaves* tenu à Lund, 10-15 Août 1953, p. 241 (1954).

the limit $\sim 10^{10}$ cm placed on classical electromagnetic geons by the onset of virtual pair phenomena. However, one at least knows where the limit is in the electromagnetic case, while in the neutrino case the critical limit could be anywhere, as indicated by the following analysis. Just as the non-linear phenomena of electromagnetic geons commence when photon-photon collisions become important, so neutrino-neutrino collisions represent a potential critical mechanism to set a lower bound on the size, and an upper limit on the density, of those pure neutrino geons that are susceptible to simple analysis. The penetrating power of a neutrino through ordinary matter is so enormous ([16]) that it seems at first sight ridiculous to consider the collision of neutrino with neutrinos. However, if the continuous spectrum of electrons from μ-meson decay is correctly interpreted in terms of the simultaneous emission of two neutrinos (or a neutrino and an antineutrino) then it necessarily follows that two neutrinos of the appropriate character running towards each other with sufficiently high energy, $(\hbar\omega_1)\cdot(\hbar\omega_2) \geqslant (207\,mc^2/2)^2$, will necessarily be capable of provoking the reaction $\nu + \nu \rightarrow \mu^- + e^+$; and from the Fermi type of β-decay theory it follows that the reaction cross-section will vary at sufficiently high energies as

(92) $$\sigma \sim (g^2/\hbar^2 c^4)\omega_1\omega_2 ,$$

where the coupling constant is of the order

(93) $$g \sim 10^{-49} \text{ erg cm}^3 .$$

The existence of this absorption mechanism for high energies implies that even low-energy neutrinos can produce virtual μ, e pairs, which reannihilate and send the neutrinos off into new directions. The cross-section for this neutrino scattering process, evaluated in the forward direction by use of the dispersion relation ([12])

(94) $$(\mathrm{d}\sigma/\mathrm{d}\Omega_2)_{\text{forward}} = \left| (\omega_2^2/2\pi^2 c)\int_0^\infty \sigma_{\text{absn}}(\omega_2')(\omega_2'^2 - \omega_2^2)^{-1}\,\mathrm{d}\omega_2' \right|^2 ,$$

is easily seen to diverge logarithmically,

(95) $$(\mathrm{d}\sigma/\mathrm{d}\Omega_2)_{\text{forward}} \sim (\omega_1\omega_2 g^2/\hbar^2 c^5)^2 \ln^2(\hbar\omega_{\text{upper}}/100\,mc^2) ,$$

unless one inserts for the indicated upper limit of infinity a finite upper limit, $\hbar\omega_{\text{upper}}$, for which one so far has no evidence. Similarly, the refractive index presented by a medium containing per unit volume n_1 neutrinos of circular

([16]) See, for example, F. Reines and C. Cowan: *Phys. Rev.*, **92**, 830 (1953).

frequency ω_1 differs from unity, according to (83), by the amount

$$n(\omega_1) - 1 \sim (g^2/\hbar^3c^3)(n_1\hbar\omega_1)\ln(\hbar\omega_{\text{upper}}/100\,mc^2)\,, \tag{96}$$

again a divergent expression.

In view of the divergence of the neutrino-neutrino interaction as evaluated from Fermi beta theory and the dispersion relation, we really have no basis to discuss neutrino geons at all, much less to set a lower limit of masses at which the theory takes a new form, as in the case of electromagnetic geons. Nevertheless, it is still of interest to see what we can say if we assume that the logarithm, instead of diverging, has a value of the order of 10^2 or less. In this case we can employ (96) to draw two conclusions. First, it will be beyond the scope of simple neutrino theory to analyse geons in which the refractive index correction is of the order of unity, or the energy density exceeds

$$\left\{\begin{aligned} n_1\hbar\omega_1 &\sim (\hbar^3c^3/g^2)[1/\ln(\hbar\omega_{\text{upper}}/100\,mc^2)] \\ &\sim 10^{47}\ \text{erg/cm}^3 \\ &\sim (10^{26}\ \text{g/cm}^3)c^2\,. \end{aligned}\right. \tag{97}$$

To yield such a density, neutrino states must be occupied up to momenta of the order p, or energies of the order cp, where

$$10^{47}\ \text{erg/cm}^3 \sim \int_0^p (cp)\,2(4\pi p^2\,\mathrm{d}p/h^3)\,, \tag{98}$$

or

$$\left\{\begin{aligned} cp &\sim (h^3c^3\,10^{47}\ \text{erg/cm}^3)^{\frac14} \\ &\sim 1\ \text{erg} \sim 10^6\,mc^2\,. \end{aligned}\right. \tag{99}$$

This energy is so great that it carries us beyond the domain of virtual μ, e processes to real production of pairs of this kind. This circumstance leads to the second conclusion, that the energy density of any geon which can be analysed in terms of simple neutrino theory can at most be equal to the right-hand side of (98), evaluated for a maximum neutrino energy, cp, of the threshold value, $100\,mc^2$:

$$\left\{\begin{aligned} \text{energy density} &\sim 2\pi(cp)^4/h^3c^3 \\ &= 3.62\cdot 10^{31}\ \text{erg/cm}^3 \\ &= (4.02\cdot 10^{10}\ \text{g/cm}^3)c^2\,, \end{aligned}\right. \tag{100}$$

corresponding according to (96) to a refractive index correction of only one part in 10^{15}. This estimate implies a mass density considerably less than a typical estimate for nuclear matter, $\sim 1.4\cdot 10^{14}$ g/cm³. It is conceivable that there is some limitation of which physics is not aware that puts a bound to the density of pure neutrino geons much smaller than (100). However, if real production of μ, e pairs sets the only limit, then it is possible in principle to treat in terms of existing theory objects built up solely out of neutrinos and gravitational forces down to a radius

$$R = [(M/R)(3/4\pi)(4\pi R^3/3M)]^{\frac{1}{2}} \sim [(c^2/G)\,1.69\cdot 10^{11}\ \text{g/cm}^3)]^{\frac{1}{2}} = 2.83\cdot 10^{8}\ \text{cm}^3\,,$$

and mass

$$M \sim (c^2/G)R = 3.82\cdot 10^{36}\ \text{g}\,. \tag{101}$$

This lower limit for pure neutrino geons is less than the corresponding limit (10) for pure electromagnetic geons (10^{11} cm, 10^{39} g) by not more than a few powers of ten. In one case the bound comes from the limiting electromagnetic field strength, or field energy density, at which pairs of positive and negative electrons begin to appear; in the other case, electron-μ-meson pairs.

Mixed geons, energized by a combination of neutrinos and electromagnetic field, will have properties similar to either kind of pure system, and hardly need separate consideration here. However, the presence of neutrinos and photons on an equal footing does raise again the question of the neutrino theory of light, developed by JORDAN, KRONIG, and others, and brought to a halt by the discovery of PRYCE that the theory in its then existing form did not possess proper relativistic invariance ([17]). The theory assumes that there exists between neutrinos a physical interaction, never introduced explicitly and never discussed, such that a photon is described by a pair consisting of one neutrino and one antineutrino; or rather, by a quantum-mechanical linear superposition of very many such pairs of states. The description implies an unavoidable complementarity, such that a statement of the occupation numbers of the photon states, and a prescription of the occupation numbers of the neutrino states, stand to each other in a mutually exclusive relation. When only neutrino states are occupied, the theory speaks of a pure neutrino field.

([17]) P. JORDAN: *Ergeb. exakt. Naturwiss.*, **7**, 158 (1928); *Zeits. Phys.*, numerous papers ending with **105**, 229 (1937); R. DE L. KRONIG: several papers ending with *Zeits. Phys.*, **100**, 569 (1936) and *Physica*, **3**, 1120 (1936); M. H. L. PRYCE: *Nature*, **141**, 976 (1938). See also DE BROGLIE, HEISENBERG and KRAMERS in *L. de Broglie, Physicien et Penseur* (Paris, 1953). I am indebted to Prof. A. WIGHTMAN for several discussions of the present status of Jordan's idea.

See K. M. CASE: *Phys. Rev.*, **106**, 1316 (1957) on ν theory of light and gravitation. Also see M. H. L. PRYCE: *Proc. Roy. Soc.*, **165** A, 247 (1938); A. SOKOLOV: *Physica*, **5**, 797 (1938).

When in addition a few antineutrino states are filled, a mixture of light and neutrinos is said to be present. With equal numbers of neutrinos and antineutrinos a pure photon field is considered to exist; and so on, up to the case of a pure antineutrino field. Such a description would evidently subsume geons of purely electromagnetic character, of purely neutrino type, and of mixed constitution, all into a unified class of systems.

Regarding the status of the neutrino theory of light, I am kindly informed by Professor EUGENE WIGNER that the conceivable mechanisms for the combination of the spinors and momentum vectors of the neutrino and antineutrino states to form in an invariant way the vector magnitudes of the photon states are far from having been explored in a comprehensive way in the literature, so that is not necessarily clear that the objections of PRYCE will forever retain their force. Second, recent studies of the decay of the μ-meson [18] show that the lifetime and the form of the electron spectrum [19] are together consistent with a universal Fermi interaction of the kind met in β-decay only if the two neutrinos are of opposite character. This result suggests, though it does not prove, that μ-decay produces one neutrino and one antineutrino. The consequences are the existence of the $\nu+\nu^* \to \mu+e$ reaction at high energies, and ν, ν^* scattering at low energies. In other words, a physical background for the interaction of the neutrino theory of light does not have to be postulated; it exists. Third, no such argument exists for an interaction between two neutrinos of the same character. Consequently it is conceivable that the theory of pure neutrino geons, or pure antineutrino geons, can be carried without meeting new physical effects to energy densities larger, and sizes smaller, than the limits of (100) and (101).

In summary, if we assume the existence of a cut-off in the Fermi interaction at high energies in eq. (95) and (96), then the door is open to analysing the properties of neutrino geons over an enormous range of sizes without going outside the scope of existing theory; but below an uncertain critical limit of sizes interesting and fundamental physical questions raise themselves.

7. – Electricity, Gauss' theorem, and gravitational field fluctuations.

What of free electricity? Consistently to complete the scheme of classical physics we find no alternative but to regard the geon as exemplar of the concept of body; but neither in this object nor in the divergence free theory behind it is there any place for charge. All lines of force continue without end. Let a sphere be drawn around the immediate neighborhood of a point. Then as many lines of force go in as out.

---

(18) L. MICHEL and A. S. WIGHTMAN: *Phys. Rev.*, **93**, 354 (1954).
(19) J. VILAIN and R. W. WILLIAMS: *Phys. Rev.*, **92**, 1586 (1953).

In applying the theorem of Gauss we have tacitly assumed space to be simply connected. One knows, however, that the notion of Riemannian manifold by itself places no such requirement upon the space-time continuum. One can consider a metric which on the whole is nearly flat except in two widely separated regions, where a double-connectedness comes into evidence as symbolized in Fig. 7. The general divergence-free electromagnetic disturbance holding sway in the space around one of these «tunnel mouths» will send forth lines of force into the surrounding space, and appear to have a charge. However, an equal number of lines of force must enter the region of disturbance from the tunnel. Consequently the other mouth of the tunnel must manifest an equal and opposite charge. In such a doubly-connected space it is evidently a matter of definition whether we say that divergence-free field equations do or do not permit the existence of electric charge. It will be convenient to say yes if the width of the tunnel is small compared to the separation of its mouths. So far we have inquired only after the behavior of the electro-magnetic field in a metric assumed to be pre-existing. However, in classical relativity theory the metric cannot be taken arbitrarily, but must be found by solution of the gravitational field equations. No investigation is known to have been made of the possibility of a self-consistent solution that is doubly-connected. Yet one would not be surprised to find that no reasonable choice of boundary conditions would permit such a classical solution. (Addendum, 1961: Such solutions *do* exist.).

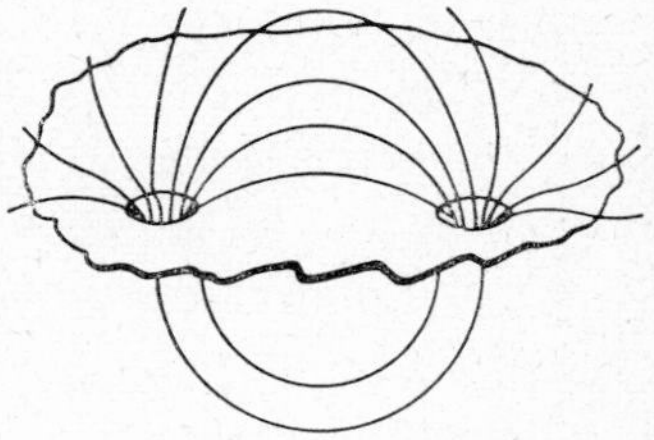

Fig. 7. – Schematic representation of lines of force in a doubly-connected space. In the upper continuum the lines of force behave much as if the tunnel mouths were the seats of equal and opposite charges.

Let one pass from the classical theory defined by the action principle (4) to the corresponding quantum theory, either by the prescription of Feynman [20],

$$(102)\qquad \psi \sim \sum_{\substack{\text{all conceivable relevant}\\ \text{field histories}}} \exp\left[(i/\hbar)\,(\text{classical action for each field history})\right],$$

or by any other standard method. Then one is forced to recognize the existence of fluctuations in all fields. Their magnitudes depend upon the size, L, of the space-cotime regions under consideration, and are given under suitable conditions by formulas of the form $\Delta F \sim (\hbar c)^{\frac{1}{2}}/L^2$; $\Delta A \sim (\hbar c)^{\frac{1}{2}}/L$; and $\Delta g \sim (\hbar G/c^3)^{\frac{1}{2}}/L$. So long as one deals with distances large in comparison with

([20]) R. P. Feynman: *Phys. Rev.*, **76**, 769 (1949).

$(\hbar G/c^3)^{\frac{1}{2}} \sim 10^{-33}$ cm, one can disregard for most purposes the fluctuations in the metric, and consider space to be simply connected. But in deriving Gauss' theorem one is driven to consider an integral over the whole of the region in question, including regions of the very smallest spatial extension. Here the inevitable fluctuations force on space-time a most complicated structure. Because it is the essence of quantum mechanics that *all* field histories contribute to the probability amplitude, the sum (102) not only may contain doubly and multiply connected metrics; it must do so. General relativity, quantized, leaves no escape from topological complexities of which Fig. 7 is only an oversimplified symbol. In this sense the door is open for the existence of charges in the quantum version of a theory that contains no charges.

Little progress has so far been made in studying the quantization of general relativity ([21]). 1) It is not yet certain whether the method of summing over configurations gives in the case of non-linear theories results that are identical to those derived from other methods of quantization. 2) It is not certain that the action function of general relativity can be given a well-defined meaning for those field configurations, classically unrealizable, that make the factor $(-g)^{\frac{1}{2}}$ in the action function a pure imaginary. This square root recalls the similar factor in relativistic electron theory, $(-\mathrm{d}x_\mu \mathrm{d}x^\mu)^{\frac{1}{2}}$, where likewise similar difficulties of interpretation arise for non-classical paths, and where the root has been replaced by Dirac's matrix expression, $\Gamma_\mu \mathrm{d}x^\mu$, associated with half-integral spins and Fermi-Dirac statistics. Thus, as of today we cannot exclude that charges will show themselves naturally and inevitably in the spinor quantization of the only comprehensive and divergence-free classical theory of fields that we possess.

8. – Conclusion.

Taking seriously and following out the consequences of the forty year old theory of general relativity, we have been led to recognize the relative stability of certain types of electromagnetic field disturbances held together by gravitational forces. These geons furnish for the first time a completely classical, divergence-free, self-consistent picture of the Newtonian concept of body over the range of masses from $\sim 10^{39}$ g to $\sim 10^{57}$ g. Two such geons interacting at a distance large compared to their characteristic dimensions behave as elementary objects. However, when one geon is followed for a long time or is allowed to interact closely with another it undergoes interesting and characteristic transformation processes.

([21]) I am indebted to Prof. J. ANDERSON and Prof. P. BERGMANN for instructive discussions of the literature of this problem.

Classical geons are not objects for study in the laboratory, nor is there any evident reason to believe that geons of the classical range of sizes now exist in nature, or ever did exist. Even were such large geons once present, a sufficient lapse of time would guarantee the decay of all but extraordinarily stable ones to a mass below the limit where these systems are capable of classical analysis.

On entry into the quantum domain of sizes, electromagnetic geons build up field strengths strong enough to produce pairs of electrons. At not very different sizes neutrino geons commence to give birth to μ-meson-electron pairs. Consequently the projection of geon theory to objects of dimensions less than $\sim 10^{10}$ cm to $\sim 10^{8}$ cm requires the analysis of new phenomena.

In conclusion, the geon makes only this visible contribution to science: it completes the scheme of classical physics by providing for the first time an acceptable classical theory of the concept of body.

One's interest in following geon theory down into the quantum domain will depend upon one's considered view of the relation between very small geons and elementary particles.

II. Thermal Geons.

E. A. POWER

Department of Mathematics, University College - London

J. A. WHEELER

Palmer Physical Laboratory, Princeton University - Princeton, N. J.

(Reprinted from *Rev. Mod. Phys.*, **29**, 480-495 (1957))

1. – Introduction and summary.

The well-established classical theory of fields with zero rest mass has rich consequences, many of which still stand unexplored today (Table I), forty years after Einstein's formulation of the general relativity theory of electromagnetism and gravitation.

One new consequence appeared in a recent investigation (1). An electromagnetic field, or a neutrino field, or a mixed field, of appropriate character and sufficient energy density can hold itself together, it was calculated, by its own gravitational attraction for a time long in comparison with the characteristic periods of the field oscillations. Or a the gravitation field, sufficiently strong, can guide an electromagnetic or neutrino wave and confine its energy to a bounded region of space. When the energy of the standing wave is great enough, it has enough mass to provide the guiding gravitational field all by itself. The wave holds itself together. Thus the gravitational and electromagnetic field equations of general relativity admit self-consistent solutions of great variety, many of which describe a reasonably stable concentration of energy. Such a « gravitational electromagnetic entity » or « geon » is endowed with mass, has a characteristic decay rate in the free state, moves through space like a Newtonian « body » when subjected to fields that vary sufficiently slowly in space and time, and under the influence of stronger fields undergoes transmutation. Geons of mass greater than 10^{38} g and radius over 10^{11} cm are subject to classical analysis. Smaller geons, even very much

(1) J. A. WHEELER: *Phys. Rev.*, **97**, 511 (1955); or pp. 131-185 of present text.

TABLE I. – *Qualitative comparison of the present state of charge- and mass-free gravitation and electromagnetism with hydrodynamic theory showing how many features of the Einstein-Maxwell field still remain to be explored.*

Hydrodynamics	Gravitation plus electromagnetism
1. Divergence condition; pressure density relation; and equations of motion.	1. Maxwell's source-free equations in curved space and Maxwell's stress-energy tensor as source term in Einstein's gravitational field equations.
2. Formulation in terms of a single action principle.	2. Formulation in terms of a single action principle.
3. Descriptions in alternative co-ordinate systems related by tensor analysis.	3. Description has same form in all co-ordinate systems, much as in group theory the laws of multiplication of the matrices that represent group elements are independent of the special choice of representation.
4. Hedlund and others have made a beginning at representing the laws of mechanics in an abstract co-ordinate-free form ([a]).	4. Nothing known to have been done to represent the Maxwell-Einstein theory in a co-ordinate-free form as abstract as the abstract theory of groups.
5. Two alternative formulations of equations, according as one analyses the time change of the hydrodynamic quantities at a given space point or at a given mass point.	5. Co-ordinate system employed, x^i, may be arbitrary, or may be given an invariant significance (A. KOMAR) by identification with four of the fourteen invariants, I_s, of Géhéniau and Debever ([b]).
6. Degree of arbitrariness in specification of initial conditions well understood.	6. Cartan-Lichnerowicz equations must be satisfied by initial conditions, but means are not yet known to generate the general solution of these initial value requirements ([c]).
7. Expansions for hydrodynamic quantities near a typical point.	7. Expansion for g_{ik} and F_{ik} and R_{ijkl} near a typical point.
8. Behavior of fluid near a stagnation point or a triple point or a vortex center.	8. Behavior of electromagnetic and gravitational field near a point of special symmetry.

(*a*) G. A. HEDLUND: *Bull. Am. Math. Soc.*, **45**, 241 (1939); also G. A. HEDLUND and M. MORSE: *Am. Journ. Math.*, **60**, 815 (1938), and W. H. GOTTSCHALT and G. A. HEDLUND: *Topological Dynamics*, in *Am. Math. Soc. Colloquium Publ.*, **36** (Providence, Rhode Island, 1955).

(*b*) A. KOMAR: *Proc. Natl. Acad. Sci. U. S.*, **41**, 758 (1955); and *P. D. Thesis*, unpublished (Princeton, 1956); T. Y. THOMAS: *Proc. Natl. Acad. Sci. U. S.*, **31**, 306 (1945); J. GÉHÉNIAU and R. DEBEVER: *Acad. Roy. de Belgique*, **42**, 114 (1956).

(*c*) A. LICHNEROWICZ: *Théories relativistes de la gravitation et de l'électromagnétisme* (Paris, 1955), chap. II.

TABLE I (*continued*).

Hydrodynamics	Gravitation plus electromagnetism
9. Fluid motion generated by an elemental source or sink.	9. Schwarzschild and Reissner-Nordström solution ([d]).
10. Expansion of density, pressure and other quantities near a point in a series of spherical harmonics.	10. Similar expansion in spherical harmonics for small departures from a condition of spherical symmetry seems not yet to have been given ([e]).
11. Sound waves; radiation pattern related to source geometry; radiation damping.	11. Electromagnetic and gravitational waves in small amplitude approximation and their radiation pattern as related to the geometry of the source. Radiation reaction analysed for electromagnetic but not for gravitational radiation.
12. Shock waves; Mach triple point; slip stream ([f]).	12. Behavior of waves of high amplitude not yet known, even qualitatively, except in very special cases.
13. Vortex ring moving in quiet fluid maintains its identity and integrity for a long time.	13. Collections of electromagnetic or gravitational waves or both under suitable conditions hold themselves together gravitationally for long period of time (« geons »).
14. Law of motion for the center of a vortex follows from the hydrodynamic equations themselves ([g]).	14. Law of motion for a geon follows from the field equations themselves; the law of motion along a geodesic does not have to be introduced as a separate postulate.
15. Turbulence under appropriate conditions describable in statistical terms.	15. Radiation — isotropic or not — under appropriate conditions also describable in statistical terms.
16. Generation of sound waves by turbulence partly studied ([h]).	16. Gravitation induced interactions between electromagnetic waves, gravitational waves and geons, and cross sections for elementary types of encounter between these objects, hardly analysed at all so far.

(*d*) H. REISSNER: *Ann. Phys.*, **50**, 106 (1916); K. NORDSTRÖM: *Proc. Amsterdam Acad.*, **21**, 68 (1918); R. LINDQUIST and J. A. WHEELER: *Rev. Mod. Phys.* **29**, 432 (1957).

(*e*) *Note added in proof.* – Small perturbations of Schwarzschild solution: T. REGGE and J. A. WHEELER, *Phys. Rev.* **108**, 1063 (1957). The stability of the expanding universe against small departures from sphericity has been partially treated by E. LIFSHITZ, *J. Phys. U.S.S.R.* **10**, 116 (1946).

(*f*) See, for example, W. BLEAKNEY and A. H. TAUB: *Rev. Mod. Phys.*, **21**, 584 (1949); C. H. FLETCHER, W. BLEAKNEY and A. H. TAUB: *Rev. Mod. Phys.*, **23**, 271 (1951).

(*g*) See, for example, H. LAMB: *Hydrodynamics*, sixth edition (London, 1953), chap. VII.

(*h*) M. J. LIGHTHILL: *Proc. Roy. Soc.* (*London*), A **211**, 564 (1952); A **222**, 1 (1954).

TABLE I (*continued*).

Hydrodynamics	Gravitation plus electromagnetism
17. Many special solutions of the hydrodynamic equations are known from similarity arguments or group theory or other special methods of analysis.	17. Problem of homogeneous isotropic closed radiation-filled universe and its expansion and subsequent contraction, and a few other special problems have been analysed. Field largely unexplored (*i*).
18. Many types of hydrodynamic instability have been analysed, among them Rayleigh-Taylor instability and Helmholtz instability and Bénard cells (*j*).	18. One does not know how small departures from sphericity grow with time in the problem of the expanding universe, nor in the Schwarzschild-Reissner-Nordström solution. The problem of stability analysis is practically untouched (*e*).
19. One has developed a set of secondary concepts adequate to describe many derived properties of the hydrodynamic field: turbulence; vorticity; acoustic impedance; radiation flux, etc.	19. Terminology for the electromagnetic field, with its six components, is extraordinarily rich; but for the gravitational field, with twenty R_{ijkl}, the present secondary conceptual structure is very rudimentary, having as yet no terms analogous to dielectric constant, permeability, Poynting vector, radiation pressure, Thomson scattering cross section, inductance, etc.

(*i*) See for example, L. LANDAU and E. LIFSHITZ: *The Classical Theory of Fields* (Cambridge, Mass., 1951), chap. XI.

(*j*) See, for example, reference (*g*), chap. XI; also Lord RAYLEIGH: *The Theory of Sound* 2nd edition (London, 1896), chap. XXI; H. BÉNARD: *Rev. gen. sci. pures appl.*, **12**, 1261 (1900); *Ann. chim. phys.*, **23**, 62 (1901).

smaller geons, presumably exist, but are specifically quantum objects. Their properties have not yet been investigated. The large, classical geons have no known connection with observational science. Their interest lies in what they tell of the richness of a pure field theory. *The* pure classical field theory, it would perhaps be better to say: the only well tested theory that one has for fields of zero rest mass; the theory of elementary fields, not fields associated with particles that are themselves complex; the only field theory long established in its own right, not invented to account for selected particles or for special features of nuclear forces.

From the pure field theory of the fields of zero rest mass, and the geon concept, this article aims only at a detailed analysis of one particular kind of geon, a *thermal* geon, with the following properties:

1) The gravitational field is static and spherically symmetric; *i.e.*, in appropriate co-ordinates the element of proper distance, ds, or proper cotime, dτ, has the form,

$$(1)\qquad (\mathrm{d}s)^2 = -(\mathrm{d}\tau)^2 = g_{\alpha\beta}\,\mathrm{d}x^\alpha\,\mathrm{d}x^\beta = e^\lambda(\mathrm{d}r)^2 + r^2[(\mathrm{d}\theta)^2 + (\sin\theta\,\mathrm{d}\varphi)^2] - e^\nu(\mathrm{d}T)^2\,,$$

where λ and ν are functions of r alone, found by numerical integration.

2) Each independent mode of vibration of the electromagnetic field is idealized to fall into one or other of two sharply separated classes. The energy of modes of the first class remains trapped for all time. The second class of vibrations carry energy freely to infinity. The one class corresponds (in the language of photon orbits) to bounded null geodesics, the other to null geodesics that lead to infinity (Fig. 1). In actuality the energy of the « bounded » modes leaks off to infinity at a non-zero rate through a refractive index barrier, after the manner of α-particle penetration through a nuclear potential barrier. The rate of leakage falls off exponentially as the ratio of the dimensions of the geon to the wavelength of the disturbance in question. In a thermal geon the wavelength of the average mode is so small in comparison with the geon's radius that the leakage rate is effectively zero for all but a very restricted class of vibration modes. These few modes on the orbit picture belong to geodesics close to the crossover from bounded orbits to free orbits. The outward transport of energy resulting from such modes is relatively small and is legitimately neglected in a first analysis of a thermal geon.

3) All free modes are assigned zero energy. Each bound mode of circular frequency Ωc is idealized to have an excitation

$$(2)\qquad m_\Omega c^2 = E_\Omega = \hbar c\Omega[-1 + \exp(\hbar c\Omega/T)]^{-1}\,.$$

All properties of the thermal geon are specified by the single parameter T, which has the dimensions of energy and which we call the temperature. Occurrence of the quantum of angular momentum, $\hbar$, in this formula makes assignment of boundary conditions no different in principle from that in any classical problem. It is an act from outside, it may or may not have a quantum origin, but it alters in no way the purely classical character of all the *rest* of the analysis.

It is easy to compare and contrast thermal geons with other gravitational-electromagnetic entities. In all such objects effective confinement of the energy demands localization of each mode of electromagnetic oscillation in a region where the dimensionless measure, $-g_{44}$, of gravitational potential ($=1-2GM/c^2r$ for Schwarzschild's point mass solution) is small compared with unity, and orientation of the flow of field energy in each mode normal to the gradient of

$-g_{44}$, or in a direction not too far from normal. In contrast, a photon that travels outward along a radius vector in a spherical geon can always escape.

That region of space where $-g_{44}$ is small compared to unity, or where the rate of ticking of a standard clock is greatly slowed, is in some ways analogous to the closed container of the theory of blackbody radiation. There every mode is confined, while here only the bounded modes—or modes

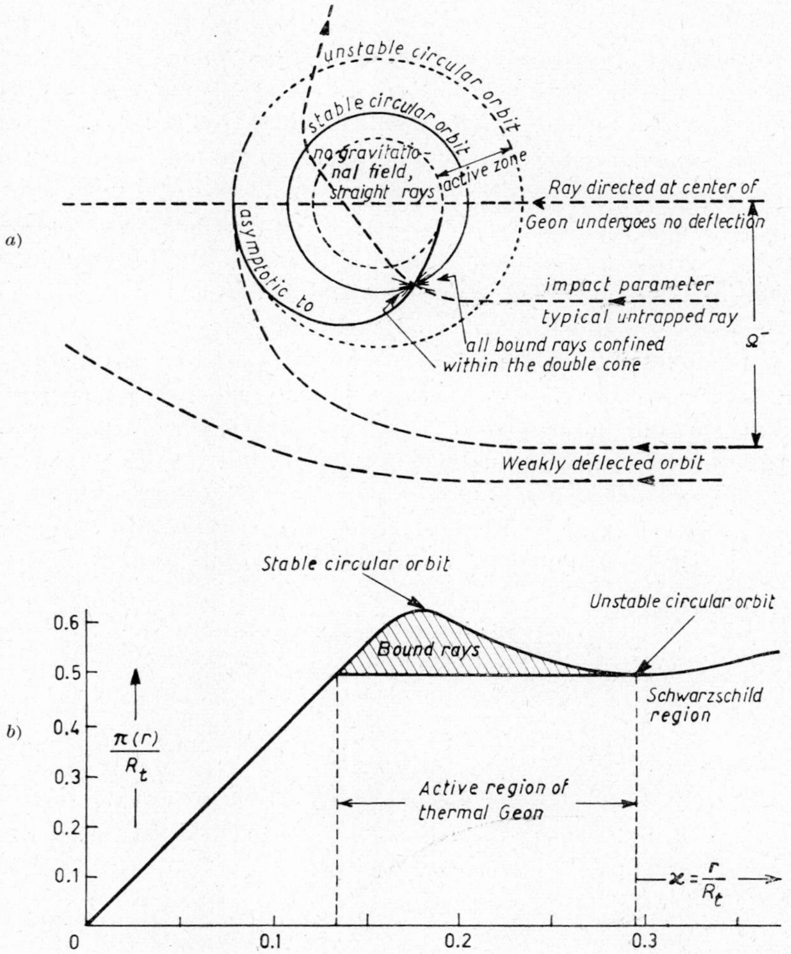

Fig. 1. – (*a*) Schematic diagram of null geodesic or ray orbits in the gravitational field of a thermal geon. Smooth curves: bound orbits. Dashed curves: orbits that come from or go to infinity. Dotted curves: inner and outer boundaries of the active region of the geon; *i.e.*, limits between which all bound rays circulate. (*b*) A ray which is to reach to the point r must have an impact parameter less than $\pi(r)$. Here $\pi(r)$ $(=re^{-\nu/2})$ is plotted as a function of r in dimensionless units. Rays that are bound must have impact parameters between $P_1=0.51R_T$ and $P_2=0.62R_T$, where R_T is a unit of length uniquely determined by the temperature.

of semitangential energy transport—properly belong to the interior of the container. Except for this difference the varieties of geon are as numerous as the states of electromagnetic field disturbance in a hohlraum. In the general case many modes of oscillation of the field are excited, each with an amplitude of its own. Then the gravitational field resulting from the average energy distribution has no particular symmetry, and the mathematical analysis is complex. There are at least three particularly simple types of geons. i) Toroidal geons. Here the electromagnetic energy is concentrated in the equatorial ring where the gravitational potential has its extreme value. The energy flows around the ring in equal or unequal measure in the positive and negative senses. The ratio of the fluxes in the two directions is unity or zero in the two special subcases of zero angular momentum and maximal angular momentum. Toroidal geons presumably have the greatest stability of all geons of a given mass and angular momentum. They have received partial mathematical analysis by F. J. Ernst (2). ii) Simple spherical geons. Here the gravitational field has nearly spherical symmetry. The electromagnetic energy is localized in a single mode of field oscillation with no radial nodes and has a large but definite number, l, of nodes in the angular variation of the field quantities. More accurately, the energy is divided over a nearly degenerate system of modes, corresponding to different spherical harmonics of the same l value but different m values. Such geons (1) require for specification two parameters: the mass and the azimuthal index number, l. The electromagnetic fields are intense in a relatively thin spherical shell, or active region. In the course of time non-linear couplings build up the strength of originally unexcited modes, and the energy distribution slowly becomes more diffuse. iii) Thermal geons. Here the gravitational field is again spherically symmetric, but the available electromagnetic energy is distributed over all confined modes according to the most natural of statistical laws. A thermal geon is in many ways the simplest to discuss because all its properties are fixed by a single parameter, the temperature.

Orders of magnitude and scaling laws for thermal geons are readily discussed. Let the energy density of blackbody radiation be denoted by $bT^4/\hbar^3c^3$, where $b = \pi^2/15$. The energy density in the active region is of the same order

$$\text{energy/volume} \sim Mc^2/R^3 \sim bT^4/\hbar^3c^3 \,. \tag{3}$$

The linear extension, R, of the active region is set by the requirement that $-g_{44}$ deviate substantially from unity inside:

$$GM/c^2R \sim 1 \,. \tag{4}$$

(2) F. J. Ernst: *Phys. Rev.*, **105**, 1662 and 1665 (1957).

From (3) and (4) the size is of the order

(5) $$R \sim R_T \equiv (\hbar^3 c^7/8\pi b G T^4)^{\frac{1}{2}} ,$$

where the factor 8π has been included for later convenience; and the mass is of order

(6) $$M \sim M_T \equiv (\hbar^3 c^{11}/8\pi b G^3 T^4)^{\frac{1}{2}} .$$

Higher temperature corresponds to geons of greater energy concentration, and of smaller mass and size.

There is a maximum temperature, and a smallest size, for which geons are free from electron pair creation and annihilation phenomena. 1) Thermal energies must be insufficient to create pairs, or the temperature T must be significantly less than $2mc^2$. 2) The electric field $\mathscr{E}$ acting on an electronic charge over the characteristic localizability distance for an electron, $\hbar/mc$, must be insufficient to raise the particle to a state of positive energy:

(7) $$\mathscr{E} < \mathscr{E}_{\text{crit}} \equiv m^2c^3/e\hbar = 4.41\cdot 10^{13}\ (\text{g/cm s}^2)^{\frac{1}{2}}\ (= 4.41\cdot 10^{13}\ \text{gauss}) .$$

Consequently the energy density of the field must be limited to values less than $\mathscr{E}^2_{\text{crit}}/8\pi$ to permit a simple analysis:

$$(\pi^2/15)T^4/\hbar^3c^3 < (m^2c^3/e\hbar)^2/8\pi$$

whence

$$T < [(15/\pi^2)(137/8\pi)]^{\frac{1}{4}}\, mc^2 = 1.70\, mc^2 (1.01\cdot 10^{10}\ ^\circ\text{K}) .$$

Corresponding to the limit $T \sim mc^2$ on the temperature there are limits

(8) $$\begin{cases} \sim (mc^2)^4/\hbar^3c^3 = 1.41\cdot 10^{25}\ \text{erg/cm}^3 \text{ on energy density} \\ \sim m^4c^3/\hbar^3 = 1.57\cdot 10^4\ \text{g/cm}^3 \text{ on mass density} \\ \sim (\hbar^3/Gm^4c)^{\frac{1}{2}} = 9.25\cdot 10^{11}\ \text{cm on size} \\ \sim (\hbar^3c^3/G^3m^4)^{\frac{1}{2}} = 1.25\cdot 10^{40}\ \text{g on mass} . \end{cases}$$

All analysis in this article is confined to geons on the high mass side of these limits.

In the realm of sizes that are free of electron physics, geons satisfy the simple scaling law implied by (5) and (6): when one geon is hotter than another by a factor or two, it has a mass and radius four times as small; but apart from this difference of scale it has the same law of fall off of activity as does the cooler geon. For this reason the calculations are carried out in terms of

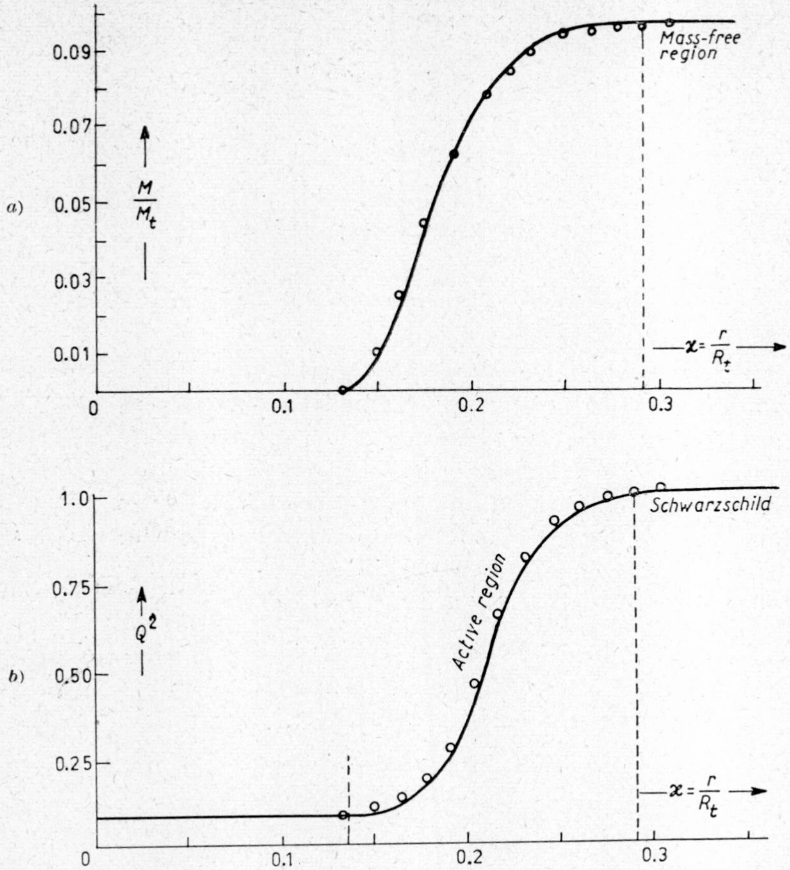

Fig. 2. – Self-consistent solution of the problem of the thermal geon. The circles represe
a function $m(x)$ having the proper analytic behavior, as given by (86) and (89), at the two
eigenvalue. The quantity e^{ν} can be regarded as a measure of the gravitational potential tha

the dimensionless scale independent variable

(9) $$x = r/R_T\,,$$

where R_B is the characteristic distance of (5). It is found that the mass has the value

(10) $$M = 0.099\, M_T\,,$$

where M_T is the characteristic mass value of (6). The total mass $M(r)$ out to the distance r, and the dimensionless measure of this mass,

$$m(x) = M(r)/M_T\,,$$

are *defined* by

(11) $$e^{-\lambda} = 1 - 2GM(r)/c^2 r = 1 - 2m(x)/x\,.$$

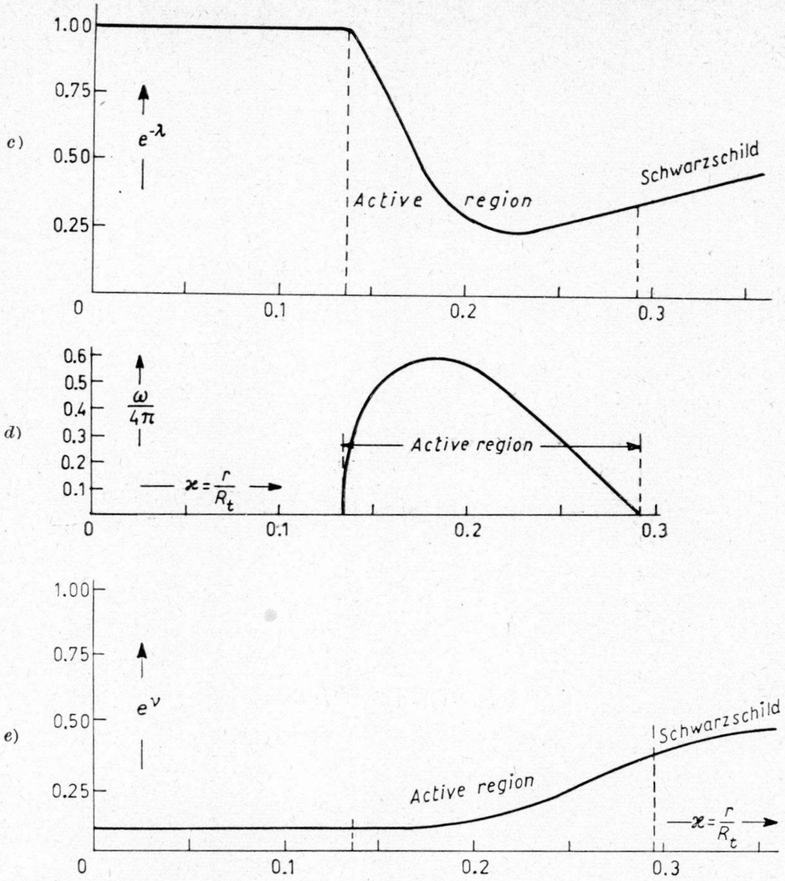

of numerical integration for the trial value of the eigenvalue parameter closest to giving
ɘ smooth curves represent an estimate of the course of the functions for the correct
;on in the orbits of Fig. 1.

The dimensionless measure of mass, $m(x)$, is shown in Fig. 2, along with the metric quantities $-g_{TT}(x) = e^{\nu}$ and $g_{rr} = e^{\lambda}$. Fig. 1 and 2 contain the principal results of this paper.

The analysis is simple in outline. If the gravitational field is temporarily assumed known, then the information is at hand to set up Maxwell's equations for characteristic vibrations of the electromagnetic field. Each solution has a well-determined proper frequency, Ωc, and is therefore assigned by Planck's formula a definite amount of energy. Distribution of this energy in space follows from the form of the field eigenfunction. Summation over all characteristic modes then gives the total energy density—and similarly the total stress—in the field at any specified point in space. The stress-energy density so found—or its time average value—constitutes the entire source for the original static gravitational field. One arrives at a coupled system of equations for the gravitational field and for the characteristic vibrations of the electromagnetic field.

In practice the number of characteristic modes of appreciable excitation is so enormous that a statistical treatment of the characteristic modes is more appropriate than any detailed solution of Maxwell's equations. The Fermi-Thomas picture of electrons in an atomic field bears a relation to the Schrödinger equation like the connection between the statistical analysis of optical rays and the solutions of Maxwell's equations in a gravitational field. In both cases the JWKB approximation method links the wave point of view to the particle or ray picture. In Section **2** Maxwell's equations in a spherically symmetric metric are separated into an angular and a radial part. The solution of the radial part in the JWKB approximation is found to depend upon a single constant, the impact parameter P. For a ray which can escape to infinity this distance is defined as the asymptotic separation of the ray and a parallel ray which comes straight through the center of the geon without deflection. For a trapped ray, the concept of ray provides an idealized description of a mode of vibration of the electromagnetic field. The amplitude is large and oscillatory in the region of trapping, falls off exponentially outside the zone of confinement, but with still greater distance starts again to oscillate, corresponding to a weak leakage wave that runs off to infinity. This leakage wave, described in ray language, has an impact parameter, P, that is a property of the mode of vibration as a whole. Bound rays in a thermal geon have impact parameters between the two limits (Fig. 1),

$$P_1 = 3^{\frac{3}{2}} GM/c^2 = 0.51 R_T$$

and

(12) $$P_2 = 0.62 R_T ,$$

and move always between the limits

(13) $$R_{\text{min}} = 0.14 R_T \quad \text{and} \quad R_{\text{max}} = 0.30 R_T .$$

Every point in space is characterized by a critical impact parameter,

(14) $$\pi(r) = r \exp[-\tfrac{1}{2}\nu(r)] .$$

No ray with impact parameter greater than $\pi(r)$ can arrive at r. Trapped rays are associated with the shaded region in Fig. 1. Among these, the bound null geodesics, there is exactly one which is circular. Its radius is

(15) $$R_{\text{circle}} = 0.19 R_T$$

and its impact parameter is

(16) $$\pi(R_{\text{circle}}) = P_{\text{circle}} = P_2 = 0.62\, R_T\,.$$

Circular motion at the radius $R = R_{\text{max}}$ is also possible, but is unstable. On receiving small disturbance the orbit spirals inward or outward from the circle, slowly at first and then with steeper pitch. This orbit, with impact parameter $P = P_1$, marks a boundary between orbits that can be trapped ($P_2 \geqslant P \geqslant P_1$) and those that can not.

The impact parameter $P = P_1$ gives the bound orbit with the greatest possible range of excursion in r, from $r = R_{\text{min}}$ to $r = R_{\text{max}}$. The bound orbit with the maximum possible impact parameter, $P = P_2$ has the minimum radial excursion: none at all.

It is easy to discuss the behavior of rays of impact parameter $P = P_1$ near the outer limit, $r = R_{\text{max}}$, of the region of trapping. All the mass M of the system lies within the radius R_{max}, and the total angular momentum of all the radiation mass-energy is zero. Consequently the metric from the point $r = R_{\text{max}}$ to infinity has the Schwarzschild value,

(17) $$e^{\nu} = e^{-\lambda} = 1 - (2GM/c^2 r)\,;$$

and throughout this same region the critical impact parameter associated with any point r is

(18) $$\pi(r) = r[1 - 2GM/c^2 r]^{-\frac{1}{2}}\,.$$

The minimum value of this quantity and the value of r at which it occurs have to be identified with the co-ordinates of the critical turning point, P_1, R_{max}, in Fig. 1. Thus, a ray coming from outside with this critical impact parameter, like a ray coming from inside, must approach the point $r = R_{\text{max}}$ without ever reaching it, in the manner of a spiral asymptotic to a circle. By differentiation of (18) we find

(19) $$\begin{cases} R_{\text{max}} = 3\,GM/c^2 \\ P_1 \quad = \pi(R_{\text{max}}) = 3^{\frac{3}{2}}\,GM/c^2\,. \end{cases}$$

The comparison between the two extreme bound orbits is striking (Fig. 1). One is exactly a circle of radius $r = R_{\text{circ}}$. The other, starting as a straight line tangent to the smaller circle R_{min}, moves out to larger r, gradually curving as it goes, crosses the circle $r = R_{\text{circ}}$, and ends up at the circle $r = R_{\text{max}}$ after an infinite number of convolutions.

Let one describe a sphere of a specific radius r between R_{min} and R_{max} and ask which of the bound orbits cut this sphere. Not all of them, unless r happens accidentally to equal R_{circle}. A typical trapped ray ($P_2 \geqslant P \geqslant P_1$) will or will not reach the distance r according as its impact parameter is less than or greater than the critical impact parameter, $\pi(r)$, associated with the point r. The extremal ray $P = \pi(r)$, that can barely touch the sphere moves at *that* part of its orbit perpendicular to the axis. A ray of a slightly smaller impact parameter cuts across the sphere of radius r both on its outward excursion and on its return, both times with only a small velocity component normal to the surface. A bound ray of minimum impact parameter P_1, cuts this sphere closer to normality than does any other bound ray. Rays of this impact parameter observed at the point r will have all azimuths. Including both outgoing and reflected portions of orbits, these rays define a double cone. This double cone bounds the bundle of directions filled out by all the trapped rays ($\pi(r) \geqslant P \geqslant P_1$). This bundle embraces the largest solid angle when $r = R_{circle}$; *i.e.*, when $\pi(r) = \pi_{max\ bound} = P_2$. The bundle narrows down to a flat disk perpendicular to the radius vector when r approaches either of the limiting values R_{min} or R_{max}; *i.e.* $\pi(r) = P_1$.

For a quantitative measure of ray direction we define an angle of inclination, $\alpha = 0$, for a ray (unbound!) that travels parallel to the radius vector. For any other ray the inclination, α, depends upon the impact parameter P that characterizes the whole course of that ray and the point r at which that ray is observed:

$$(20)\qquad \begin{cases} \operatorname{tg}\alpha = \dfrac{\mathrm{d}\,(\text{proper distance} \perp r)}{\mathrm{d}\,(\text{proper distance} \parallel r)} = r\,\mathrm{d}\theta/\exp[\lambda/2]\,\mathrm{d}r = [\pi^2(r)/P^2 - 1]^{-\frac{1}{2}}\,; \\ \sin\alpha = P/\pi(r)\,. \end{cases}$$

The bundle of bound rays has, at the point r, angles of inclination that range from

$$(21)\qquad \alpha = \arcsin[P_1/\pi(r)]$$

for outgoing rays of the minimum impact parameter P_1, through $\alpha = \pi/2$ for rays of the local extremal impact parameter $\pi(r)$, to

$$(22)\qquad \alpha = \pi - \arcsin[P_1/\pi(r)]$$

for returning rays of the minimum impact parameter, P_1. The allowed rays fill a fraction of the entire solid angle given by

$$(23)\qquad \omega/4\pi = \cos\alpha = [1 - P_1^2/\pi^2(r)]^{\frac{1}{2}}\,.$$

Normal blackbody radiation would have the energy density

$$(24)\qquad bT^4/\hbar^3c^3 = (\pi^2/15)T^4/\hbar^3c^3\,.$$

The actual energy density is less because only a portion of the solid angle is filled with blackbody radiation (23) and because the effective temperature at the point r is not T, but

$$T/(-g_{44})^{\frac{1}{2}} = T \exp[-\tfrac{1}{2}\nu(r)]\,, \tag{25}$$

according to TOLMAN [3]. Thus the energy per unit volume is

$$T_T^{\,T} = (bT^4/\hbar^3c^3)(\omega/4\pi)\exp[-2\nu]\,. \tag{26}$$

The same result is obtained from first principles in Section **3** by evaluating the energy density of each individual bound mode of vibration of the electromagnetic field and summing over all bound modes. The JWKB approximation is used, together with the wave-ray correspondence. All summations are replaced by integrations in view of the enormous number of proper vibrations of appreciable energy content. A similar calculation gives for the radial component of the electromagnetic stress energy tensor

$$T_r^{\,r} = (1/3)(bT^4/\hbar^3c^3)(\omega/4\pi)^3\exp[-2\nu]\,. \tag{27}$$

The circumstance that one has in principle to deal with a practically infinite number of eigenvalue problems in treating the trapped modes of vibration far from causing difficulties, helps to express the stress-energy tensor in terms of purely geometrical quantities.

In Section **4** the self-consistent system of equations of the geon is analysed and solved. Thus, (26) and (27) with (23) and (14) give the source of gravitational field—the electromagnetic stress energy tensor—in terms of the gravitational field itself. In addition we require only the law to find the gravitational field from its sources—Einstein's generalization of the equation of Newtonian theory,

$$\nabla^2\varphi = 4\pi G\varrho\,, \tag{28}$$

where φ is Newtonian potential and ϱ is the mass density.

The field equations of general relativity give the second derivatives of the g_{ik} in terms of the ten source strengths T_{ik}, of which the component, T_{44}, divided by c^2 is the mass density. The metric tensor, g_{ik}, is completely known except for the two dilatation functions, $\lambda(r)$ and $\nu(r)$. Consequently, two of the ten equations are sufficient to determine the potentials in terms of the

(3) R. C. TOLMAN: *Relativity, Thermodynamics and Cosmology* (Oxford, 1934), p. 318. T corresponds to Einstein's « wahre Temperatur »; $T\exp[-\frac{1}{2}\nu]$ to Ehrenfest's « Taschentemperatur ».

source strengths:

$$R_T^2[e^{-\lambda}(r^{-1}\,\mathrm{d}\nu/\mathrm{d}r + r^{-2}) - r^{-2}] = (8\pi G R_T^2/c^4)T_r{}^r = (\tfrac{1}{3})(\omega/4\pi)^3 e^{-2\nu}, \tag{29}$$

$$R_T^2[e^{-\lambda}(r^{-2} - r^{-1}\,\mathrm{d}\lambda/\mathrm{d}r) - r^{-2}] = (8\pi G R_T^2/c^4)T_T{}^T = -(\omega/4\pi)e^{-2\nu}. \tag{30}$$

Here the expressions (26) and (27) for the energy stress tensor in terms of the solid angle have been used. In terms of the dimensionless independent variable, $x = r/R_T$, these are

$$e^{-\lambda}(x^{-1}\,\mathrm{d}\nu/\mathrm{d}x + x^{-2}) - x^{-2} = (\tfrac{1}{3})(\omega/4\pi)^3 e^{-2\nu} = (\tfrac{1}{3})(1 - x_1^2 x^{-2} e^{\nu})^{\frac{3}{2}} e^{-2\nu}, \tag{31}$$

$$e^{-\lambda}(x^{-2} - x^{-1}\,\mathrm{d}\lambda/\mathrm{d}x) - x^{-2} = -(\omega/4\pi)e^{-2\nu} = -(1 - x_1^2 x^{-2} e^{\nu})^{\frac{3}{2}} e^{-2\nu}. \tag{32}$$

These are the two differential equations for the self-consistent solution of the thermal geon problem.

In (31) and (32) the quantity x_1 is an eigenvalue parameter which measures the critical impact parameter P_1 in dimensionless units. Also it determines what mass M is required to give stability to a thermal geon of temperature T:

$$x_1 \equiv P_1/R_T = (3^{\frac{3}{2}} GM/c^2)/(GM_T/c^2) = 3^{\frac{3}{2}} M/M_T. \tag{33}$$

This parameter has to be chosen in such a way as to yield a solution that is acceptable in the following sense:

1) The metric dilatation parameters must join on smoothly to the Schwarzschild values at the outer boundary of the active region; 2) The metric must become flat at the inner boundary of the active region. Specifically, from eq. (17), (18), and (19), the conditions at the outer join point, $x = x_{\max}$, are

$$\begin{cases} x_{\max} = x_1/3^{\frac{1}{2}}, & \\ e^{\nu} = \tfrac{1}{3}; & \mathrm{d}\nu/\mathrm{d}x = 3^{\frac{1}{2}}(2/x_1), \\ e^{\lambda} = 3; & \mathrm{d}\lambda/\mathrm{d}x = -3^{\frac{1}{2}}(2/x_1). \end{cases} \tag{34}$$

At the inner join point, $x = x_{\min}$, the boundary conditions are

$$\begin{cases} (xe^{-\frac{1}{2}\nu}) \text{ at } x_{\min} = x_1 \text{ (definition of } x_{\min}) \\ \mathrm{d}\nu/\mathrm{d}x = \mathrm{d}\lambda/\mathrm{d}x = 0. \end{cases} \tag{35}$$

For convenience in numerical integration of the self-consistent equations these boundary conditions on $\lambda(x)$ were expressed as boundary conditions on a variable, $m(x)$—the effective mass up to a distance x, defined by the question

(36) $$e^{-\lambda} = 1 - 2m(x)/x\,.$$

At $x_{max} = x_1/3^{\frac{1}{2}}$ we have $m(x_{max}) = (\frac{1}{3})x_{max}$ and $(dm/dx) = 0$; at the inner point both $m(x)$ and (dm/dx) are zero. The differential equations were integrated with an electronic digital computer starting at a specific inner join point and proceding outwards until either $m(x) = x/3$ or $dm/dx = 0$. In the former case the deviation from flatness was noted, the inner join point made larger, and the integration repeated from the start. When $m(x)$ became flat before reaching the value $(\frac{1}{3})x_{max}$, the inner joint point was made smaller and again the integration repeated. Fig. 1 and 2 report the results of the integration for the best value of x_1 found with the limited machine time available

(37) $$x_1 = 0.51\,.$$

Details of the present analysis of thermal geons follow.

2. – The proper vibrations of the electromagnetic field.

2·1. *Analysis in spherical harmonics.* – The electromagnetic field $F_{jk}(F_{23}\sim H_x;\ F_{14}\sim E_x)$ satisfies the eight source-free Maxwell equations

(38) $$(-g)^{-\frac{1}{2}}(\partial/\partial x^\alpha)(-g)^{\frac{1}{2}}F^{i\alpha} = 0$$

and

(39) $$\{i\alpha\beta\gamma\}\,\partial F_{\alpha\beta}/\partial x^\alpha = 0\,.$$

Here the numbers $\{ijkl\}$ are defined by $\{1234\} = 1$ and by $\{ijkl\}$ changing sign on reversal of any two indexes. Also g is the determinant of the g_{ik}: $g = -r^4\cdot\sin^2\theta\exp[\lambda(r)+\nu(r)]$. In the static spherically symmetric gravitation field the Maxwell equations are invariant with respect to a group of transformations built from the following elementary operations: 1) rotation of the space frame of reference; 2) translation of time; 3) inversion of the space frame in the center of symmetry; 4) reflection in a plane through this center; 5) reversal of time; 6) interchange of the roles of electric and magnetic fields, according to the substitution

(40) $$F^{II}_{jk} = \tfrac{1}{2}(-g)^{\frac{1}{2}}\{ik\alpha\beta\}g^{\alpha\mu}g^{\beta\nu}F^{I}_{\mu\nu}\,,$$

such that $E^{II}\sim H^{I}$, $H^{II}\sim -E^{I}$. For a flat space time continuum one knows the irreducible representations of this group of transformations and the basic set of functions on which these transformations operate ([4]), and it is very easy to modify the results for the present spherically symmetrical curved static space-time continuum. The basic solutions are characterized by a circular frequency, Ω/c, by two angular momentum quantum numbers, l and m, and by the statement that the disturbance is of electric or magnetic multipole character, as the case may be, in the following sense: 1) Magnetic multipole field: the electric field is everywhere exactly perpendicular to the radius vector; the parity of the electric field with respect to space inversion is $(-1)^l$; the parity of the magnetic field is $(-1)^{l+1}$; and the field is expressed in terms of a four-potential A_i

$$F_{jk} = \partial A_k/\partial x^j - \partial A_j/\partial x^k \,, \tag{41}$$

which lies always on the surface of a sphere with center at the origin, and points always in the direction of the electric field. Thus $A_r = A_T = 0$, and the space vector $\boldsymbol{A}$ is a function of r multiplied by $\boldsymbol{r}\times\nabla$ acting on a spherical harmonic. The normalized spherical harmonic ([4]) is denoted by $Y_l^{(m)}(\theta, \varphi)$. We write

$$Q \equiv Y_l^{(m)}(\theta, \varphi)\exp[-i\Omega T]\,; \tag{42}$$

then the non-zero components of the vector potential for the mode in question have the form

$$\begin{cases} A_\theta = a(r)\,im\,Q/\sin\theta + \text{complex conjugate}\,, \\ A_\varphi = -\,a(r)\sin\theta\,\partial Q/\partial\theta + \text{complex conjugate}\,, \end{cases} \tag{43}$$

where the radial function $a(r)$ has the dimensions $(\text{g cm}^3/\text{s}^2)^{\frac{1}{2}}$ or gauss cm^2 or cm electrostatic volts. The field itself, F_{jk}, is expressed relative to the coordinate system that appears in the metric 1). However, the field is more easily visualized in a local orthonormal co-ordinate system that is aligned along the r, θ, φ, T axes. In this frame we shall call the field $(\boldsymbol{E}, \boldsymbol{H})$. From (43) we derive

$$\begin{cases} \exp[\nu/2+\lambda/2]E_r = F_{rT} = 0 \\ r\exp[\nu/2]E_\theta = F_{\theta T} = -\,\Omega a m Q/\sin\theta + \text{c.c.} \\ r\sin\theta\exp[\nu/2]E_\varphi = F_{\varphi T} = -\,\Omega a i\sin\theta\cdot\partial Q/\partial\theta + \text{c.c.} \\ r^2\sin\theta\, H_r = F_{\theta\varphi} = l(l+1)a\sin\theta\, Q + \text{c.c.} \\ r\sin\theta\exp[\lambda/2]H_\theta = F_{\varphi r} = (\mathrm{d}a/\mathrm{d}r)\sin\theta\cdot\partial Q/\partial\theta + \text{c.c.} \\ r\exp[\lambda/2]H_\varphi = F_{r\theta} = (\mathrm{d}a/\mathrm{d}r)\,im\,Q/\sin\theta + \text{c.c.} \end{cases} \tag{44}$$

([4]) See, for example, J. M. Blatt and V. F. Weisskopf: *Theoretical Nuclear Physics* (New York, 1952), pp. 799 ff. for formulas and references to the original literature.

2) Electric multipole field: the magnetic field is everywhere exactly perpendicular to the radius vector; space inversion multiplies the electric field by $(-1)^{l+1}$, the magnetic field by $(-1)^{l}$. This type of field is obtained from the magnetic multipole field by two steps: *a*) replace $a(r)$ in (43) by $b(r)$ and call the field F so calculated « F^{I} »: *b*) substitute this field into (40) and calculate the field « F^{II} ». This is the desired electric multipole field:

$$(45)\quad \begin{cases} F_{rT} = l(l+1)\Omega^2 r^{-2}\exp[\lambda/2+\nu/2]\,b(r)Q+\text{c.c.} \\ F_{\theta T} = \Omega\exp[-\lambda/2+\nu/2](\mathrm{d}b/\mathrm{d}r)(\partial Q/\partial\theta)+\text{c.c.} \\ F_{\varphi T} = \Omega\exp[-\lambda/2+\nu/2](\mathrm{d}b/\mathrm{d}r)\,imQ+\text{c.c.} \\ F_{\theta\varphi} = 0 \\ F_{\varphi r} = \exp[\lambda/2-\nu/2]\,b(r)\,mQ+\text{c.c.} \\ F_{\theta r} = \exp[\lambda/2-\nu/2]\,b(r)\,i(\partial Q/\partial\theta)+\text{c.c.} \end{cases}$$

2·2. *Radial function.* – The radial factors $a(r)$ and $b(r)$ in the field expressions (44) and (45) satisfy a common differential equation ([5]),

$$(46)\qquad \mathrm{d}^2 f/\mathrm{d}r^{*2} + [\Omega^2 - l(l+1)e^{\nu}/r^2]f = 0$$

where

$$\mathrm{d}r^* = \exp[\lambda/2-\nu/2]\,\mathrm{d}r\,.$$

We demand a solution of (46) that is regular at the origin. Near the origin λ and ν are constant, and λ is zero ([1]). Consequently, f varies as r^{l+1} near the origin. At larger r, f increases roughly exponentially until the first zero of the square bracket in (46): $r=r_1$. Beyond this point the quantity

$$(47)\qquad l(l+1)e^{\nu}/\Omega^2 r^2$$

falls below unity, the square bracket is positive, and the solution is oscillatory. With further increase in r there are two possibilities which are familiar from the closely analogous problem of α-decay: 1) The quantity (47) never rises above unity again. In this case the solution remains oscillatory to infinite r, ultimately approaching the behavior

$$(48)\qquad f(r) \sim c_1 \sin(\Omega r + c_2)\,.$$

([5]) Eq. 26, p. 151. See also A. Eddington: *The Mathematical Theory of Relativity* (Cambridge, 1923), p. 175, where the vector wave equation is written in the form

$\Box A^m + R_{\alpha}{}^m A_{\alpha} = 0$, with $\Box\psi \equiv g^{\alpha\beta}\psi_{;\alpha\beta}$ (equivalent to our $(\partial/\partial x^{\alpha})(-g)^{\frac{1}{2}}F^{m\alpha}=0$).

Such a solution represents an electromagnetic wave that runs freely to infinity (analogous to an α-particle with energy that exceeds the potential barrier). Since such a wave carries energy away from the geon, it is not of interest in constructing a relatively stable object. Such modes of oscillation of the electromagnetic field are assigned zero energy. 2) The quantity (47) rises above unity again at a point $r = r_2$ (analogous to inner radius of potential barrier for an α-particle with energy below the top of the barrier). A sufficiently great increase in r will result in (47) once again falling below unity at some point, $r = r_3$. The solution, $f(r)$ of (46) rises monotonically from the origin to r_1, oscillates from r_1 to r_2, behaves between r_2 and r_3 as a linear combination of a function that falls roughly exponentially and another function that rises roughly exponentially, and resumes an oscillatory character from r_3 to ∞. The wave in this outer region transports energy away from the geon. The rate of transport is the smaller, the less is the ratio of the amplitudes of oscillation in the outer and inner regions. This ratio has a minimum value for certain characteristic values of Ω, designated as Ω_{nl}. At such a value of Ω the solution $f(r)$ decreases monotonically and roughly exponentially all the way from r_2 and r_3. For such characteristic solutions the region from $r_1(\Omega_{nl})$ to $r_2(\Omega_{nl})$ is called the region of activity. As a first approximation exponential fall-off is supposed to continue indefinitely beyond the point r_2.

2·3. *Eigenvalues, eigenfunctions, and averages.* – The characteristic values, Ω_{nl}, of eq. (46) in the sense just defined, are given in the JWKB approximation by the implicit equation,

$$\int_{r_1}^{r_2} [1 - l(l+1)e^{\nu}/\Omega_{nl}^2 r^2]^{\frac{1}{2}} \Omega_{nl} \, \mathrm{d}r^* = (n + \tfrac{1}{2})\pi \,. \tag{49}$$

The solutions themselves [6] in the same approximation have the form

$$f_{nl}(r) = C_{nl}[1 - l(l+1)e^{\nu}/\Omega_{nl}^2 r^2]^{-\frac{1}{4}} \sin\left\{\int_{r_1}^{r} [1 - l(l+1)e^{\nu}/\Omega_{nl}^2 r^2]^{\frac{1}{2}} \Omega_{nl} \, \mathrm{d}r^* + \frac{\pi}{4}\right\}. \tag{50}$$

The value of $|f|^2$, averaged over a region appreciable in comparison with one wavelength, but very small relative to the size of the region of activity, is

$$\langle |f|^2 \rangle \doteq \tfrac{1}{2} |C_{nl}|^2 [1 - l(l+1)e^{\nu}/\Omega_{nl}^2 r^2]^{-\frac{1}{2}} \tag{51}$$

---

[6] See, for example, W. Pauli: *Handb. d. Phys.* (Berlin, 1933), 2nd ed., vol. **24**, part 2, p. 171.

inside the active region, and practically zero outside. This measure of intensity, like the limits of activity, depends, not upon l and Ω individually, but only upon these two quantities in the single combination of an *impact parameter*,

$$P \equiv [l(l+1)/\Omega^2]^{\frac{1}{2}} . \tag{52}$$

At a given point in the active region of the geon this quantity can have any value between the minimum value P_1 for binding (Fig. 1) and the maximum value, $\pi(r)$ $(= re^{-\nu/2})$, appropriate to that point.

The number of bound modes of vibration that contribute to the electromagnetic field intensity at the point r in the active region is obtained by taking the product of the following factors and summing:

$$\begin{aligned} 2\,, &\quad \text{for polarizations} \\ 2l+1\,, &\quad \text{for values of } m \\ \mathrm{d}l\,, &\quad \text{for values of } l \\ \mathrm{d}n\,, &\quad \text{for values of } n\,. \end{aligned}$$

Summations over l and n are replaced by integrations and then by integrations over all the relevant values of the impact parameter P between P_1 and $\pi(r)$ and over the circular cofrequency Ω by virtue of eq. (30), and (33). One finds that

$$\mathrm{d}l\,\mathrm{d}n = \frac{\partial(l, n)}{\partial(P, \Omega)} = \pi^{-1}\Omega \int [1 - P^2 e^{\nu}/r^2]^{-\frac{1}{2}}\, \mathrm{d}r^*\, \mathrm{d}P\, \mathrm{d}\Omega\,,$$

and consequently the total number of modes within specified limits of Ω and P is

$$\mathrm{d}N = (2/\pi)\Omega^2\, \mathrm{d}\Omega\, \mathrm{d}(P^2) \int [1 - P^2 e^{\nu}/r^2]^{-\frac{1}{2}}\, \mathrm{d}r^* . \tag{53}$$

It is of interest to have not only the local average (51) of $|f|$, but also the local average of the square of its derivative

$$\langle |\mathrm{d}f/\mathrm{d}r^*|^2 \rangle \doteq \tfrac{1}{2} |C_{nl}|^2\, \Omega_{nl}^2 [1 - l(l+1)e^{\nu}/\Omega_{nl}^2 r^2]^{\frac{1}{2}} . \tag{54}$$

The symbol $\langle\!\langle\ \rangle\!\rangle$ denotes an average with respect to time and with respect to position over a spherical shell of thickness large compared to a typical wave length ($\sim 10^{-11}$ cm)but small compared to the dimension of the active region

($>\sim 10^{11}$ cm). We note

$$(55)\qquad \langle\!\langle |Y_l^{(m)}|^2 \rangle\!\rangle = \frac{1}{4\pi}\,; \qquad \langle\!\langle |\partial Y_l^{(m)}/\partial\theta|^2 + m^2 \sin^{-2}\theta\, |Y_l^{(m)}|^2 \rangle\!\rangle = l(l+1)/4\pi\,.$$

For a typical mode of the form (43) and (44),

$$\left.\begin{aligned} \langle\!\langle F_{\theta\varphi} F^{\theta\varphi} \rangle\!\rangle &= P^2 e^{\nu}/r^2 \\ \langle\!\langle F_{\varphi r} F^{\varphi r} + F_{r\theta} F^{r\theta} \rangle\!\rangle &= (1 - P^2 e^{\nu}/r^2) \\ \langle\!\langle F_{\theta T} F^{\theta T} + F_{\varphi T} F^{\varphi T} \rangle\!\rangle &= -1 \end{aligned}\right\} \begin{aligned} &\text{times} \\ &|C_{nl}|^2 \{l(l+1)/4\pi r^2\}\, \Omega^2 e^{-\nu} [1 - P^2 e^{\nu}/r^2]^{-\frac{1}{2}}\,. \end{aligned}$$

The sum, $\frac{1}{2} F_{\alpha\beta} F^{\alpha\beta} = H^2 - E^2$, of the quantities on the left represents the action invariant for the field oscillator. The action disappears on the time average for this oscillator as it does for every harmonic oscillator (7).

3. – Energy-density stress-density tensor.

3·1. *Radial stress- and energy-density of one mode.* – The source of the gravitational field is the stress-energy tensor of the electromagnetic field, with components

$$(56)\qquad T_i^{\,k} = (4\pi)^{-1} F_{i\alpha} F^{k\alpha} - (16\pi)^{-1} \delta_i^{\,k} F_{\alpha\beta} F^{\alpha\beta}$$

so that in flat space-time $-T_{44} = T_4^{\,4} = -(E^2 + H^2)/8\pi$. In a geon with a negligible rate of leakage of energy we can assume time symmetry as well as spherical symmetry. In the r, θ, φ, T system of co-ordinates, all off-diagonal elements of the stress-energy tensor vanish. Among the diagonal elements there exists the equality $T_\theta^{\,\theta} = T_\varphi^{\,\varphi}$, and also a general relation expressing these two tangential tensions in terms of the radial tensions—in terms of $T_r^{\,r}$ $T_T^{\,T}$, and $\mathrm{d}T_r^{\,r}/\mathrm{d}r$. This knowledge of $T_\theta^{\,\theta}$ and $T_\varphi^{\,\varphi}$ does not help in the determination of the gravitational field from the field equations

$$(57)\qquad G_i^{\,k} = (8\pi G/c^4) T_i^{\,k}$$

because there is an identity between $G_\theta^{\,\theta}$, $G_\varphi^{\,\varphi}$ and $G_r^{\,r}$, $G_T^{\,T}$, and $\mathrm{d}G_r^{\,r}/\mathrm{d}r$, which makes them automatically satisfy the same radial-tangential equilibrium con-

(7) The integral of $E^2 - H^2$ over all space for a field that is a superposition of two modes gives zero for the integral of the cross term in virtue of the orthogonality that follows from the eigenvalue eq. (46) for radial functions of the same l and different n.

dition as the corresponding components of the T's. For this reason it is enough to consider only the two remaining components of the stress-energy tensor, $T_r^{\ r}$ and $T_T^{\ T}$.

The intensity of the particular mode of field oscillation characterized in (55) results in this mode contributing to the energy-density and radial stress:

$$(58)\quad \begin{cases} \langle\langle T_T^{\ T}\ (\text{one mode})\rangle\rangle = \\ \quad = (8\pi)^{-1}\langle\langle F_{rT}F^{rT} + F_{\theta T}F^{\theta T} + F_{\varphi T}F^{\varphi T} - F_{\theta\varphi}F^{\theta\varphi} - F_{\varphi r}F^{\varphi r} - F_{r\theta}F^{r\theta}\rangle\rangle = \\ \qquad = -(\Omega^2/16\pi^2r^2)e^{-\nu}l(l+1)\,|C_{nl}|^2[1-P^2e^{\nu}/r^2]^{-\frac{1}{2}} \\ \langle\langle T_r^{\ r}\ (\text{one mode})\rangle\rangle = \\ \quad = (8\pi)^{-1}\langle\langle F_{\varphi r}F^{\varphi r} + F_{r\theta}F^{\theta r} + F_{rT}F^{rT} - F_{\theta\varphi}F^{\theta\varphi} - F_{\theta T}F^{\theta T} - F_{\varphi T}F^{\varphi T}\rangle\rangle = \\ \qquad = (\Omega^2/16\pi^2r^2)e^{-\nu}l(l+1)\,|C_{nl}|^2[1-P^2e^{\nu}/r^2]^{\frac{1}{2}}. \end{cases}$$

3·2. *Many modes; total mass.* – The electromagnetic stress energy tensor being bilinear in the field, the fields of all individual standing waves must be added before commencing the evaluation. For the time average value of the energy density, we assume that the elementary disturbances are incoherent (1): the average contribution from cross terms between modes vanishes. Thus, we write

$$(59)\qquad \langle T_T^{\ T}\rangle = \sum_{n,l,m,p}\langle\langle T_T^{\ T}(n,l,m,p;r,\theta,\varphi)\rangle\rangle\,,$$

where the sum goes over all values of the angular index, l, and m; over all the values of the index number n of the radial proper function f_{nl} associated with the cofrequency Ωnl; and over both types of polarization: $p=$ electric or magnetic multipole. There is a similar expression for the radial stress.

There are two simple ways to get the total mass (8).

1) Write

$$(60)\qquad e^{-\lambda} = 1 - 2GM(r)/c^2r$$

as a definition of the effective mass, $M(r)$; insert this expression into differential eq. (30) to derive an expression for $\mathrm{d}M(r)/\mathrm{d}r$; integrate from $r=0$ to

(8) R. C. Tolman: *Phys. Rev.*, **35**, 875 (1930); see also L. Landau and E. Lifschitz: *The Classical Theory of Fields*, translated by M. Hamermesh (Cambridge, Mass., 1951), pp. 309 and 323.

$r = \infty$; and find

$$(61)\qquad Mc^2 = c^2 M(r = \infty) = -\int_0^\infty \sum_{\text{modes}} \langle\!\langle T_T{}^T \text{ (one mode)} \rangle\!\rangle\, 4\pi r^2\, \mathrm{d}r\,.$$

2) Write down the expression for the local density of *gravitational plus electromagnetic* energy; integrate over all space; use the fact that the gravitational part is expressible in terms of a surface integral; use also the fact that this surface integral does not involve any details of the gravitational field when the metric is asymptotically flat; finally, use the fact that the trace of the electromagnetic stress-energy tensor is zero:

$$(62)\qquad Mc^2 = \iiint \langle T_r{}^r + T_\theta{}^\theta + T_\varphi{}^\varphi - T_T{}^T \rangle (-g)^{\frac{1}{2}}\, \mathrm{d}r\, \mathrm{d}\theta\, \mathrm{d}\varphi =$$
$$= -2\int \sum_{\text{modes}} \langle\!\langle T_T{}^T \text{ (one mode)} \rangle\!\rangle \exp\left[\lambda/2 + \nu/2\right] 4\pi r^2\, \mathrm{d}r\,.$$

Expression (62) is more convenient than (61) because the radial integral i easier to calculate.

3'3. *Contraction effect.* – To define the energy of one mode, one can think of measuring the gravitational field far away from a geon before and after the stilling of that particular vibration. One might be tempted to write for this change in mass

$$(63)\ \text{(wrong)}\qquad c^2\,\Delta M = I_{\text{mode}}\,,$$

where

$$(64)\qquad I_{\text{mode}} = -2\int \langle\!\langle T_T{}^T(\text{mode}) \rangle\!\rangle \exp\left[\lambda/2 + \nu/2\right] 4\pi r^2\, \mathrm{d}r\,.$$

This would be wrong. As the radiation in question leaks out of the geon, less pressure is available to sustain the geon against gravitational forces. Consequently the geon contracts. Thus every other mode finds itself more tightly confined. Its frequency rises. Accordingly by the principle of adiabatic invariance there is a proportional *increase* in energy. Therefore, the mass of the geon will decrease by an amount less than given by (63).

The fractional change in mass due to stilling of a single mode is fantastically small. For a first primitive analysis the effect on the geon is primarily a scale transformation to smaller size. Mass and radius transform in parallel. Frequency goes up inversely as radius, and therefore inversely as mass. The same applies—according to adiabatic invariance—to the contribution, I_{mode}, to the energy from every mode except the selected mode:

$$\frac{\Delta I_{\text{mode}}\,(\text{increase})}{I_{\text{mode}}} = \frac{\Delta M\,(\text{decrease})}{M}. \tag{65}$$

(see qualification below). On this basis we compare the geon before,

$$Mc^2 = I_{\text{one}} + \sum I_{\text{others}} \tag{66}$$

and after

$$(M - \Delta M)c^2 = 0 + \sum \left(1 + \frac{\Delta M}{M}\right) I_{\text{others}}, \tag{67}$$

the mode is stilled. Subtraction gives

$$c^2 \Delta M = \frac{I_{\text{one}}}{1 + (1/Mc^2)\sum I_{\text{others}}} = \frac{1}{2} I_{\text{one}}. \tag{68}$$

We are considering a classical geon that has a great many proper models $s = 1, 2, \dots$, where s stands for the quartet (n, l, m, p). Each mode has a reduced action variable J_s ($=$ action$/2\pi$) associated with it. The energy consists of two parts: electromagnetic energy of individual modes and gravitational energy of interaction between modes. The sum of both energies (61) is a function of the action variables of all these oscillators:

$$c^2 M = c^2 M(J_1, \dots J_s, \dots).$$

The circular frequency of a given oscillator is given by

$$c\Omega_s(J) = c^2 \frac{\partial M(J)}{\partial J_s}. \tag{69}$$

If a particular action variable decreases slowly from its normal value to zero, during this change all other action variables keep their original values, according to the principle of adiabatic invariance.

Then the change in mass is

$$c^2 \Delta M = c\Omega_s(J)\,\mathrm{d}J_s = \tfrac{1}{2} I_s = -\int \langle\langle T_T{}^T\ (\text{chosen mode } s)\rangle\rangle \exp[\lambda/2 + \nu/2]\, 4\pi r^2\, \mathrm{d}r. \tag{70}$$

A weakness in the foregoing reasoning is that it assumes that stopping of the given vibration produces a change in the field of gravitational force that is represented with sufficient accuracy simply by a change of scale. Perhaps the change in metric field will act in different ways on different modes, raising some in I value less than others. It is at least conceivable that such a differentiation might take place. Since the quantity of interest is not the I value of one mode, but the sum of the changes in I values of all the modes, we need not (65) for every mode individually, but only a weaker equation for this sum of changes:

$$\frac{\sum I_{\text{others}}\,(\text{increase})}{I_{\text{others}}} = \frac{\Delta M\;(\text{decrease})}{M}\,. \tag{71}$$

The question about correctness of (71) could be answered by an appeal back to first principles:

1) Determine the effect on a single mode of an adiabatic change in the metric field. *a*) Insert in the action principle of the electromagnetic field a trial function of the product form (43), where however the time factor, $\exp[-i\Omega T]$, is replaced by an arbitrary undetermined function of cotime $\psi(T)$. *b*) From the variational principle derive the second-order differential equation for this function. *c*) Solve by the JWKB method. *d*) This gives a general expression for properties of a single mode under arbitrary adiabatic changes in the Schwarzschild metric, containing one arbitrary amplitude constant, independent of both r and T.

2) Calculate the stress energy associated with this mode, and find all over again the expressions (58), with the difference that not C_{nl}, but D_{nl}, is constant under adiabatic changes, where

$$C_{nl} = D_{nl}\,\Omega_{nl}^{-\frac{1}{2}}\left[\int[1-P^2e^{\nu}/r^2]^{-\frac{1}{2}}\,dr^*\right]^{-\frac{1}{2}}. \tag{72}$$

(1961 addendum: exponents -1 of original text changed here to $-\frac{1}{2}$).

3) Write down the eq. (29) and (30) of the self-consistent geon field for two problems: *a*) with all modes s excited to specific metric-independent amplitudes D_s; and *b*) with all modes but one so excited.

4) By differencing these two sets of non-linear equations derive linear equations for the small changes $\delta\lambda(r)$, $\delta\nu(r)$, produced in the metric by quenching one mode.

5) Derive expressions for these changes in the metric.

6) Find how these changes alter the I value of each mode individually and hence

7) compute the change in mass of the system as a whole due to stopping one vibration.

3·4. *Test of adiabatic analysis against Ehrenfest-Tolman formula.* – For thermal geons there is an extra simplification with which we can check the correctness of (68), without the more detailed analysis just outlined. Considering blackbody radiation in equilibrium in a gravitational field for an asymptotic temperature T, we know from EHRENFEST and TOLMAN ([9]) that the energy density has the value appropriate to the temperature $T(-g_{44})^{-\frac{1}{2}}$, rather than T itself. Here this means an energy density proportional to $T^4 e^{-2\nu}$, multiplied by the fractional solid angle filled by trapped rays. This result comes from the normalization (70).

The energy leaked out of the geon by quenching one mode is equated to the thermal energy of a harmonic oscillator, as given by Planck's formula:

$$(73)\qquad \hbar c\Omega_{nl}\,[-1+\exp\,[\hbar c\Omega_{n'}/T]]^{-1} = c^2\Delta M = \tfrac{1}{2} I_s =$$
$$= -\int \langle\!\langle T_T{}^T(\text{chosen mode})\rangle\!\rangle \exp\,[\lambda/2+\nu/2]\, 4\pi r^2\, \mathrm{d}r =$$
$$= (\Omega^2/4\pi)\, l(l+1)\,|C_{nl}|^2 \int [1-P^2\, e^{\nu}/r^2]^{-\frac{1}{2}}\, \mathrm{d}r^* \,.$$

Solving this for the amplitude $|C_{nl}|$, and inserting this value of $|C_{nl}|$ into eq. (38) we find *the energy density and radial stress due to one normalized mode*:

$$(74)\qquad \langle\!\langle -T_T{}^T\ (\text{or } +T_r{}^r)\rangle\!\rangle = \hbar c\Omega_{nl}[-1+\exp\,[\hbar c\Omega_{nl}/T]^{-1}\cdot$$
$$\cdot\,[1-P^2 e^{\nu}/r^2]^{\{-\frac{1}{2}\,(\text{or }+\frac{1}{2})\}}\,(e^{-\nu}/4\pi r^2)\left\{\int [1-P^2 e^{\nu}/r^2]^{-\frac{1}{2}}\,\mathrm{d}r^*\right\}^{-1}.$$

We multiply (74) by the number of modes, $\mathrm{d}N$, as in (53), in the interval $\mathrm{d}\Omega\,\mathrm{d}P$, and sum over all modes by integrating over the wave number Ω and the equivalent impact parameter P. This gives the local value of the total energy density and radial stress:

$$(75)\qquad \langle\!\langle -T_T{}^T\ (\text{or } +T_r{}^r)\rangle\!\rangle_{\text{local total}} =$$
$$= \int \hbar c\Omega[-1+\exp\,[\hbar c\Omega/T]]^{-1}\,\Omega^2\,\mathrm{d}\Omega\,(\tfrac{1}{2}e^{-\nu}/r^2)\int_{P_1}^{P_{\max}=r\exp[-\nu/2]} [1-P^2 e^{\nu}/r^2]^{\{-\frac{1}{2}(\text{or}+\frac{1}{2})\}}\,\mathrm{d}(P^2) =$$
$$= (\pi^2 T^4/15\hbar^3 c^3)\, e^{-2\nu}\{[1-P_1^2 e^{\nu}/r^2]^{\frac{1}{2}}\ (\text{or } \tfrac{1}{3}[1-P_1^2 e^{\nu}/r^2]^{\frac{3}{2}})\}\,.$$

([9]) R. C. TOLMAN and P. EHRENFEST: *Phys. Rev.*, **36**, 1791 (1930); see also TOLMAN, ref. ([3]), p. 318.

In terms of the solid angle, ω, spanned by the trapped rays, the complete stress energy tensor has the form

$$(76)\qquad \langle\langle T_j^{\,i}\rangle\rangle_{\text{local total}} = (\pi^2 T^4 e^{-2\nu}/15\pi^3 c^3)\cdot$$

$$\cdot\begin{vmatrix} \frac{1}{3}(\omega/4\pi)^3 & & & \\ & \frac{1}{2}(\omega/4\pi)-\frac{1}{6}(\omega/4\pi)^3 & & \\ & & \frac{1}{2}(\omega/4\pi)-\frac{1}{6}(\omega/4\pi)^3 & \\ & & & -(\omega/4\pi) \end{vmatrix}.$$

The stress-energy tensor calculated here by consideration of individual modes agrees with the usual blackbody value, corrected properly as demanded by the Ehrenfest-Tolman argument and by the solid angle factor. No such agreement would have resulted if the factor $\frac{1}{2}$ in (70) for the loss of mass on stilling of one mode is left out. Thus the contraction effect is essential.

Expressions (76) as derived here were used as described in the introduction to set up (29) and (30) for the self-consistent thermal geon field.

To restate the results of the present analysis, the total mass of the geon is given by the superficially paradoxical formula,

$$(77)\qquad Mc^2 = \tfrac{1}{2}\sum_{\text{all modes}}\big(\text{Planck formula for energy of one mode, as in (2)}\big)\,.$$

4. – Numerical solution of the differential equations.

In the dimensionless variable $x = r/R_T$ the equations for the geon field are

$$(78)\qquad e^{-\lambda}(x\,\mathrm{d}\nu/\mathrm{d}x+1)-1=(x^2/3)(1-x_1^2e^{\nu}/x^2)^{\frac{3}{2}}e^{-2\nu}\,,$$

$$(79)\qquad e^{-\lambda}(1-x\,\mathrm{d}\lambda/\mathrm{d}x)-1=-x^2(1-x_1^2e^{\nu}/x^2)^{\frac{1}{2}}e^{-2\nu}\,.$$

Let $m(x)$ represent the effective mass, in units M_T, out to the distance $r = xR_T$, as *defined by*

$$(80)\qquad m(x)=x(1-e^{-\lambda})/2\,.$$

Thus the mass of the geon is

$$M = m(\infty)M_T\,.$$

Also define a scale factor, Q, by the equation

$$(81)\qquad Q^2=\exp[\lambda+\nu]\,.$$

These variables behave as follows (Fig. 2). From $x=0$ to the radius $x = x_{\min}$, the dimensionless mass variable, m, is zero. Then it increases up to

$$m = m(\infty) = x_{\max}/3 = x_1/3^{\frac{3}{2}} \tag{82}$$

at the outer boundary

$$x_{\max} = x_1/3^{\frac{1}{2}} \tag{83}$$

of the active region. Here x_1 is a measure of the critical impact parameter for trapped rays:

$$x_1 = P_1/R_T \,. \tag{84}$$

Thereafter it remains constant at the value $m(\infty)$. The curve for m as a function of x has a horizontal slope at $x = x_{\min}$ and $x = x_{\max}$. A similar description applies to Q, with these exceptions: Q is not zero, but has a constant value between 0 and 1 for $x < x_{\min}$; and Q has the constant Schwarschild value of unity for $x > x_{\max}$. Between these limits these quantities satisfy the equations

$$\frac{\mathrm{d}m}{\mathrm{d}x} = x^2 \frac{[1 - x_1^2 x^{-2} Q^2(1 - 2m/x)]^{\frac{1}{2}}}{2\,Q^4(1 - 2m/x)^2}\,, \tag{85}$$

$$\frac{\mathrm{d}Q^2}{\mathrm{d}x} = x \frac{\{[1 - x_1^2 x^{-2} Q^2(1 - 2m/x)]^{\frac{1}{2}} + [1 - x_1^2 x^{-2} Q^2(1 - 2m/x)]^{\frac{3}{2}}/3\}}{Q^2(1 - 2m/x)^3}\,. \tag{86}$$

Near the outer limit, $x_{\max} = x_1/3^{\frac{1}{2}}$, of the zone of trapping, write

$$x = x_{\max}(1 + s)\,, \tag{87}$$

where s is understood to be a small *negative* quantity. Then, from the differential equations and the boundary conditions the following behavior follows for the physically relevant quantities:

$$\left\{\begin{aligned} m(x) &= (x_1/3^{\frac{3}{2}}) - (3x_1^3/4)s^2 + \dots \\ Q^2(x) &= 1 - (3^{\frac{5}{2}}/2)x_1^2 s^2 + \dots \\ e^{-\lambda} &= (\tfrac{1}{3}) + (\tfrac{2}{3})s + (\tfrac{2}{3})[(3^{\frac{5}{2}}x_1^2/4) - 1]s^2 + \dots \\ e^{\nu} &= (\tfrac{1}{3}) + (\tfrac{2}{3})s - (\tfrac{2}{3})s^2 + \dots \\ \omega/4\pi &= -\,3^{\frac{1}{2}} s + \dots\,. \end{aligned}\right. \tag{88}$$

The power series expressions for $e^{-\lambda}$ and e^{ν} join on smoothly to the accurate exterior values,

$$e^{\nu} = e^{-\lambda} = (1 - 2x_1/3^{\frac{3}{2}}x)\,. \tag{89}$$

Near the inner limit, for $x \sim x_{\min}$, write

$$x = x_{\min}(1 + u)\,. \tag{90}$$

Then

$$\left\{\begin{aligned} m(x) &= (2/3)(x_1^4/x_{\min})u^{\frac{3}{2}} + \dots \\ Q^2(x) &= (x_{\min}^2/x_1^2) + (2^{\frac{3}{2}}/3)x_1^2 u^{\frac{3}{2}} + \dots \\ e^{-\lambda} &= 1 - (2^{\frac{5}{2}}/3)(x_1^4/x_{\min}^2)u^{\frac{3}{2}} + \dots \\ e^{\nu} &= (x_{\min}^2/x_1^2) + (2^{\frac{7}{2}}/15)x_1^2 u^{\frac{5}{2}} + \dots \\ \omega/4\pi &= 2^{\frac{1}{2}}u^{\frac{1}{2}} + \dots \end{aligned}\right. \tag{91}$$

and, for $x_1 \leqslant x_{\min}$,

$$e^{-\lambda} = 1\,; \qquad e^{\nu} = (x_{\min}^2/x_1^2)\,; \qquad m = 0\,.$$

It is reasonable to assume a trial value for the eigenvalue parameter x_1, and start a numerical integration working inward from $x_{\max} = x_1/3^{\frac{1}{2}}$ with the starting series (88). The solid angle will first increase, then decrease. When it goes to zero, one wants $e^{-\lambda}$ to be unity. This condition is not satisfied in general. Accordingly, a new choice for x_1 is made. One proceeds by trial and error until $e^{-\lambda}$ goes to 1 as the solid angle goes to zero. This procedure was not adopted because the series expansion (88) was not available when the numerical work was done.

In the procedure that was used the coupled eq. (85) and (86) were integrated from the interior boundary $x_{\min}$ although the initial value of Q^2 depends not on a chosen value of x_1 alone, but also on the value of $x_{\min}$. To make the integration depend on a single parameter, the invariance of the equations to scale change, similar to that used in reference [1], was utilized. Defining $\bar{x}$, $\bar{m}$ and $\bar{Q}$ and c by the relations

$$x = b\bar{x}\,, \qquad Q^2 = b\bar{Q}^2\,, \qquad m = b\bar{m}\,, \qquad x_1^2 = bc^2\,; \tag{92}$$

one has for $\bar{m}$ and $\bar{Q}^2$

$$\begin{aligned} \mathrm{d}\bar{m}/\mathrm{d}\bar{x} &= \big(\bar{x}^2/2\bar{Q}^4(1 - 2\bar{m}/\bar{x})^2(\omega/4\pi)\big) \\ \mathrm{d}\bar{Q}^2/\mathrm{d}\bar{x} &= \big(\bar{x}/\bar{Q}^2(1 - 2\bar{m}/\bar{x})^3\big)\{(\omega/4\pi) + (\omega/4\pi)^3/3\}\,, \end{aligned}$$

where

$$\omega/4\pi = [1 - c^2\bar{x}^{-2}\bar{Q}^2(1 - 2\bar{m}/\bar{x})]^{\frac{1}{2}} . \tag{93}$$

The choice $b = x_1^2/x_{\min}^2$ or, equivalently, $c = \bar{x}_{\min}$, gives the simple boundary conditions at $\bar{x}_{\min}$:

$$\begin{cases} \bar{Q}^2(c) = 1 , & \mathrm{d}\bar{Q}^2/\mathrm{d}\bar{x}|_c = 0 , \\ \bar{m}(c) = 0 , & \mathrm{d}\bar{m}/\mathrm{d}\bar{x}|_c = 0 ; \end{cases} \tag{94}$$

and the integration can be carried through for any c. At the outer boundary, $\bar{x}_{\max} = \Gamma$, the correct boundary values, following from (88) are

$$\begin{cases} \bar{Q}^2(\Gamma) = 3(\Gamma/c)^2 , & \mathrm{d}\bar{Q}^2/\mathrm{d}\bar{x}|_\Gamma = 0 , \\ \bar{m}(\Gamma) = \Gamma/3, & \mathrm{d}\bar{m}/\mathrm{d}\bar{x}|_\Gamma = 0 ; \end{cases} \tag{95}$$

but in general these will not be satisfied for a particular choice of c. Starting at an arbitrary c the equations were integrated, on a punched card programmed electronic computer, using the Kutta-Runge method; $\bar{m}$ was plotted as a function of $\bar{x}$. If a c is chosen smaller than the actual eigenvalue then, when $\bar{m}(\bar{x}) = \bar{x}/3$, the slope $(\mathrm{d}\bar{m}/\mathrm{d}\bar{x})$ will not vanish. In such cases the integration was stopped at the point where $\bar{m}(\bar{x}) = \bar{x}/3$ and the slope examined. A larger c, still less than the eigenvalue, will reduce the slope at the critical point. If c is chosen greater than the eigenvalue then $\mathrm{d}\bar{m}/\mathrm{d}\bar{x}$ vanishes before $\bar{m}(\bar{x})$ has decreased to $\bar{x}/3$. Thus, the correct eigenvalue for c can be approached both from above and below. With the limited machine time available the nearest value of c to its true eigenvalue for which a numerical integration was carried out was 1.875: the corresponding values for Γ and $\bar{m}(\infty)$ are $\Gamma = 4.05$ and $\bar{m}(\infty) = 1.35$. In Fig. 2 $m(x)$ and $Q^2(x)$ are plotted, by a dotted line, for this value of c, for which $b = 0.071$ (and therefore $x_{\min} = 0.134$ and $x_{\max} = 0.289$). The smooth curves represent an estimate of $m(x)$, $Q^2(x)$, $e^{-\lambda(x)}$, $e^{\nu(x)}$ and $\omega(x)/4\pi$ for the correct eigenvalue.

5. – Variational principle for the thermal geon.

All the differential equations of the Maxwell-Einstein theory, can be derived from the action principle

$$\delta I = 0 , \tag{96}$$

where

$$I = \iiiint \mathscr{L}(-g)^{\frac{1}{2}} \mathrm{d}x^1\, \mathrm{d}x^2\, \mathrm{d}x^3\, \mathrm{d}x^4 \tag{97}$$

and where

$$16\pi c \mathscr{L} = (c^4/G) R_\alpha^{\ \alpha} - F_{\alpha\beta} F^{\alpha\beta} \tag{98}$$

and where the independent variables are the ten metric quantities g^{ik} and the four electromagnetic potentials A_j. Similarly, one can derive the differential equations of the simple spherical geon [1],

$$\left\{\begin{aligned} &\mathrm{d}^2\varphi/\mathrm{d}x^2 + jk\varphi = 0 \\ &\mathrm{d}k/\mathrm{d}x + \varphi^2 = 0 \\ &\mathrm{d}j/\mathrm{d}x = 3 - [1 + (\mathrm{d}\varphi/\mathrm{d}x)^2]/k^2 \end{aligned}\right. \tag{99}$$

from the variational principle

$$\left\{\begin{aligned} &\delta I = 0 \\ &I = \int \mathscr{L}(u)\, \mathrm{d}u \\ &\mathrm{d}u = k - \mathrm{d}x \\ &\mathscr{L} = k^{-1} + 3k + jk\, \mathrm{d}k/\mathrm{d}u + j\varphi^2 - k - (\mathrm{d}\varphi/\mathrm{d}u)^2 , \end{aligned}\right. \tag{100}$$

as recently shown by Ernst [2]. Encouraged by this result, we found that we could derive the equations for the thermal geon from the principle

$$\left\{\begin{aligned} &\delta I = 0 , \\ &I = \int \mathscr{L}(x)\, \mathrm{d}x , \\ &\mathscr{L}(x) = (1 - x\, \mathrm{d}\lambda/\mathrm{d}x) \exp[\nu/2 - \lambda/2] - \exp[\nu/2 + \lambda/2] - \\ &\qquad - (x^2/3) \exp[\lambda/2](\exp[-\nu] - x_1^2 x^{-2})^{\frac{3}{2}} . \end{aligned}\right. \tag{101}$$

However, here the eigenvalue parameter x_1, which we would like to know, already enters the variational principle. The situation resembles that in which we would find ourselves if we tried to express the content of the Schrödinger equation in a variational principle built upon the function

$$\mathscr{L}(x) = (\nabla\psi)^2 + (V - \varepsilon)\psi^2 . \tag{102}$$

We will always find the trivial solution $\psi(x) = 0$ for this variational problem unless ε happens to be an eigenvalue: not a very happy way to find eigenvalues! Much more appropriate is the more familiar Ritz variation principle

$$\varepsilon = \frac{\int[(\Delta\psi)^2 + V\psi^2]\,dx}{\int\psi^2\,dx} = \text{minimum} , \tag{103}$$

into which we can substitute *any* well-behaved trial function and obtain an upper limit on ε.

Correspondingly, we take for variation principle

$$\delta(A^*B^*) = 0 , \tag{104}$$

$$A^* = \int_b^1 \exp[\lambda^*/2 + \nu^*/2](d/dy)\big[y(1 - \exp[-\lambda^*])\big]\,dy , \tag{105}$$

$$B^* = \int_b^1 (y^2/3)\exp[\lambda^*/2](\exp[-\nu^*] - 3y^{-2})^{\frac{3}{2}}\,dy . \tag{106}$$

The independent variable here is y:

$$\begin{cases} x = sy ; \quad \lambda(x) = \lambda^*(y) ; \quad \nu(x) = \nu^*(y) ; \\ e^{-\lambda^*} = 1 - 2m^*/y ; \quad s = x_{\max} = x_1/3^{\frac{1}{2}} \\ x_{\min} = sy_{\min} = sb . \end{cases} \tag{107}$$

The boundary conditions are

$$e^{-\lambda^*} = m^* = e^{\nu^*} = \tfrac{1}{3} \quad \text{at} \quad y = 1 \tag{108}$$

$$\begin{cases} e^{\lambda^*} = 1 , \quad m^* = 0 , \quad e^{\nu^*} = b^2/3 \\ d\lambda^*/dy = 0 , \quad dm^*/dy = 0 , \end{cases} \qquad \text{at } y = b . \tag{109}$$

From the variational principle (104) follow differential equations for λ^* and ν^* as functions of y which are identical in form to eq. (78) and (79) for λ and ν as functions of x *except* for the introduction on the right-hand side of (78) and (79) of an extra factor

(110) $$s^2 = A^*/B^* .$$

The logic proceeds so: 1) Introduce into (105), (106) trial functions $\lambda^*(y)$ and $\nu^*(y)$ that satisfy (108), (109) and that contain one or more adjustable parameters, among them the lower limit b. 2) Calculate (A^*B^*) and extremize with respect to choice of these parameters. 3) From (110) calculate s^2 and hence x_1 and the geon mass

(111) $$M = M_T x_1/3^{\frac{3}{2}} = M_T s/3 .$$

If instead the quantities λ and ν are calculated as functions of x by solution of *differential* eq. (78) and (79) for a trial eigenvalue x_1, an improved estimate of the eigenvalue is given by

$$x_1/3^{\frac{1}{2}} = s = (AB)^{\frac{1}{4}} ,$$

where A and B are the analogs of (105) and (106) for $\lambda(x)$ and $\nu(x)$.

6. – Photon-photon collisions in a thermal geon.

The electromagnetic energy content of a thermal geon decreases slowly not only by the monomolecular process of barrier penetration but also by bimolecular processes in which two photons collide, either to produce a pair of electrons, or to go off as photons in new directions [1]. We wish to estimate the rate of these two processes in a very active part of a thermal geon: at the radius of the stable circular orbit (Fig. 1), where the solid angle occupied by bound rays is the largest,

(112) $$(\text{solid angle}/4\pi) \doteqdot 0.59$$

and where the effective temperature is

(113) $$T_{\text{eff}} = Te^{-\nu/2} \doteqdot 3.3\,T .$$

Here the number of photons Ω_1 per unit volume in the interval of circular wave number $\mathrm{d}\Omega_1$, and in the interval of solid angle $\mathrm{d}\omega$ (within the allowed cone) will be

(114) $$\mathrm{d}n_1 = (\mathrm{d}\omega/4\pi)\Omega_1^2\,\mathrm{d}\Omega_1(-1 + \exp[\hbar c\Omega_1/T_{\text{eff}}])^{-1} .$$

The collision between two photons ([10]) of wave numbers Ω_1 and Ω_2 whose directions of motion make an angle θ will look like the collision between two photons of equal wave number Ω^* and opposite direction, in a suitably selected local Lorentz system, where

$$\Omega^* = (\Omega_1\Omega_2)^{\frac{1}{2}} \sin \tfrac{1}{2}\theta \, . \tag{115}$$

The total collision cross-section, integrated over all angles of the emergence of the pair (for process 1) or of the scattered photons (for process 2) will be

$$\sigma = \sin^2 \tfrac{1}{2}\theta\sigma^*(\Omega^*) \, , \tag{116}$$

where Ω^* is the cross-section calculated for equally energetic but oppositely moving photons. For the pair process the cross-section σ^* vanishes below the threshold, $\Omega^* = mc/\hbar$, and reaches a maximum value of the order $(e^2/mc^2)^2$ for a wave number that is a small multiple of this threshold value. For temperatures small compared to mc^2 it follows from the Planck formula that the number of pair production processes is exponentially small, with an exponential factor qualitatively of the form

$$\exp\left[-\left(\mu mc^2/T\right)\right] \, , \tag{117}$$

where μ is of the order of unity.

The cross-section for elastic photon-photon collisions also reaches a peak for wave numbers, Ω^*, of the order $mc/\hbar$. The peak value of σ^* for this process is of the order $(e^2/\hbar c)^2(e^2/mc^2)^2$, much smaller than that for the pair production mechanism. However, the cross-section has no threshold and varies at low wave numbers in accordance with the formula ([11])

$$\sigma^* = (52/1125\pi)(e^2/\hbar c)^2(e^2/mc^2)^2(\Omega^*\hbar/mc)^6 \, . \tag{118}$$

For low temperatures the effective cross-section for collision between two photons consequently varies as T^6, and therefore dominates over an exponentially small factor of the form (117). For this reason we can disregard pair production processes, relative to elastic collisions, so long as the temperature is considerably less than mc^2.

([10]) G. Breit and J. A. Wheeler: *Phys. Rev.*, **46**, 1087 (1934).

([11]) H. Euler and B. Kockel: *Naturwiss.*, **23**, 246 (1935); W. Heisenberg and H. Euler: *Zeits. Phys.*, **98**, 714 (1936).

Not all photon collision processes result in loss of photons from the system. In some cases one or both of the new quanta still move in bound orbits. Only those are lost whose directions are thrown outside the cone of trapping angles. In particular a new photon escapes from the system if it is moving along a radius.

For an order-of-magnitude estimate of the rate of loss of energy we disregard details of the differences between trapping and escaping directions and consider the product of the following factors:

$$(119)\quad \left\{\begin{array}{ll} \text{number of photons } \Omega_1 \text{ per cm}^3 & \sim T^3/\hbar^3c^3 \\ \text{number of photons } \Omega_2 \text{ per cm}^3 & \sim T^3/\hbar^3c^3 \\ \text{collision velocity} & c \\ \text{cross-section} & \sim (e^2/\hbar c)^2(e^2/mc^2)^2(T/mc^2)^6 \\ \text{energy loss from geon on collision} & \sim T \\ \hline \text{product, energy loss per cm}^3 \text{ and per s} & \sim (e^2/\hbar c)^4(mc^2/\hbar)(mc^2)^4\hbar^{-3}c^{-3}(T/mc^2)^{13} \end{array}\right.$$

In contrast, the energy on hand per unit volume is of the order $T^4/\hbar^3c^3$. This quantity, divided by (119), fixes a characteristic scale of time, τ, for depletion of the geon by photon-photon collisions:

$$(120)\qquad \tau^{-1} \sim \frac{(\text{energy loss/cm}^3\text{ s})}{(\text{energy/cm}^3)} \sim (e^2/\hbar c)^4(mc^2/\hbar)(T/mc^2)^9 \sim (10^{12}\text{ s}^{-1})(T/mc^2)^9 .$$

For a characteristic time as long as a year it is sufficient to have a temperature of the order

$$T \sim 10^{-20/9} mc^2 \sim 10^{-2} mc^2$$

corresponding to a geon mass of the order

$$M_T \sim 10^{44} g$$

and radius

$$R_T \sim 10^{16}\text{ cm} .$$

As the energy loss continues, the thermal geon shrinks, grows denser and hotter, and loses energy at a rapidly increasing rate. As the temperature rises to the neighborhood of mc^2, pair production processes rapidly increase in importance. Then the physics of the system takes on quite a different character which we do not analyze here.

7. – Zero-point energy.

We have consistently disregarded quantum effects, or rather have consistently attempted to choose conditions where quantum effects are unimportant, in all except the considerations of very hot geons in the last section. However, at all temperatures one has to reckon with zero-point fluctuations in the electromagnetic field, as well as with the fluctuations due to the thermal radiation itself. One can formally associate these zero-point fluctuations with a zero-point energy, $\frac{1}{2}\hbar c\Omega$, that goes with each field oscillator. Usually this energy is left out in the bookkeeping of the energy of the electromagnetic field. The subtracted density of zero point energy of the vacuum is infinite. Normally one deals with field physics at the level of special relativity, where such an infinite quantity can be disregarded. However, in general relativity there is no such thing as an arbitrary additive constant in the density of field energy. Energy density curves space, and an increase in energy density produces an increase of curvature. Our analysis of thermal geons is based on the tacit assumption that the zero-point energy does not have to be counted, either as energy or as a source of curvature. We hope this point of view is correct, as it gives reasonable results in familiar situations. Nevertheless, a deeper approach to the problem of zero-point energy is needed—a problem whose overriding importance to all of field physics NIELS BOHR has often stressed.

APPENDIX

Appendix on ray-wave equivalence.

There is a close correlation between the field theory solutions of (44), (45), and (50) and the motion of a classical corpuscle of light or « pseudophoton » along a geodesic in the same gravitational field. Superposition of standing waves of slightly different Ω_{nl}, l, and m values allows one to build up a wave packet. This concentration of energy will remain the better defined in space and time the larger are the relevant values of l and n — that is, the shorter the wavelength of the disturbances of significant amplitude in comparison with the scale of distances over which the gravitational field changes appreciably. The correspondence between waves and pseudophoton orbits in the idealized limit which disregards the spreading of a wave packet may be analysed this way: 1) we pass from the wave itself to its phase,

$$\text{(A.1)} \qquad (\text{vector potential}) = \\ = (\text{slowly varying vector function of position}) \exp [i\cdot \text{phase}] ,$$

where $\exp[i\cdot\text{phase}]$ varies rapidly with position; 2) we approximate the differential equation for the phase by neglecting the slow change of the amplitude with distance in comparison with the rapid change of the phase with distance. Thus we pass from the accurate phase of (A.1) to the pseudophase (or eikonal) — the central concept in William Rowan Hamilton's method of treating problems in geometrical optics as well as in mechanics (*). The equation for the pseudophase has the Hamilton-Jacobi form

$$g^{\alpha\beta}(\partial\Phi/\partial x^{\alpha})(\partial\Phi/\partial x^{\beta}) = 0 . \tag{A.2}$$

[Instead of deriving this from the wave equation by the substitution (A.1), one can start directly with the picture of a surface propagating parallel to itself with the speed of light. The surface and its propagation with time can be expressed in the form

$$\Phi(x^1, \dots, x^4) = 17.2 . \tag{A.3}$$

Let x^4 be one value of the cotime, and x^1, x^2, x^3 the co-ordinates of one point on the surface at that time. Let $x^i + \mathrm{d}x^i$ denote a neighboring point on the same moving surface, $\Phi = 17.2$, at a slightly later time. The space and time separations of the two points are connected by the relation

$$(\partial\Phi/\partial x^{\mu})\,\mathrm{d}x^{\mu} = 0 . \tag{A.4}$$

The requirement that the surfaces of (A.4) move with the speed of light leads directly to (A.2)]; 3) we recognize not only single solutions, $\Phi(x^1 \dots x^4)$ of the pseudophase equation, but also a typical family of pseudophase functions

$$\Phi = \text{function of } (x^1, \dots, x^4;\ \beta^1, \beta^2, \beta^3) + \beta^4(\beta^1, \beta^2, \beta^3) , \tag{A.5}$$

where each number of the family is characterized by a specific set of values for the three numbers β^1, β^2, β^3. These numbers might correspond in the case of physical optics to components of the wave vector for a monochromatic wave, but need not have such an immediate interpretation. The fourth constant of integration β^4, represents an additive phase constant, always allowed because (A.2) contains only derivatives of the pseudophase, never Φ itself; 4) we impose the requirement of constructive interference. Several neighboring solutions of the wave equation of the form (A.1) are superposed in such a way as to build up a wave packet. To make this requirement clean cut, we go to the pseudophase picture, and enquire how a pseudophoton must move in order that it shall always lie at the point where four pseudophase functions of nearly identical β values have a common value. The pseudophase need not be constant along the path of the pseudophoton. It is only

(*) See, for example, J. L. SYNGE: *Geometrical Mechanics and de Broglie Waves* (Cambridge, 1954), chap. II; or L. LANDAU and E. LIFSHITZ: *The Classical Theory of Fields*, ref. (8), p. 271.

required that at each point of the path, $x^i(\sigma)$ the four pseudophase functions should have a common value:

$$\begin{aligned}\Phi(x(\sigma);\ \beta^1, \beta^2, \beta^3;\ \beta^4(\beta^1, \beta^2, \beta^3)) &= \\ = \Phi(x(\sigma);\quad & \beta^1 + \mathrm{d}\beta^1, \beta^2, \beta^3; \quad \beta^4(\beta^1 + \mathrm{d}\beta^1, \beta^2, \beta^3)) \\ = \Phi(x(\sigma);\quad & \beta^1, \beta^2 + \mathrm{d}\beta^2, \beta^3; \quad \beta^4(\beta^1, \beta^2 + \mathrm{d}\beta^2, \beta^3))\,, \\ = \Phi(x(\sigma);\quad & \beta^1, \beta^2, \beta^3 + \mathrm{d}\beta^3; \quad \beta^4(\beta^1, \beta^2, \beta^3 + \mathrm{d}\beta^3))\,,\end{aligned}$$

or

(A.6) $$\partial\Phi(x;\beta)/\partial\beta^s + (\partial\Phi/\partial\beta^4)(\partial\beta^4/\partial\beta^s) = 0 \qquad (=1, 2, 3):$$

These three equations connect the three position co-ordinates of the pseudophoton with the time, and therefore suffice completely to determine its motion. From (A.2) and its first derivatives with respect to the β's, this motion proceeds along a null geodesic,

$$\mathrm{d}^2x^k/\mathrm{d}\sigma^2 + \Gamma_{\mu\nu}{}^k\,(\mathrm{d}x^\mu/\mathrm{d}\sigma)\,(\mathrm{d}x^\nu/\mathrm{d}\sigma) - (\text{undetermined function of } \sigma)\,(\mathrm{d}x^k/\mathrm{d}\sigma) = 0\,,$$

as expected. As an illustration how one gets all details of the pseudophoton motion from (A.6), one can ask for the velocity components of the motion. For this one differentiates (A.6) once with respect to σ and solves for the $\mathrm{d}x^i/\mathrm{d}\sigma$ by the method of determinants, finding

(A.7) $$\mathrm{d}x^i/\mathrm{d}\sigma = f(\sigma)\{i\lambda\mu\nu\}(\partial^2\Phi/\partial x^\lambda\,\partial\beta^1)(\partial^2\Phi/\partial x^\mu\,\partial\beta^2)(\partial^2\Phi/\partial x^\lambda\,\partial\beta^3)\,.$$

Here the arbitrary functions $f(\sigma)$ in the solution appear because σ itself represented an arbitrary parametrization of the path of the pseudophoton. The same method gives the acceleration and other details of the motion.

For the spherically symmetric metric of the thermal geon the pseudophase propagation equation takes the form

(A.8) $$e^{-\lambda}(\partial\Phi/\partial r)^2 + r^{-2}(\partial\Phi/\partial\theta)^2 + (r\sin\theta)^{-2}(\partial\Phi/\partial\varphi)^2 - e^{-\nu}(\partial\Phi/\partial T)^2 = 0\,,$$

which possesses separable solutions of the form

(A.9) $$\begin{aligned}\Phi = \int_{r_{\min}}^{r} [1 - l(l+1)e^\nu/\Omega\, r^2]^{\frac{1}{2}}\,\Omega \exp\,[\lambda/2 - \nu/2]\,\mathrm{d}r\, + \\ + \int_{\theta_{\min}}^{\theta} [l(l+1) - m^2\sin^2\theta]^{\frac{1}{2}}\,\mathrm{d}\theta + m\varphi - \Omega T + \beta^4(\beta^1, \beta^2, \beta^3)\,.\end{aligned}$$

Here the three constants of integration, β^1, β^2, β^3, have been expressed in the form Ω, l, and m to bring out the identity between the pseudophase and the phase of the JWKB approximation to the solution of the wave equation. We can superpose waves of different l, m, and Ω values to build up a wave packet that will trace out the designated geodesic.

The nature of the geodesic curve is independent of its orientation; consequently it is sufficient to consider m values close to zero, corresponding to motion in a meridian plane. *Which* meridian can be specified in the wave picture by the relative phase or β^4 values with which one superposes waves of slightly different m values; in the eikonal formulation, by setting equal to zero the derivative of the pseudophase with respect to m; thus $\partial\Phi/\partial\beta^3 = \partial\Phi/\partial m = 0$ gives an equation for φ. However, as there is no interest in this angle, it is appropriate to overlook this relation, and set m equal to a fixed value: $m = 0$. Likewise the first equation of stationary pseudophase, $\partial\Phi/\partial\beta^1 = \partial\Phi/\partial\Omega = 0$ is also irrelevant for our purpose; we do not care *when* the pseudophoton arrives at a given point in its orbit. We are left with the second equation of constructive interference, $\partial\Phi/\partial\beta^2 = \partial\Phi/\partial l = 0$, to determine the *shape* of the geodesic:

$$0 = -\int_{r_{\min}}^{r} [r^2/e^\nu P^2 - 1]^{-\frac{1}{2}} \exp[\lambda/2]\, dr/r + \theta + \text{const.} \tag{A.10}$$

Here the quantity P is an abbreviation for the expression $[l(l+1)]^{\frac{1}{2}}/\Omega$ and represents the *impact parameter* of the pseudophoton — the distance of closest approach in the absence of gravitational forces. Evidently *this single constant determines the shape of the geodesic*, not Ω or l individually. From (A.10) we derive the properties of the geodesic already discussed in the main text and pictured in Fig. 1. All the information gained about geodesics carries over to the characteristic solutions of the wave equation. The limits of motion, $r_1(P)$ and $r_2(P)$, of the rays correspond to the points where the field amplitudes change from oscillation to exponential fall off. Inclination of the nodal surfaces of the field is closely related to the inclination of the rays; and the energy carried by the rays or the wave fields has to supply the gravitating mass that holds the geon together.

III. Classical Physics as Geometry.

Gravitation, Electromagnetism, Unquantized Charge, and Mass as Properties of Curved Empty Space (*).

C. W. MISNER (**) and J. A. WHEELER (*.*)

Lorentz Institute, University of Leiden - Leiden
Palmer Physical Laboratory, Princeton University - Princeton, N. J.

(Reprinted from *Ann. of Phys.*, **2**, 525-603 (1957))

« I transmit but I do not create;
I am sincerely fond of the ancient ».
CONFUCIUS

1. – Is the space-time continuum only an arena, or is it all? Classical physics, regarded as comprising gravitation, electromagnetism, unquantized charges and unquantized mass; all four concepts described in terms of empty curved space without any addition to accepted theory; the electromagnetic field as the « Maxwell square root » of the contracted curvature; unquantized charge described in terms of source-free Maxwell field in a multiply-connected space; unquantized mass associated with collection of electromagnetic field energy held together by its own gravitational attraction; history of ideas of physics as geometry; summary of paper.

Two views of the nature of physics in sharp contrast:

1) The space time continuum serves only as *arena* for the struggles of field and particles. These entities are foreign to geometry. They must be added to geometry to permit any physics.

2) There is nothing in the world except empty curved space. Matter, charge, electromagnetism, and other fields are only manifestations of the bending of space. *Physics is geometry.*

(*) Part VI of a critique of classical field theory. Part V appeared in *Phys. Rev.*, **97**, 51 (1956).

(**) National Science Foundation Predoctoral Fellow.

(*.*) Holder for part of the period of this work of a John Simon Guggenheim Fellowship at the Lorentz Institute of the University of Leiden.

To understand how far one can go in regarding classical physics as geometry is the object of this paper. Nothing will be said here about the fascinating issue [1] of quantizing this classical pure « geometrodynamics » (Table I).

TABLE I. – *The distinction between classical and quantum physics as envisaged in this paper* [a].

Classical physics as defined here	Description in terms of the geometry of empty curved space	Quantum physics: not discussed in this paper
Gravitation	Defined by curving of geodesics in a Riemannian space.	Gravitons; photons; spin; neutrinos; *quantization* of charge; *quantization* of mass; electrons, mesons and other particles; characteristic fields that do not have zero rest mass, apparently associated with some of these particles; particle transformation processes; also all phenomena where quantum fluctuations in the metric are more important than any static gravitational fields.
Electromagnetism	Determined by curvature, and its rate of change, in this same Riemannian space (Fig. 2).	
Unquantized charge	Manifestation of lines of force trapped in a multiply connected topology (Fig. 3).	
Unquantized mass	Geons: semistable collection of electromagnetic or gravitational wave energy held together by its own gravitational attraction.	
$G = 6.67\cdot10^{-8}$ cm³/g s² and c define no characteristic length, mass, or time. Electromagnetic field $F_{\mu\nu}$ (in gauss or electrostatic volts per cm or $(\text{g/cm s}^2)^{\frac{1}{2}}$) translated into purely geometric quantities $f_{\mu\nu}$ (in units of cm⁻¹) by multiplication with $G^{\frac{1}{2}}/c^2 = 1/3.49\cdot10^{24}$ G cm.		G, c, and $\hbar$ define the characteristic units first introduced by Planck: $L^* = (\hbar G/c^3)^{\frac{1}{2}} = 1.63\cdot10^{-33}$ cm; $T^* = L^*/c$; and $M^* = (\hbar c/G)^{\frac{1}{2}} = 2.18\cdot10^{-5}$ g.

(*a*) The unquantized classical charge and mass in the table have no *direct* relation whatsoever with the elementary masses and charges that are seen in the quantum world of physics.

In describing classical physics (in the sense of Table I) as geometry, we invent no new ideas. We accept Maxwell's 1864 electrodynamics of empty space, his formulation of the stress-momentum-energy tensor of the electromagnetic field, and Einstein's forty-one-year old description of gravitation in terms of curved space. Restricting attention to classical concepts (Table I) we take as source of metric fields, $g_{\mu\nu}$, *exclusively* electromagnetic fields,

(1) See, however, C. W. MISNER: *Rev. Mod. Phys.*, **29**, 497 (1957) and J. A. WHEELER: *Ann. of Phys.*, **2**, 604 (1957) for a partial discussion of some features of this problem.

$F_{\alpha\beta}=(c^2/G^{\frac{1}{2}})f_{\alpha\beta}$, and electromagnetic fields that are themselves *free of all sources* (²):

(1) $(3!)^{-1}[\alpha\beta\gamma\delta](\partial f_{\beta\gamma}/\partial x^\delta) = 0$ (half of Maxwell's equations),

(2) $(-g)^{-\frac{1}{2}}(\partial/\partial x^\beta)(-g)^{\frac{1}{2}}f^{\alpha\beta} = 0$ (the other half),

$$« \Box g_{\alpha\beta} » \equiv R - \tfrac{1}{2}g_{\alpha\beta}R = 2f_{\alpha\delta}f_\beta{}^\delta - \tfrac{1}{2}g(f_{\sigma\tau}f^{\sigma\tau})$$

(3) (curvature of metric by Maxwell stress-momentum-energy density).

These equations describe electromagnetism and gravitation as a coupled but closed dynamical system.

(²) We accept the following familiar conventions: Greek labels refer to four dimensional space; Latin labels refer to three dimensional space. The fourth co-ordinate, x^0 ($=T=ct=$« cotime » in flat space) receives the label 0 to prevent confusion with the occasional use in special relativity of x^4 to designate ict. The proper distance, ds, or proper interval of cotime, $d\tau$, between two neighboring events is given by

$$(ds)^2 = -(d\tau)^2 = g_{\alpha\beta}dx^\alpha dx^\beta .$$

In flat space and Euclidean co-ordinates, the metric tensor is diagonal with -1, 1, 1, 1 in the diagonal. Many of the considerations of this article deal with space like manifolds, on which it is a great convenience to have a positive definite metric, as given by the present convention (see also PAULI, LANDAU and LIFSHITZ, JAUCH and ROHRLICH). The determinant, $|g_{\alpha\beta}|$, of the metric in four-space is designated by g, and the determinant, $|g_{ik}|$, of the metric on a spacelike manifold is designated by ${}^3g$. Other important quantities include the bending coefficients,

$$\Gamma_{\alpha\beta,\gamma} = \tfrac{1}{2}(\partial g_{\beta\gamma}/\partial x^\alpha + \partial g_{\alpha\gamma}/\partial x^\beta - \partial g_{\alpha\beta}/\partial x^\gamma) ;$$

the Riemann curvature tensor, with its twenty distinct components, $R_{\mu\nu\sigma\tau}$, where

$$R_\nu{}^\mu{}_{\sigma\tau} = \partial\Gamma_{\nu\tau}{}^\mu/\partial x^\sigma - \partial\Gamma_{\nu\sigma}{}^\mu/\partial x^\tau + \Gamma_{\sigma\eta}{}^\mu\Gamma_{\nu\tau}{}^\eta - \Gamma_{\tau\eta}{}^\mu\Gamma_{\nu\sigma}{}^\eta ;$$

the symmetric Ricci tensor or contracted Riemann tensor,

$$R_{\mu\sigma} = R_\mu{}^\alpha{}_{\alpha\sigma} ;$$

the curvature invariant, $R=R_\alpha{}^\alpha$; the generalization of the notion of d'Alembertian of the gravitational potentials,

$$« \Box g_{\mu\nu} » = R_{\mu\nu} - \tfrac{1}{2}g_{\mu\nu}R ;$$

and the electromagnetic potentials, A_α, such that

$$F_{\alpha\beta} = \partial A_\beta/\partial x^\alpha - \partial A_\alpha/\partial x^\beta .$$

The alternating quantity that is often written in the form $\varepsilon_{\alpha\beta\gamma\delta}$ is not a tensor and is here written in the form $[\alpha\beta\gamma\delta]$. It changes sign on interchange of any two indices, and $[0123]$ has the value unity. The dual, $(*F)_{\mu\nu}$, of an alternating tensor, $F_{\alpha\beta}$, is defined by the equation

$$(*F)_{\mu\nu} = \tfrac{1}{2}(-g)^{\frac{1}{2}}[\mu\nu\sigma\tau]g^{\sigma\alpha}g^{\tau\beta}F_{\alpha\beta} .$$

Associated with the geometrized electromagnetic field quantities, $f_{\alpha\beta}=(G^{\frac{1}{2}}/c^2)F_{\alpha\beta}$, are

Solve eq. (3) for the reduced electromagnetic field, $f_{\sigma\tau}$, in terms of the contracted curvature tensor, $R_{\alpha\beta}$. Substitute the resulting espressions into Maxwell's equations. Thus re-express the content of the Maxwell-Einstein equations in a *purely geometrical form*. This program was carried out by RAINICH in an important paper (3) that has long lain neglected. The result is simple. 1) The symmetric Ricci tensor, $R_{\alpha\beta}$, can be expressed as the « Maxwell square », as in eq. (3), of an alternating tensor, $f_{\sigma\tau}$, if and only if this tensor (Fig. 1) *a*) has zero trace and *b*) has a square which is a multiple of the unit matrix:

(4) $$R \equiv R_\alpha^{\ \alpha} = 0 ,$$

(5) $$R_\alpha^{\ \beta} R_\beta^{\ \gamma} = \delta_\alpha^{\ \gamma}(R_{\sigma\tau}R^{\sigma\tau}/4) .$$

We therefore demand these conditions of the Ricci tensor. 2) Then this contracted curvature tensor determines the local value of the reduced electromagnetic field tensor, $f_{\sigma\tau}$, uniquely up to an arbitrary angle, α, by way of an equation which we write symbolically in the form (4)

(6) $$f_{\sigma\tau} = (R_{\text{Maxwell root}})_{\sigma\tau}\cos\alpha + (*R_{\text{Maxwell root}})_{\sigma\tau}\sin\alpha .$$

---

the geometrized electromagnetic potentials, $a_\alpha = (G^{\frac{1}{2}}/c^2)A_\alpha$, which are dimensionless. In flat space and Euclidean co-ordinates,

$$\mathrm{d}x^1 = \mathrm{d}x_1 = \text{displacement in } x\text{-direction} ,$$
$$\mathrm{d}x^0 = -\mathrm{d}x_0 = \text{interval of cotime} ,$$
$$A^1 = A_1 = x\text{-component of usual vector potential} ,$$
$$A^0 = -A_0 = \text{usual scalar potential, V (es volts)} ,$$
$$F_{23} = -F_{32} = x\text{-component of magnetic field} ,$$
$$F_{10} = -F_{01} = x\text{-component of electric field} .$$

(3) G. Y. RAINICH: *Trans. Am. Math. Soc.*, **27**, 106 (1925). Even Rainich's later book, *The Mathematics of Relativity* (New York, 1950), does not summarize this paper, primarily because he was motivated by a different view of classical physics than that under investigation in the present article. We undertook the problem of expressing (1), (2), and (3) in « already unified form », and one of us (C. M.) independently derived Rainich's results, before becoming aware of his valuable contribution. The possibility of such an « already unified theory » was first suggested to us by Dr. H. EVERETT.

(4) We wish to express our appreciation to Prof. V. BARGMANN for bringing eq. (5) and (6) to our attention two years ago, noting that their gist had been independently discovered by several investigators, and expressing their content in essentially the above exceptionally simple form. An early proof is given by Rainich himself (3). The result is implicit in Theorem V of a study by J. L. SYNGE: *Principal Null-Directions defined in Space-Time by an Electromagnetic Field*, no. 1 in the University of Toronto Studies, Applied Mathematics Series, (Toronto, 1935); see also SYNGE's book *Relativity: The Special Theory* (Amsterdam, 1956), p. 326, a paper by W. B. BONNOR: *Proc. Phys. Soc.*, A **67**, 225 (1954), and the thesis of L. MARIOT: *Thesis. Le champ électromagnétique pur en relativité générale*, (Paris), mimeograph, privately reproduced (April 6, 1957), for which we are indebted to M. MARIOT.

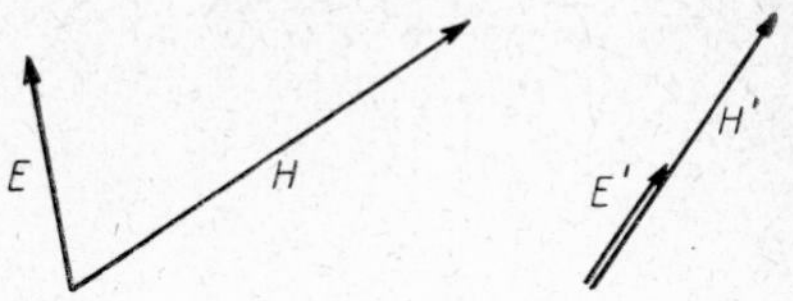

Fig. 1. – Simplification of the analysis of the Maxwell stress-momentum-energy tensor by passage to a locally Lorentz frame of reference in which $\boldsymbol{E}$ and $\boldsymbol{H}$ are parallel. Left: electric and magnetic vectors in the original reference system. Calculate the energy flux, $c(\boldsymbol{E}\times\boldsymbol{H})/4\pi$, and the energy density, $(\boldsymbol{E}^2+\boldsymbol{H}^2)/8\pi$, and their ratio, $c\boldsymbol{n}$ tgh 2θ, where $\boldsymbol{n}$ is a unit vector. Right: view the fields in a frame of reference moving with the velocity $\boldsymbol{v}=c\boldsymbol{n}$ tgh θ (not $c\boldsymbol{n}$ tgh 2θ as in the original publication!). The energy flux must vanish. Therefore $\boldsymbol{E}'$ and $\boldsymbol{H}'$ must be parallel. Let their common direction be called the x' axis. There is a Maxwell tension $(\boldsymbol{E}'^2+\boldsymbol{H}'^2)$ along this axis, and equally strong Maxwell pressures along the two perpendicular y' and z' axes. Therefore the stress-momentum-energy tensor has the form

$$(F'^2/8\pi)\begin{pmatrix} -1 & & & \\ & -1 & & \\ & & 1 & \\ & & & 1 \end{pmatrix},$$

where F'^2 is an abbreviation for the invariant

$$F'^2 = \boldsymbol{E}'^2 + \boldsymbol{H}'^2 = [(\boldsymbol{E}'^2 - \boldsymbol{H}'^2)^2 + 4(\boldsymbol{E}'\cdot\boldsymbol{H}')^2]^{\frac{1}{2}} =$$
$$= [(\boldsymbol{E}^2 - \boldsymbol{H}^2)^2 + 4(\boldsymbol{E}\cdot\boldsymbol{H})^2]^{\frac{1}{2}} = [(\boldsymbol{E}^2 + \boldsymbol{H}^2)^2 - 4(\boldsymbol{E}\times\boldsymbol{H})^2]^{\frac{1}{2}}.$$

This tensor has two important properties: 1) its trace is zero 2) its square is a multiple of the unit matrix. Both features are invariant to change of co-ordinate system. They hold whether the Maxwell tensor is diagonal or not. — Conversely, consider a real symmetric tensor which enjoys the properties 1) and 2). One can find a co-ordinate system with a favored direction, x', which puts it in the above diagonal form. In particular, one can find at once the invariant field magnitude,

$$F' = [(8\pi \text{ Maxwell tensor})^2/(\text{unit matrix})]^{\frac{1}{4}}.$$

Then pick any angle α, and *define* vectors $\boldsymbol{E}'$ and $\boldsymbol{H}'$ that point in the favored direction, x', with magnitudes

$$E' = F' \sin\alpha, \qquad H' = F' \cos\alpha.$$

The vectors $\boldsymbol{E}'$ and $\boldsymbol{H}'$ are determined uniquely apart from the single freely disposable parameter, α. Transform the electromagnetic field so defined back to the original reference system. Operating on this field, the Maxwell prescription for the stress energy tensor will produce the symmetric tensor with which one started. — These proofs break down when the electromagnetic field is a null field, with $\boldsymbol{E}$ perpendicular to $\boldsymbol{H}$ and equal in magnitude to $\boldsymbol{H}$, but the statement in the text is still true.

3) The expression for the electromagnetic field in terms of the Ricci curvature is substituted into Maxwell's equations. The laws of electrodynamics thereby take on the following purely geometrical character. First, out of the derivative of the Ricci tensor form the vector a_τ *defined* by the equation

$$\alpha_\tau = (-g)^{\frac{1}{2}}[\tau\lambda\mu\nu]R^{\lambda\beta;\mu}R_\beta^{\ \nu}/R_{\gamma\delta}R^{\gamma\delta}. \tag{7}$$

(The null-case where $R_{\gamma\delta}R^{\gamma\delta}$ vanishes requires special treatment). Second, demand that the curl of this vector shall vanish:

$$\alpha_{\tau;\eta} - \alpha_{\eta;\tau} = \alpha_{\tau,\eta} - \alpha_{\eta,\tau} = 0 \,. \tag{8}$$

4) *This differential eq.* (8), *plus the algebraic eq.* (4) *and* (5), *summarize in complete geometrical form both the whole of source-free Maxwell electromagnetism in curved space, and Einstein's laws for the production of curvature by this field.* These three equations, (4), (5), (8), comprise what we shall call « *already* unified field theory ». Electric and magnetic fields are not signals to *invent* a unified field theory or to introduce one or another new kind of geometry. The « *already* unified field theory » of Maxwell, Einstein and Rainich, summarized in this paper, describes electric and magnetic fields in terms of the rate of change of curvature of pure Riemannian geometry, and nothing more.

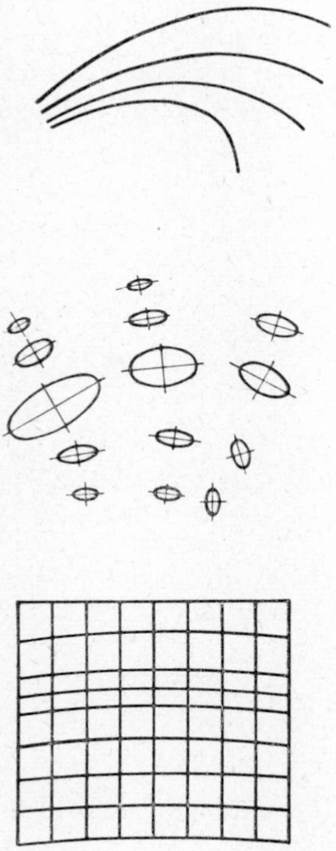

Fig. 2. – Relation between the electromagnetic field and geometry, schematically represented. Above: lines of force. Middle: Maxwell stress tensor due to these lines of force. This stress tensor serves as source of the gravitational field and equals the contracted curvature tensor of the space-time continuum, up to a multiplicative constant, according to Einstein. Below: the metric of four-space as distorted by this curvature. In brief, the electromagnetic field leaves its footprints on space. Moreover, these footprints on the metric are so specific and characteristic that from them one can work back and find out all that needs to be known about the electromagnetic field. One has a purely geometrical description of electromagnetism.

The nature of this unification can be stated in mathematical terms as follows: Maxwell's equations are of the second order, and so are Einstein's; the two sets of equations can be combined into one set of eq. (8) of the fourth order. In more physical terms, the electromagnetic field leaves an *imprint* [5] upon the metric that is so characteristic (Fig. 2), that from that imprint one can read back to find out all that one needs to know about the electromagnetic field.

Given a purely metric field that satisfies eq. (4), (5), and (8) of already unified field theory, one finds the electromagnetic field as follows. First, calculate everywhere the vector field α_μ of eq. (7). Second, from some standard point 0 calculate the integral

$$\alpha(x) = \int_0^x \alpha_\mu \, dx^\mu + \alpha_0 \,. \tag{9}$$

---

[5] We are indebted for this phrase to Prof. P. Bergmann.

Since α_μ is curl free, the integral is independent of path, so long as alternative paths are continuously deformable into one another. (When instead the space is multiply connected, new considerations will be needed.) We therefore have a dimensionless number or angle, α, defined as a function of position, up to an additive *constant*, α_0. Finally, we substitute this angle into eq. (6) to find the electric and magnetic field at every point in space.

We find that long established theory has a well defined means to describe gravitation and electromagnetism in terms of empty curved space. What about charge?

EINSTEIN emphasized that the field equations of electromagnetism and general relativity have a purely local character. They relate conditions at one point to conditions at points an infinitesimal distance away. They tell nothing about the topology of space in the large. EINSTEIN was led by Mach's principle (6) to consider a space not topologically equivalent to Euclidean space, a spherical or nearly spherical universe. But EINSTEIN confesses his indebtedness to a thinker who had still more far reaching ideas. RIEMANN (7) in his famous inaugural lecture envisaged a connection between physics and a curvature of space that would be sensible not only at very great distances, but also at very small distance: «... es kann dann in jedem Punkte das Krümmungsmaß in drei Richtungen einen beliebigen Werth haben, wenn nur die ganze Krümmung jedes meßbaren Raumtheils nicht merklich von Null verschieden ist; ...». Dying of tuberculosis twelve years later, occupied with an attempt at a unified explanation of gravity and electromagnetism, RIEMANN communicated to BETTI his system of characterization of multiply-connected topologies (8). What is the character of charge-free electromagnetism in a space endowed with such a multiply connected topology?

---

(6) A. EINSTEIN: *The Meaning of Relativity*, 3rd ed. (Princeton, 1950), p. 107.

(7) In the opening passage of this lecture B. RIEMANN (1826-1866), Habilitationsvorlesung of June 10, 1854 on entry into the philosophical faculty of the University of Göttingen, *Über die Hypothesen welche der Geometrie zu Grunde liegen*, in B. RIEMANN: *Gesammelte Mathematische Werke* (H. WEBER, ed.), 2nd ed., Reprinted by Dover Publications, (New York, 1953), declares that «the properties which distinguish space from other conceivable triply extended magnitudes are only to be deduced from experience» (translation of W. K. CLIFFORD: *Nature*, **8**, 14 (1873).

(8) H. WEYL: *Raum Zeit Materie*, 4th ed., Sect. **34** (Berlin, 1921); quotation from WEYL'S: *Philosophy of Mathematics and Natural Science* (translated by O. HELMER) (Princeton, 1949), p. 91, emphasizes that the field equations provide no means whatever to rule out either multiply-connected spaces, or spaces which are non orientable, such as a Klein bottle. He notes (original German in 1927; translation and revision in 1949) «that a more detailed scrutiny of a surface might disclose that, what we had considered an elementary piece, in reality has tiny handles attached to it which change the connectivity character of the piece, and that a microscope of ever greater magnification would reveal ever new topological complications of this type, *ad infinitum*. The Riemann point of view allows, also for real space, topological conditions entirely different from

One can outline a complete classification of the everywhere regular initial conditions for Maxwell's equations in a closed space. This analysis *forces* one to consider situations—such as described by one of us (⁹) (Fig. 3)—where there is a net flux of lines of force through what topologists would call a handle of the multiply-connected space and what physicists might perhaps be excused for more vividly terming a « wormhole ». The flux of lines of force that emerge from the mouth of a small wormhole appears to an observer endowed with poor resolving power to come from an elementary electric charge. But there is nowhere that one can put his finger and say, « This is where some charge is located (¹⁰). » Lines of force never end. This freedom from divergence by no means prevents changes in field strengths. Lines of forces which are not trapped into the topology can be continuously shrunk to extinction, as in familiar examples of electromagnetic induction and electromagnetic waves. However, lines of force which are trapped in wormholes cannot diminish in number. The flux out of the mouth of a wormhole cannot change with time, no matter how violent the disturbances in the electromagnetic field, no matter how roughly the metric changes, no matter how rapidly corresponding wormholes recede or approach, up to the moment when they actually coalesce and change the topology. Either Maxwell's equations, or Faraday's equivalent physical picture of lines of force, plus the conception of multiply connected space, force one to the conclusion that the wormhole flux remains invariant. *This constant of the motion represents the charge.*

The charge or wormhole flux is unquantized. It can have one value as well as another. It has nothing whatsoever directly to do with the quantized charge observed on the elementary particles of quantum physics. This circumstance is not an objection to the concept of a classical unquantized charge.

---

those realized by Euclidean space. I believe that only on the basis of the freer and more general conception of geometry which had been brought out by the development of mathematics during the last century, and with an open mind for the imaginative possibilities which it has revealed, can a philosophically fruitful attack upon the space problem be undertaken ». A. EINSTEIN and N. ROSEN: *Phys. Rev.*, **48**, 73 (1935). proposed in 1935 to regard ordinary space as connected with a duplicated « mirror » space by short tubes. This topology is much more particular than anything contemplated here or in the following paper (J. A. WHEELER: *Ann. of Phys.* **2**, 604 (1957)). EINSTEIN and ROSEN also took the electromagnetic field to have a *negative*-definite energy density, in contradiction to experience. We learn that Prof. J. L. SYNGE also once mentioned in a lecture at Dublin in 1947 the idea of multiply connected space.

(9) J. A. WHEELER: *Phys. Rev.*, **97**, 511 (1955).

(10) In 1895 the great physicist H. A. ROWLAND said, « ... electricity no longer exists, for the name electricity as used up to the present time signifies at once that a substance is meant, and there is nothing more certain than that electricity is not a substance ». (Quoted by K. K. DARROW: *Physics Today*, **9**, no. 8, 24 (1956). His words are apropos here!

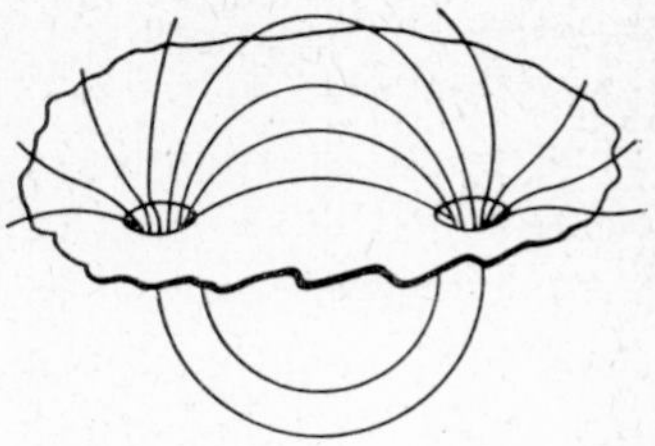

Fig. 3. – Symbolic representation of the unquantized charge of classical theory. For ease of visualization the number of space dimensions is reduced from three to two. However, the two dimensional curved and multiply-connected space is pictured as imbedded in a three dimensional Euclidean space. The third dimension, measured off the surface, has no physical meaning. Of course the topology and geometry of the 2-space receives its best mathematical formulation in intrinsic terms, without this imbedding of the manifold in a space of higher dimensionality. The 2-space is multiplyconnected, but free of all singularities. An imaginary ant crawling over the surface and entering the tunnel or handle or « wormhole » finds there the same two-dimensional space he experienced everywhere else. Electric lines of force that converge on the right-hand mouth of the tunnel continue to obey at each point Maxwell's equation div $\boldsymbol{E}=0$. The field is everywhere free of singularity. The lines of force have no escape but to continue through the tunnel. They emerge from the left-hand mouth. Outside the tunnel mouths the pattern of lines of force is identical with that due to equal positive and negative charges. An observer endowed with poor vision sees evidence for two point charges. He may even construct a boundary around the right-hand charge, determine the flux through this boundary, incorrectly apply the theorem of Gauss, and « prove » that there is a charge inside the boundary. He does not recognize that he has been making tacit and unjustified assumptions about the topology of space. He is not aware that his « boundary » does not bound any region interior to it. He assumes, either that Maxwell's equations fail in the vicinity of the charge, or that there exists there some magic substance at which lines of force end and to which he gives the name « electricity ». But a closer inspection discloses that the lines of force do not end. Neither is there any violation of Maxwell's equations for charge-free space. Nowhere can one place his finger and say, « Here there is some charge ». Such is the purely topological picture of unquantized electric charge which is adopted in this paper. This classical charge has no *direct* relation whatsoever to quantized electric charge. At this classical level there is a freedom of choice in the strength of the charge, and an individuality about the connection between one charge and another, that must be entirely changed in any proper *quantum* theory of electricity. — The distance along the wormhole from one mouth to the other need have no correspondence whatever with the distance in the open space between the same two mouths. The connection can be as short as the radius of the wormhole itself, for example, even when the openings are very far apart in the upper space, as one sees by bending the upper space to bring the backs of the two holes into coincidence (diagram reproduced from ref. ([9])).

It is a warning that quantized charge is quite another concept. This distinction is not unacceptable at a time when one has learned how great a difference there is between the « undressed » and « dressed » charge of quantum electrodynamics ([11]). To limit attention to purely classical unquantized charge will

---

([11]) See, for example, F. DYSON: *Advanced Quantum Mechanics*, mimeographed notes, (Ithaca, 1954), pp. 120, 167.

therefore not appear unreasonable in an article that restricts itself to classical physics (Table I).

Around the mouth of a wormhole lies a concentration of electromagnetic energy that gives *mass* to this region of space. Mass arises even in singly connected space, where there is no charge connected with the source-free Maxwell field. The equations of Maxwell and Einstein predict the possibility of a long-lived concentration of electromagnetic energy, or « geon », held together by its own attraction. Both in the multiply-connected space and in the singly-connected continuum, the mass with which one has to do is classical, non-localized, and unquantized. It has nothing whatsoever directly to do with the quantized mass of elementary particles.

Summarized in paradoxical form, the existing well-established already unified classical theory (eq. (4), (5), (8)) allows one to describe in terms of empty curved space.

1) gravitation without gravitation

2) electromagnetism without electromagnetism

3) charge without charge

4) mass without mass.

It has *nothing at all* to contribute directly to an understanding of

5) spin without spin

6) elementary particles without elementary particles,

or any other issues of quantum physics. Nevertheless, we would hardly have taken up the analysis of classical geometrodynamics if we did not hope ultimately to find out what, if anything, *quantum* geometrodynamics has to do with elementary particle physics. It is our long range objective to discover if quantum physics, like classical physics (Table I), can be expressed in terms of pure geometry, and nothing more.

It is not customary today to adopt either extreme view, either that space time is only an arena, or that it is everything. One analyzes the states of particles and fields into plane waves that move as foreign elements in a pre-assigned flat space. At the same time one thinks of the curvature of space, not as exactly zero, but only as very small over distances short compared to the extension of the universe. Einstein's geometrical description of gravitation is taken seriously. His attempts at an equally geometric description of electromagnetism—by *modifying* Riemannian theory—are recognized to be incompatible ([12]) with the well-tested Lorentz law of force and are rejected. Par-

---

([12]) L. Infeld: *Acta Phys. Pol.*, **10**, 284 (1950); J. Callaway: *Phys. Rev.*, **92**, 1567 (1953).

ticles, and fields other than gravitation, are considered to be added to geometry, not as derived from geometry. Nature can be said to be described today in a mixed fashion, partly in terms of pure geometry, partly in terms of foreign entities.

To go to the logical extreme, however, and think of a purely geometrical description of nature, was not a new idea even before one knew enough to distinguish between classical and quantum physics. The distinguished mathematician CLIFFORD delivered a paper to the Cambridge Philosophical Society on February 21, 1870 *On the Space-Theory of Matter*, in which he proposed that « in the physical world nothing else takes place but this variation [of the curvature of space], subject (possibly) to the law of continuity »; and later he spoke of considerations « which indicate that distance or quantity may come to be expressed in terms of *position* in the wide sense of the analysis situs »; and again about the finite volume of a uniformly curved space, but with the explicit statement that « The assumptions here made about the Zusammenhang of space are [merely] the simplest » ([13]). Before EINSTEIN, CLIFFORD, and RIEMANN—and Riemannian geometry—was there ever current, anything like the concept of physics as geometry? What were Newton's views of field theory and the idea that empty space is the universal building material? His letter to BENTLEY has long been known: « That one body may act upon another at a distance through a vacuum, without the mediation of anything else, by and through which their action and force may be conveyed from one to another, is to me so great an absurdity, that I believe no man, who has in philosophical matters a competent manner of thinking, can ever fall into it » ([14]). MAXWELL says, « We find in his "Optical Queries" and in his letters to Boyle, that Newton has very early made the attempt to account for gravitation by means of the pressure of a medium, and that the reason he did not publish these investigations "proceeded from hence only, that he found he was not able, from experiment and observation, to give a satisfactory account of this medium, and the manner of its operation in producing the chief phenomena of Nature". »

New insight into Newton's ideas and their origins comes from the recent scholarly and most interesting analysis by FIERZ ([15]). FIERZ cites especially

---

([13]) First quote from W. K. CLIFFORD: *Mathematical Papers* (R. TUCKER, ed.) (London, 1882), p. 21. Second and third quotes from W. K. CLIFFORD: *Lectures and Essays* (L. STEPHEN and F. POLLOCK, eds.), vol. **1** (London, 1879), pp. 244 and 322, respectively.

([14]) This and the following quotation come from notes of F. CAJORI: revision of Motte's English translation of I. NEWTON's *Mathematical Principles of Natural Philosophy* (Berkeley, 1934).

([15]) M. FIERZ: *Gesnerus*, **11**, 62 (1954).

PATRIZZI ([16]), who writes of space as a substance, « Spacium ergo hoc, quod ante mundum fuit, et post quod mundus est, et quod mundum at capit, et excedit, quidnam tandem est.... Quid ergo substantia ne est? Si substantia est, id quod per substat, spacium maxime omnium substantia est. » Also some of the Vedas of old India ([17]) suggest ([18]) that the idea is very old, that nature derives its whole structure and way of action from properties of space.

Can space be regarded as a marvellous creation of all-encompassing properties? Independent of the origins of this idea, both ancient and modern, let us now proceed to analyze it.

In Section **2** we recapitulate in present day notation the derivation of the equations of Rainich for already unified field theory. The starting point, the theory of Einstein and Maxwell, deals entirely with local properties and so does Rainich's final system of equations.

([16]) F. PATRIZZI: *Nova de Universis Philosophia ...*, part IV; *Pancosmia*, book I; *de Spacio Physico* (Venice, 1593).

([17]) *The Taittirîya Upanishad with commentaries* (translated by A. MAHADEVA SASTRI) (Mysore, 1903), pp.293 and 305-307. See also vol. **3** of *The Upanishads* (translated by SWAMI NIKHILANANDA) (New York 1956).

([18]) For very early ideas related to « physics is geometry » we have been referred by Prof. G. L. CHANDRATREYA to the Indian Vedas. In this connection we wish to thank SWAMI NIKHILANANDA who explains to us the relevant writings: « According to the Vedas, *akasa* (often translated as "space" or "ether") is the rudimentary first element from which the other elements, namely, air, fire, water, and earth, have evolved. These five are the only material elements spoken of by the Vedas. Hindu philosophers postulated five elements because a man reacts to the outside world in five ways: through his hearing, touch, sight, taste, and smell ... [quoting in this connection from Taittirîya Upanishad II. i. 3.] » Thus we find *akasa* as the primary element in this early (c. 700 B.C.) sketch of physics. (Brahman, although preceding *akasa*, is pure spirit, outside the realm of physics). We can say that in this physics space was the primary element out of which all else was to have come, only if we can satisfy ourselves that *akasa* meant something like the current word space. In this connection we quote the most authoritative early commentators on the Upanishad just mentioned ([17]). Sankarâchârya (A. D. 788-820) tells us « *Akasa* is that thing which has sound for its property and which affords space to all corporeal substances ». Then Sâya*n*a elucidates: « ... the power of *akasa* to afford space to all (corporeal) things constitutes its own peculiar nature ... And it has sound for its property. The echo heard in mountain-caves etc, is supposed to be inherent in *akasa* and is therefore said to be the property of *akasa* ». Except for the curious references to sound, these explanations seem to corroborate a tentative identification of *akasa* with space: a physicist might write « space provides room for all things » where the translator wrote « *akasa* affords space to all things ». The reference to sound is understood when we recall that the five elements were chosen to correspond to the five senses. Sankarâchârya writes « Thence, *i.e.*, from *akasa*, comes into being V*a*yu, the air, with two properties, the property of touch which is its own, and the property of sound belonging to *akasa* already evolved ». It is perhaps too much to expect that at such an early date men would know that sound is transmitted through the air, and not through empty space.

To pass from local to global or topological properties, and still to keep the discussion simple, we return in Section **2** to the more familiar dual language of metric *plus* field. We sketch out the necessary topological background, and introduce the theorem of Gauss and the theory of harmonic vector fields in the necessary generality. Much of the required mathematics is most readily expressed in terms of Cartan's calculus of exterior differential forms. Most results we give both in this notation and in the familiar tensor form. A few conclusions would appear so complicated in the tensor formalism that we omit their transcription to the conventional notation. We prove that Maxwell's equations demand the conservation of flux through each wormhole independently, thus justifying the identification of this flux with charge.

Section **4** deals with specific examples of non-singular multiply-connected metrics in non-singular form, to put into evidence the special case of a space free of either charge or mass—in the conventional sense of those words—which nevertheless exhibits mass. Next a non-singular form of the Reissner Nordström metric is exhibited. It describes a spherically symmetric space free of all « real » charge and mass which nevertheless exhibits both properties. Finally, a closed mathematical form is given for a class of metrics endowed with a plurality of wormhole mouths, each with its own charge and mass. The initial conditions being thus specified, the future evolution of the space with time is of course determined by the field equations. In other words, the arguments of EINSTEIN, INFELD, and HOFFMAN apply to this situation. The entire dynamics of the system of singularity-free charges and masses becomes a matter of pure geometrodynamics.

Section **5** outlines points that require further investigation to complete classical geometrodynamics and to extend its domain of application.

2. – Rainich's already unified field theory: the Maxwell tensor; duality; duality rotations; invariance of Maxwell tensor to duality rotation; complexion of field defined; square of Maxwell tensor; the algebraic relations on the curvature; the reverse problem — from the curvature to find the field; resulting differential equations of the curvature.

2·1. *The Maxwell tensor.* – We begin by recalling the relation between the electromagnetic field $F_{\mu\nu}$ and the Maxwell stress-momentum-energy tensor $T_{\mu\nu}$. This relation is purely algebraic. Hence we may concentrate our attention on a single point of space-time and, when convenient, use co-ordinates that give the metric components, $g_{\mu\nu}$, their Minkowski values at that point. To keep geometry to the fore, we shall use instead of $\boldsymbol{F}$ the « geometrized » or « reduced » field strength, $\boldsymbol{f}=(G^{\frac{1}{2}}/c^2)\boldsymbol{F}$, and instead of the electric and magnetic field strengths, $\boldsymbol{E}$ and $\boldsymbol{H}$, the reduced field strengths, $\boldsymbol{e}=(G^{\frac{1}{2}}/c^2)\boldsymbol{E}$ and $\boldsymbol{h}=(G^{\frac{1}{2}}/c^2)\boldsymbol{H}$ (dimensions cm^{-1}). When the metric is Minkowskian, the reduced field tensor has the form

$$(10)\qquad f_{\mu\nu} = \begin{bmatrix} 0 & -e_x & -e_y & -e_z \\ e_x & 0 & h_z & -h_y \\ e_y & -h_z & 0 & h_x \\ e_z & h_y & -h_x & 0 \end{bmatrix} (\mathrm{cm}^{-1}) ;$$

and the dual tensor,

$$(11)\qquad *f_{\mu\nu} = \tfrac{1}{2}(-g)^{\frac{1}{2}}[\mu\nu\alpha\beta]f^{\alpha\beta} ,$$

differs from $\boldsymbol{f}$ only by the interchange $\boldsymbol{e} \to \boldsymbol{h}$, $\boldsymbol{h} \to -\boldsymbol{e}$. Two familiar invariants form themselves out of the field tensor:

$$(12)\qquad \begin{cases} \boldsymbol{f}^2 \equiv \frac{1}{2}f_{\mu\nu}f^{\mu\nu}\ (= \boldsymbol{h}^2 - \boldsymbol{e}^2 \text{ in a Minkowski frame}), \\ \boldsymbol{f}\times\boldsymbol{f} \equiv \frac{1}{2}f_{\mu\nu}{*f}^{\mu\nu} (= 2\boldsymbol{e}\cdot\boldsymbol{h} \text{ in a Minkowski frame}) . \end{cases}$$

The equations connecting the contracted curvature tensor with the stress tensor, and that in turn with the field,

$$(13)\qquad R_{\mu\nu} - \tfrac{1}{2}g_{\mu\nu}R = (8\pi G/c^4)T_{\mu\nu} = (8\pi G/c^4)[(1/4\pi)(F_{\mu\alpha}F_\nu^{\ \alpha} - \tfrac{1}{4}g_{\mu\nu}F_{\alpha\beta}F^{\alpha\beta})] ,$$
$$= 2(f_{\mu\alpha}f_\nu^{\ \alpha} - \tfrac{1}{4}g_{\mu\nu}f_{\alpha\beta}f^{\alpha\beta}) \equiv \mathfrak{T}(\boldsymbol{f})$$

justify one in using interchangeably for the quantity on the right the terms « reduced » or « geometrized » stress energy tensor, or contracted curvature tensor, insofar as one deals with pure geometrodynamics. In the Minkowski frame of reference, typical components of (13) are

$R_{00} = R^{00} = -R_0^{\ 0} = (\boldsymbol{e}^2 + \boldsymbol{h}^2) = (8\pi G/c^4)$ (energy density);

$-R_{10} = R^{10} = R_1^{\ 0} = 2\boldsymbol{e}\times\boldsymbol{h} = (8\pi G/c^4)$ (density of c times x-component of momentum) $= (8\pi G/c^4)$ (flow of electromagnetic energy per cm^2 of area normal to x and per cm of elapsed cotime);

$R_{11} = R^{11} = R_1^{\ 1} = (-e_x^2 + e_y^2 + e_z^2 - h_x^2 + h_y^2 + h_z^2) = (8\pi G/c^4)$ (pressure) $=$ $= (8\pi G/c^4)$ (force exerted in x direction, per unit area normal to x, by electromagnetic fields in medium at $x - \varepsilon$, acting on medium at $x + \varepsilon$);

$R_{12} = R^{12} = R_1^{\ 2} = -2e_xe_y - 2h_xh_y = (8\pi G/c^4)$ (shear) $= (8\pi G/c^4)$ (force exerted in x direction, per unit area normal to y, by electromagnetic forces due to medium ad $y - \varepsilon$ acting upon medium at $y + \varepsilon$).

The invariance of the stress energy tensor under the interchange $\boldsymbol{e} \to \boldsymbol{h}$ $\boldsymbol{h} \to -\boldsymbol{e}$, is apparent from (14), but does not show itself clearly in (13). Therefore it is preferable to rewrite the reduced stress tensor, or the « Maxwell square of $\boldsymbol{f}$ », on the right-hand side of (13) in the more symmetrical form

$$\mathfrak{T}(\boldsymbol{f}) = f_{\mu\alpha} f_{\nu}^{\ \alpha} + {*f_{\mu\alpha}} {*f_{\nu}^{\ \alpha}} , \tag{14a}$$

as follows from the identity [19]

$$f_{\mu\alpha} f^{\nu\alpha} - {*f_{\mu\alpha}} {*f^{\nu\alpha}} = \tfrac{1}{2} \delta_{\mu}^{\ \nu} f_{\alpha\beta} f^{\alpha\beta} \equiv \delta_{\mu}^{\ \nu} \boldsymbol{f}^2 . \tag{15}$$

2·2. *Duality rotation* [4]. – The stress tensor, or Maxwell square of $\boldsymbol{f}$, shows a further symmetry. Note that the operation of taking the dual of $\boldsymbol{f}$, twice repeated, leads back to $-\boldsymbol{f}$, so that the square of the operation $*$ is the negative of the identity operation. Consider therefore an angle α and define the operation $e^{*\alpha}$ by the equation

$$e^{*\alpha} \boldsymbol{f} = \boldsymbol{f} \cos\alpha + {*\boldsymbol{f}} \sin\alpha . \tag{16}$$

In a Minkowski co-ordinate system this operation takes the form

$$\begin{cases} h_{x\ \text{new}} = h_x \cos\alpha + e_x \sin\alpha \\ e_{x\ \text{new}} = - h_x \sin\alpha + e_x \cos\alpha \end{cases} \qquad \text{(same for } x, y, z) . \tag{17}$$

This operation appears at first to be an ordinary rotation: applied to any linearly polarized monochromatic wave, with $|\boldsymbol{e}| = |\boldsymbol{h}|$ and $\boldsymbol{e} \perp \boldsymbol{h}$, it turns the direction of polarization through the angle α around the direction of propagation. However, when this operation is applied to less special fields, it produces no such simply describable result. Moreover, it treats all three space axes alike. It is not an ordinary rotation in 3-space. We shall therefore call it a *duality rotation*. It has the additivity property

$$e^{*\alpha} e^{*\beta} = e^{*\beta} e^{*\alpha} = e^{*(\alpha+\beta)} \tag{18}$$

and the special value

$$e^{*\pi/2} = * . \tag{19}$$

---

[19] A special case of the relation

$$A_{\mu\alpha} B^{\nu\alpha} - {*A_{\mu\alpha}} {*B^{\nu\alpha}} = \tfrac{1}{2} \delta_{\mu}^{\ \nu} A_{\alpha\beta} B^{\alpha\beta} ,$$

which is valid for every pair of antisymmetric tensors, $\boldsymbol{A}$, $\boldsymbol{B}$, in 4-space.

The dual of the duality rotation yields the field tensor

$$*(e^{*\alpha}\boldsymbol{f}) = -\boldsymbol{f}\sin\alpha + *\boldsymbol{f}\cos\alpha\,. \tag{20}$$

The duality rotation has the following important property as a consequence of (14), (16), and (20): *The Maxwell square of a duality-rotated field is identical with the Maxwell square of the original field*:

$$\mathfrak{T}(e^{*\alpha}\boldsymbol{f}) = \mathfrak{T}(\boldsymbol{f})\,. \tag{21}$$

The electric and magnetic fields individually are changed, but every component of the stress energy tensor is unaltered. In contrast (Table II) the duality

TABLE II. – *Contrast between proper Lorentz transformations and duality rotations.*

Quantity	General proper Lorentz transformation	Duality rotation
Components of the Maxwell tensor or Maxwell square of $\boldsymbol{f}$	Transformed	Unchanged
The invariants, $\boldsymbol{f}^2$ and $\boldsymbol{f}\times\boldsymbol{f}$	Unchanged	Transformed

rotation alters the invariants of the field. Make the definition

$$\boldsymbol{\xi} = e^{-*\alpha}\boldsymbol{f} \tag{22}$$

for a field which has undergone a duality rotation by the angle $-\alpha$. Then the invariants transform as by a rotation through the angle -2α:

$$\left\{\begin{aligned} \boldsymbol{\xi}^2 &= (\boldsymbol{f}\cos\alpha - *\boldsymbol{f}\sin\alpha)^2 \\ &= \boldsymbol{f}^2\cos 2\alpha - \boldsymbol{f}\times\boldsymbol{f}\sin 2\alpha\,, \\ \boldsymbol{\xi}\times\boldsymbol{\xi} &= \boldsymbol{f}^2\sin 2\alpha + \boldsymbol{f}\times\boldsymbol{f}\cos 2\alpha\,. \end{aligned}\right. \tag{23}$$

Assume that the invariants, $\boldsymbol{f}^2$ and $\boldsymbol{f}\times\boldsymbol{f}$, of the original field do not both vanish. Then choose the angle α so that the one invariant quantity, $\boldsymbol{\xi}\times\boldsymbol{\xi}$, is zero:

$$\operatorname{tg} 2\alpha = -(\boldsymbol{f}\times\boldsymbol{f})/\boldsymbol{f}^2\,. \tag{24}$$

Then solve for $\sin 2\alpha$ and $\cos 2\alpha$ up to a $\pm$ ambiguity and evaluate the other invariant, finding

$$\boldsymbol{\xi}^2 = \pm[(\boldsymbol{f}^2)^2 + (\boldsymbol{f}\times\boldsymbol{f})^2]^{\frac{1}{2}}\,. \tag{25}$$

Demand that the *minus* sign shall appear on the right, thus determining the angle 2α uniquely up to a positive or negative additive integral multiple of 2π. Then the field tensor $\boldsymbol{\xi}$ represents a pure *electric* field along the x-axis, or a Lorentz transformation thereof (Table III). We say that the original field

TABLE III. – *Transformations of the general (non-null) electromagnetic field tensor* $\boldsymbol{f}=(\boldsymbol{e},\boldsymbol{h})$ *in a locally Minkowskian reference system.*

Field values	At start	After canonical duality rotation
At start	$\boldsymbol{e}$, $\boldsymbol{h}$	$\boldsymbol{e}''$ and $\boldsymbol{h}''$ perpendicular, and $\boldsymbol{e}''$ greater than $\boldsymbol{h}''$
After canonical Lorentz transformation	$\boldsymbol{e}'$ and $\boldsymbol{h}'$ parallel to each other and to the x-axis	$\boldsymbol{e}$ parallel to x axis; $\boldsymbol{h}=0$

has received a duality rotation into an *extremal* field, or into an essentially *electric field*. In a preferred Lorentz system where this field has no magnetic components, and points along the x-axis, the field magnitude is

$$(26)\qquad \begin{cases} e_x''' = [(\boldsymbol{h}^2-\boldsymbol{e}^2)^2+(2\boldsymbol{e}\cdot\boldsymbol{h})^2]^{\frac{1}{4}}\,, \\ \quad\;\; = [(\boldsymbol{h}^2+\boldsymbol{e}^2)^2-2(\boldsymbol{e}\times\boldsymbol{h})^2]^{\frac{1}{4}}\,. \end{cases}$$

2·3. *The complexion of the field.* – Referred to an extremal, or essentially electric field, $\boldsymbol{\xi}$, as standard of reference, the actual field, $\boldsymbol{f}$, evidently arises by a duality rotation through the angle α:

$$f = e^{*\alpha}\boldsymbol{\xi}\,.$$

Under a Lorentz transformation the components of the three tensors, $\boldsymbol{f}$ and $\boldsymbol{\xi}$, and $*\boldsymbol{\xi}$, transform alike. *The angle* α therefore remains unchanged. *It is a significant and Lorentz-invariant scalar property of the field,* $\boldsymbol{f}$. We shall call the angle α the *complexion* of the electromagnetic field.

When the field $\boldsymbol{f}$ is a *null* field, with

$$(\boldsymbol{e}\cdot\boldsymbol{h})=0 \qquad\text{and}\qquad \boldsymbol{h}^2-\boldsymbol{e}^2=0$$

or

$$\boldsymbol{f}\times\boldsymbol{f}=0 \qquad\text{and}\qquad \boldsymbol{f}^2=0$$

then eq. (24) for the angle α becomes indeterminate. Then the complexion is not definable on a purely local basis.

2·4. *The square of the Maxwell tensor and the algebraic relation on the curvature.* – Now return to the case where the field is not a null field. Evaluate the Maxwell square—or stress-energy tensor—of the original field by using its equality to the Maxwell square of the extremal field (see eq. (21)) or the Maxwell square of the dual of the extremal field

$$\left\{\begin{aligned} &\mathfrak{T}_\mu^{\ \varkappa}(\boldsymbol{f}) = \mathfrak{T}_\mu^{\ \varkappa}(\boldsymbol{\xi}) = 2\xi_{\mu\alpha}\xi^{\varkappa\alpha} - \delta_\mu^{\ \varkappa}(\xi^2)\,, \\ &\mathfrak{T}_\varkappa^{\ \nu}(\boldsymbol{f}) = \mathfrak{T}_\varkappa^{\ \nu}(*\boldsymbol{\xi}) = 2\,{*\xi_{\varkappa\sigma}}\,{*\xi^{\nu\sigma}} + \delta_\varkappa^{\ \nu}(\boldsymbol{\xi}^2)\,. \end{aligned}\right. \tag{27}$$

Now *square* the Maxwell square of $\boldsymbol{f}$ by multiplying the first tensor by the second. The cross terms between $\boldsymbol{\xi}$ and $*\boldsymbol{\xi}$ that arise in the calculation reduce to zero by reason of the identity [19]

$$2\xi_{\mu\alpha}\,{*\xi^{\varkappa\alpha}} = \tfrac{1}{2}\,\delta_\mu^{\ \varkappa}\,\xi_{\sigma\tau}\,{*\xi^{\sigma\tau}} = \delta_\mu^{\ \varkappa}(\boldsymbol{\xi}\times\boldsymbol{\xi}) \tag{28}$$

and the extremal property, $\boldsymbol{\xi}\times\boldsymbol{\xi} = 0$. We also used in the evaluation the identity (15). We find for the square the result

$$\left\{\begin{aligned} \mathfrak{T}_\mu^{\ \varkappa}\mathfrak{T}_\varkappa^{\ \nu} &= 2(\boldsymbol{\xi}^2)(\xi_{\mu\alpha}\xi^{\nu\alpha} - {*\xi_{\mu\alpha}}\,{*\xi^{\nu\alpha}}) - \delta_\mu^{\ \nu}(\boldsymbol{\xi}^2)^2 \\ &= \delta_\mu^{\ \nu}(\boldsymbol{\xi}^2)^2 \\ &= \delta_\mu^{\ \nu}[(\boldsymbol{f}^2)^2 + (\boldsymbol{f}\times\boldsymbol{f})^2] \\ &= \delta_\mu^{\ \nu}[(\boldsymbol{h}^2 - \boldsymbol{e}^2)^2 + (2\boldsymbol{e}\cdot\boldsymbol{h})^2] \\ &= \delta_\mu^{\ \nu}[(\boldsymbol{h}^2 + \boldsymbol{e}^2)^2 - (2\boldsymbol{e}\times\boldsymbol{h})^2]\,. \end{aligned}\right. \tag{29}$$

The proof of the same result in the case of a null field is even simpler, $\boldsymbol{f}\times\boldsymbol{f} = 0$ and $\boldsymbol{f}^2 = 0$ and the right-hand side of eq. (29) vanishes. In summary, *the square of the Maxwell stress-energy-momentum tensor is a multiple of the unit matrix.* This beautiful and interesting relation is central in Rainich's already unified field theory. In terms of curvature components, it has the form

$$\mathfrak{T}_\mu^{\ \alpha}\mathfrak{T}_\alpha^{\ \nu} = R_\mu^{\ \alpha}R_\alpha^{\ \nu} = \delta_\mu^{\ \nu}(\tfrac{1}{4}R_{\alpha\beta}R^{\alpha\beta})\,. \tag{30}$$

Here the value of the constant is obtained by comparing the traces of the two sides of the equation. To this relation he adds the vanishing of the trace of the reduced Maxwell tensor,

$$\mathfrak{T}_\alpha^{\ \alpha} = R_\alpha^{\ \alpha} \equiv R = 0\,, \tag{31}$$

(eq. (4)), that follows directly from the equation of definition, (13), and the statement (eq. (14)) that the electromagnetic energy density is positive definite:

$$\mathfrak{T}_{00} = R_{00} \geqslant 0 \, . \tag{32}$$

In other words, for any time ike vector $\boldsymbol{v}$ the quantity

$$v^{\alpha} \mathfrak{T}_{\alpha\beta}(\boldsymbol{f}) v^{\beta} \tag{33}$$

is non-negative. Eq. (30), (31), and (32) summarize the algebraic relations on the curvature in already unified field theory.

It is *necessary* that the contracted curvature tensor $R_{\mu\nu}$ satisfy (30), (31), and (32) if it is to be representable as the Maxwell square of some antisymmetrical field tensor, $\boldsymbol{f}$. Fig. 1 derives the same conditions in a slightly different way.

It is evident from Fig. 1 that a suitable Lorentz transformation puts the tensor $R_{\mu\nu} = \mathfrak{T}_{\mu}^{\ \nu}$ associated with a non-null field $\boldsymbol{f}$, into a diagonal form,

$$[(\boldsymbol{f}^2)^2 + (\boldsymbol{f} \times \boldsymbol{f})^2]^{\frac{1}{2}} \begin{pmatrix} -1 & & & \\ & -1 & & \\ & & 1 & \\ & & & 1 \end{pmatrix} . \tag{34}$$

The diagonal form necessarily has this appearance for any symmetric tensor with a zero trace and a square which is a non-zero multiple of the unit matrix. The tensor $R_{\mu}^{\ \nu}$ defines what in the language of SCHOUTEN is a *two-bladed structure* ([20]) in space-time at the point in question ([21]). A rotation in the yz plane about the x-axis leaves the tensor (34) unchanged; electric and magnetic fields remain parallel to the x-axis (Fig. 1). That picture of parallel field vectors is also left unchanged by any Lorentz transformation in the x, T plane. The yz plane and the xT plane are the two *blades* defined by the Maxwell tensor $\mathfrak{T}_{\mu}^{\ \nu}(\boldsymbol{f})$, and therefore in turn defined by $\boldsymbol{f}$ itself.

In diagonal form the Maxwell tensor is characterized by a single parameter. To this parameter there are added only four additional parameters by the general 6-parameter proper Lorentz transformation, because rotations in the

---

([20]) J. A. SCHOUTEN: *Ricci-Calculus: An Introduction to Tensor Calculus and its Geometrical Applications*, 2nd ed. (Berlin, 1954), pp. 36 and 46. See also footnote ([4]) of present paper.

([21]) We are indebted to Prof. SCHOUTEN for several illuminating discussions.

yz and xT planes have no effect. Therefore a total of five parameters characterize the contracted curvature tensor, $R_{\mu\nu}$, of « electromagnetic Riemannian geometry » or « geometrodynamics » (Table IV)—this despite the fact that the

TABLE IV. – *Partial classification of Riemannian geometry.* (See C. D. PAPAKYRIAKOPOULOS: *Am. Math. Soc. Bull.*, **64**, 317 (1958) regarding the topological classification of all three-manifolds; also J. W. SMITH: *U. S. Nat. Acad. Sci., Proc.*, **46**, 111 (1960).

Feature	Name	Remarks
$R_{\alpha\beta\gamma\delta}=0$	Uncurved space	All such 3-spaces recently classified by L. AUSLANDER and L. MARKUS: *Amer. Math. Soc.* Memoir No. 30, *Flat Lorentz 3-Manifolds*, (Providence, 1959).
$R_{\mu\nu}=0$	Pure gravitational field	The 10 « local » components of $R_{\alpha\beta\gamma\delta}$ are zero, but the other 10 « remote action » components of $R_{\alpha\beta\gamma\delta}$ have to be found by solving the differential equations $R_{\mu\nu}=0$ for the metric. No free components for $R_{\mu\nu}$.
$R_\mu^{\ \mu}=0$; $R_{00}\geqslant 0$; $R_\mu^{\ \alpha}R_\alpha^{\ \nu} = \delta_\mu^{\ \nu}(\frac{1}{4}R_{\alpha\beta}R^{\alpha\beta}) = (\boldsymbol{h}^2-\boldsymbol{e}^2)^2+(2\boldsymbol{e}\cdot\boldsymbol{h})^2$	« Electromagnetic Riemannian geometry » or « geometrodynamics ».	Five free components for $R_{\mu\nu}$. Metric must be found by solving field equations of already unified theory.
$R_\mu^{\ \mu}=0$; $R_{00}\geqslant 0$; $R_\mu^{\ \alpha}R_\alpha^{\ \nu}=0$	Null field; $\boldsymbol{e}\cdot\boldsymbol{h}=0$ and $\boldsymbol{h}^2-\boldsymbol{e}^2=0$; a special case of electromagnetism	$R_{\mu\nu}=\mathfrak{T}_{\mu\nu}(\boldsymbol{f})=k_\mu k_\nu$, where $\boldsymbol{k}$ is a null vector; only three free parameters in $R_{\mu\nu}$.
$R_\mu^{\ \mu}=0$; $R_{00}\geqslant 0$; $R_\mu^{\ \alpha}R_\alpha^{\ \nu}\neq 0$; α = constant for all space and time	Static field; by a change of names (duality rotation) can be translated into a condition where there is an electric field but never any magnetic field; another special case of electromagnetism	Extra non local (differential) requirements imposed on $R_{\mu\nu}$ in addition to the standard field equation of already unified field theory
$R_{\mu\nu}$ arbitrary	Unrestricted Riemannian geometry	No physical laws

general $R_{\mu\nu}$ has 10 distinct components, and despite the fact that (29) and (31) can be said to constitute 10 conditions on these 10 components. Evidently these non-linear algebraic equations are not all independent.

It is not only *necessary*—as previously shown—but also *sufficient* that the contracted curvature tensor $R_{\mu\nu}$ *satisfy the Rainich conditions* (30), (31), and (32) in order that one be *then able to represent* $R_{\mu\nu}$ *as the Maxwell square of an electromagnetic field* tensor, $f_{\mu\nu}$. Moreover, this field tensor is *unique* up to a duality rotation. We call this field tensor the *Maxwell root* of the Ricci curvature tensor, $R_{\mu\nu}$. We give separately the proofs for the cases where $R_{\mu\nu}$ is not a null tensor and where it *is* a null tensor ($R_{\mu\nu}R^{\mu\nu}=0$; only 3 free parameters left in $R_{\nu\mu}$).

1) Form the « Ricci part » $E_{\tau\sigma}{}^{\mu\nu}$ of the Riemannian tensor

$$E_{\tau\sigma}{}^{\mu\nu} \equiv \tfrac{1}{2}(-\delta_\tau{}^\mu R_\sigma{}^\nu + \delta_\sigma{}^\mu R_\tau{}^\nu - \delta_\sigma{}^\nu R_\tau{}^\mu + \delta_\tau{}^\nu R_\sigma{}^\mu)\,. \tag{35}$$

It has the same symmetries as the Riemann curvature tensor, contracts to the same Ricci curvature tensor,

$$E_{\tau\alpha}{}^{\alpha\nu} = -\tfrac{1}{2}R_\tau{}^\nu + 2R_\tau{}^\nu - \tfrac{1}{2}R_\tau{}^\nu + 2R_\alpha{}^\alpha\delta_\tau{}^\nu = R_\tau{}^\nu \equiv R_{\tau\alpha}{}^{\alpha\nu}\,, \tag{36}$$

by virtue of the condition $R_\alpha{}^\alpha = 0$, and introduces the antisymmetry we need for taking the Maxwell root. 2) Define the *extremal Maxwell root* $\xi_{\mu\nu}$ of the Ricci tensor—a pure electric field—up to a single $\pm$ sign by the equation

$$\xi_{\mu\nu}\xi_{\sigma\tau} = -\tfrac{1}{2}E_{\mu\nu\sigma\tau} - \tfrac{1}{2}(R_{\alpha\beta}R^{\alpha\beta})^{-\frac{1}{2}}E_{\mu\nu\gamma\delta}E_{\sigma\tau}{}^{\gamma\delta}\,. \tag{37}$$

Find any given component, $\xi_{\mu\nu}$, up to a $\pm$ sign by setting $(\sigma, \tau) = (\mu, \nu)$ and taking the root of (37). Then use (37) to determine the relative sign of different components, $\xi_{\mu\nu}$ and $\xi_{\sigma\tau}$. The consistency of the magnitudes is guaranteed by the Rainich conditions.

The prescription just given for the Maxwell square root is checked most easily in a Minkowskian reference system where the Ricci curvature tensor has the diagonal form

$$R_\mu{}^\nu = \begin{pmatrix} -(\xi_{01})^2 & & & \\ & -(\xi_{01})^2 & & \\ & & +(\xi_{01})^2 & \\ & & & +(\xi_{01})^2 \end{pmatrix}, \tag{38}$$

where ξ_{01} is a real positive number, known as soon as $R_\mu{}^\nu$ is known. Use this number to *define* an antisymmetrical extremal field tensor, $\boldsymbol{\xi}$, of which all the components vanish in the present Lorentz system except ξ_{01} and $\xi_{10} = -\xi_{01}$. Then the dual of this tensor has all components zero except

$$(*\xi)_{23} = -(*\xi)_{32} = -\xi_{01}\,.$$

Thus the extremal field has the properties

$$\boldsymbol{\xi}^2 = \tfrac{1}{2}\xi_{\alpha\beta}\xi^{\alpha\beta} = -(\xi_{01})^2 =$$

$$= \begin{pmatrix}\text{magnetic component of}\\ \text{reduced extremal field}\end{pmatrix}^2 - \begin{pmatrix}\text{electric component of}\\ \text{reduced extremal field}\end{pmatrix}^2 = -\tfrac{1}{2}(R_{\mu\nu}R^{\mu\nu})^{\frac{1}{2}};$$

$$\boldsymbol{\xi}\times\boldsymbol{\xi} = 0 = (\text{magnetic component})\cdot(\text{electric component})\ ;$$

$$(*\xi)^2 = +(\xi_{01})^2 = -\boldsymbol{\xi}^2\ ; \qquad *\xi\times *\xi = 0\ . \tag{39}$$

In this same Minkowski frame the only non-vanishing distinct components of the tensor E of (35) are

$$E_{01}{}^{01} = -\tfrac{1}{2}(R_1{}^1 + R_0{}^0) = (\xi_{01})^2$$

and

$$E_{23}{}^{23} = -\tfrac{1}{2}(R_3{}^3 + R_2{}^2) = -(\xi_{01})^2 = -(*\xi_{23})^2\ . \tag{40}$$

Therefore the general tensor component of C can be written in the covariant form

$$E_{\alpha\beta\gamma\delta} = -\xi_{\alpha\beta}\xi_{\gamma\delta} - *\xi_{\alpha\beta}*\xi_{\gamma\delta}\ . \tag{41}$$

The product of this tensor by itself has the value

$$\begin{cases} E_{\alpha\beta\gamma\delta}E^{\gamma\delta}{}_{\mu\nu} = 2(\xi_{01})^2(-\xi_{\alpha\beta}\xi_{\mu\nu} + *\xi_{\alpha\beta}*\xi_{\mu\nu}) \\ \qquad = (R_{\sigma\tau}R^{\sigma\tau})^{\frac{1}{2}}(-\xi_{\alpha\beta}\xi_{\mu\nu} + *\xi_{\alpha\beta}*\xi_{\mu\nu})\ . \end{cases} \tag{42}$$

by virtue of the properties (39) of the extremal field. Multiply (41) by $-\tfrac{1}{2}$ and (42) by $-\tfrac{1}{2}(R^{\sigma\tau}R_{\sigma\tau})^{-\frac{1}{2}}$ and add, to cancel out the terms in the dual field. There results eq. (37) for the components of the reduced extremal electromagnetic field tensor. Being a tensor equation true in the simple co-ordinate system, it must be true in all co-ordinate systems. So much for the machinery for taking the Maxwell square root when the Ricci tensor is non-null; that is, when its square is a non-zero multiple of the unit matrix.

Consider now the other case where the contracted curvature tensor is a null tensor,

$$R_{\mu\nu}R^{\mu\nu} = 0\ , \tag{43}$$

but a tensor which is not identically zero. As before, discuss the tensor in a Minkowski reference system, where the components, $g_{\mu\nu}$, of the metric tensor have their Lorentz values. The frame of reference is still free to the extent of a 6-parameter Lorentz transformation. Make such a rotation in 3-space (3 parameters) as will diagonalize the 3×3, space-space part of $R_{\mu\nu}$; thus, $R_{12}=R_{23}=$ $=R_{31}=0$. The vanishing of the square of $R_\mu{}^\nu$ (Table IV),

$$(g^{\alpha\beta})_{\text{Lorentz}} R_{\mu\alpha} R_{\beta\nu} = 0\,, \tag{44}$$

then makes conditions of the form

$$\text{time-time:} \qquad -R_{00}^2 + R_{10}^2 + R_{20}^2 + R_{30}^2 = 0\,, \tag{45}$$

$$\text{time space:} \qquad -R_{00}R_{01} + R_{01}R_{11} + 0 + 0 = 0\,, \tag{46}$$

$$\text{space}_1\text{-space}_1\text{:} \qquad -R_{01}^2 + R_{11}^2 + 0 + 0 = 0\,, \tag{47}$$

$$\text{space}_1\text{-space}_2\text{:} \qquad -R_{10}R_{02} + 0 + 0 + 0 = 0\,. \tag{48}$$

We conclude from equations of the type (48) that only one of the components, R_{01}, R_{02}, R_{03}, can differ from zero. Let this non-zero component be R_{01}, and let the sense of the x axis be so chosen that R_{01} is a negative quantity, $-2\varkappa^2$. Then R^{01} is positive, corresponding to a Poynting flux in the plus x direction. Then from eq. (45)–(48) plus the requirement, $R_{00}\geqslant 0$, of positive definite energy density it follows that the Ricci curvature tensor has the form

$$R_{\mu\nu} = \begin{pmatrix} 2\varkappa^2 & -2\varkappa^2 & 0 & 0 \\ -2\varkappa^2 & 2\varkappa^2 & 0 & 0 \\ 0 & 0 & 0 & 0 \\ 0 & 0 & 0 & 0 \end{pmatrix} \begin{matrix} \text{row } 0 \\ 1 \\ 2 \\ 3 \end{matrix}\,. \tag{49}$$

This tensor may be written

$$R_{\mu\nu} = 2k_\mu k_\nu\,, \tag{50}$$

where $\boldsymbol{k}$ is the null vector

$$\begin{cases} k_\mu = (-\varkappa,\ \varkappa,\ 0,\ 0)\,; \\ \boldsymbol{k}^2 = k_\alpha k^\alpha = 0\,. \end{cases} \tag{51}$$

Being covariant and true in one reference system, the decomposition (50) is valid in any reference system.

There is no Lorentz transformation that will diagonalize a null Ricci tensor any more than there is a Lorentz transformation that will make a null vector timelike, or parallelize field vectors $\boldsymbol{e}$ and $\boldsymbol{h}$ that satisfy the null condition,

$(\boldsymbol{e}\cdot\boldsymbol{h}) = 0$, $\boldsymbol{h}^2 - \boldsymbol{e}^2 = 0$. The theorem that every symmetric tensor can be reduced to diagonal form does not hold when the metric is indefinite, a circumstance for the elucidation of which we are indebted to our colleague, Professor V. BARGMANN. This feature in no way prevents taking the Maxwell root of (49):

$$f_{\mu\nu} = \begin{pmatrix} 0 & 0 & -\varkappa & 0 \\ 0 & 0 & \varkappa & 0 \\ \varkappa & -\varkappa & 0 & 0 \\ 0 & 0 & 0 & 0 \end{pmatrix} \tag{52}$$

or

$$\boldsymbol{e} = (0, \varkappa, 0)\ ; \qquad \boldsymbol{h} = (0, 0, \varkappa) \tag{53}$$

as one checks by direct substitution in formula (13) or (14) for the Maxwell square. The tensor (49) describes a flow of energy in the x-direction at the speed of light, and (52) or (53) decompose the Poynting flux into factors, $\boldsymbol{e}$ and $\boldsymbol{h}$. The polarization direction alone is free in the Maxwell square root. Application of a duality rotation of parameter α to the field (52) rotates the polarization vector by the angle α about the direction of propagation, leaving unaltered its Maxwell square, $R_{\mu\nu}$.

The prescription for the Maxwell square of a null Ricci tensor can be summarized in covariant form: 1) Take the « ordinary » square root, k_μ, according to eq. (50). 2) Take a four-vector $\boldsymbol{v}$ which a) has unit magnitude,

$$\boldsymbol{v}^2 = v_\alpha v^\alpha = 1 \tag{54}$$

and b) stands normal to $\boldsymbol{k}$,

$$k_\alpha v^\alpha = 0 \tag{55}$$

and c) in the special Minkowski frame of (49) and (52)—for example—has the components

$$\boldsymbol{v} = (0, 0, 1, 0)\ . \tag{56}$$

3) Form the antisymmetrical product

$$f_{\mu\nu} = k_\mu v_\nu - k_\nu v_\mu \tag{57T}$$

or—in the so-called intrinsic notation—

$$\mathsf{V} = \boldsymbol{f}\boldsymbol{a}\ \boldsymbol{k}\ . \tag{57I}$$

4) Then *the reduced field tensor* (57) *is a Maxwell square root of the null tensor* $R_{\mu\nu}$, *and apart from a duality rotation, is the only Maxwell square root of* $R_{\mu\nu}$.

The reduced field $\boldsymbol{f}$ is a null field in the Minkowski frame which we have used by preference, as one easily shows from (51), (54), and (55). Therefore it is a null field in any other frame of reference. The same is true of the field after it has experienced a duality rotation

The effect of a duality rotation on $\boldsymbol{f}$ can be stated in terms of the constituent factors of $\boldsymbol{f}$; thus, $\boldsymbol{k}$ is left unchanged, and $\boldsymbol{v}$ is rotated about $\boldsymbol{k}$. However, $\boldsymbol{v}$ is never uniquely determined by $\boldsymbol{f}$: the new vector, $\boldsymbol{v}' = \boldsymbol{v} + (\text{constant})\ \boldsymbol{k}$, gives the same field, $\boldsymbol{f}$, and satisfies the conditions (54) and (55) as well as does $\boldsymbol{v}$ itself. Moreover, the descriptive word « polarization » should be taken cautiously, as indicating in the present context only the orientation of the mutually perpendicular pair of 3-vectors, $\boldsymbol{e}$ and $\boldsymbol{h}$. It does not stand for the polarization of a monochromatic directed wave train, which could not be determined without a knowledge of the field at nearby points—even if one had a monochromatic directed wave to talk about,

2·4.1. The two-way connection between field and curvature. – In summary, any reduced electromagnetic field tensor, $f_{\mu\nu}$, null or not, produces a Ricci curvature that satisfies the Rainich conditions. Conversely, any Ricci curvature tensor, null or not, that satisfies the Rainich conditions, has a Maxwell square root, f_{ik}, that is unique up to a duality rotation. In addition, in the non-null case the Ricci curvature—or the field—determines a structure with two blades, A and B, at each point in space-time.

2·4.2. The blades do not mesh. – How is the geometric structure at one point in space-time related to that at a neighboring point? A geometrical description of the electromagnetic field has to answer this question. It therefore appeared useful to us to raise the issue, what happens when one moves in the local two-dimensional surface, or tangent plane, of blade A to neighboring points where blade A is tilted at slightly different orientations. Will one arrive in this way at a well defined two-dimensional surface,

$$x^{\mu} = x_A^{\ \mu}(u, v)? \tag{58}$$

Or will the pattern of the blades lead to structures like those in a spiral dislocation in a crystal, so that one can get from one point to any other point by moving about on blades A via a suitably selected route? In this case no surface of the type (58) will exist. Does the *demand* that blades fit into a surface of type (58) lead to Maxwell's equations? We investigated and found that this demand is too restrictive to be satisfied by the general solution of the equation of electromagnetism. Therefore we decided to let Maxwell's equations speak for themselves. We expressed the electromagnetic field as the Maxwell root of the Ricci tensor, where

$$\text{(59)}\qquad \begin{cases} f_{\mu\nu} = e^{*\alpha}\xi_{\mu\nu}\,, \quad \text{or} \quad \boldsymbol{f} = e^{*\alpha}\boldsymbol{\xi}\,, \\ \boldsymbol{\xi} = \text{extremal Maxwell root of } R_{\mu\nu}\,, \end{cases}$$

inserted into Maxwell's equations,

$$\text{(60)}\qquad \begin{cases} f^{\mu\nu}{}_{;\nu} = 0\,, \\ *f^{\mu\nu}{}_{;\nu} = 0\,, \end{cases}$$

and learned at first hand what Rainich had already learned before us about the true geometrical content of electromagnetism.

2.4.3. Four of Maxwell's equations as consequences of the identities satisfied by the curvature or stress-energy tensor. – The eight eq. (60) of electrodynamics take the form

$$\text{(61)}\qquad \begin{cases} 0 = f^{\mu\nu}{}_{;\nu} = (\xi^{\mu\nu}{}_{;\nu} + *\xi^{\mu\nu}\,\partial\alpha/\partial x^\nu)\cos\alpha + (*\xi^{\mu\nu}{}_{;\nu} - \xi^{\mu\nu}\,\partial\alpha/\partial x^\nu)\sin\alpha\,, \\ 0 = *f^{\mu\nu}{}_{;\nu} = (-\,\xi^{\mu\nu}{}_{;\nu} - *\xi^{\mu\nu}\,\partial\alpha/\partial x^\nu)\sin\alpha + (*\xi^{\mu\nu}{}_{;\nu} - \xi^{\mu\nu}\,\partial\alpha/\partial x^\nu)\cos\alpha\,, \end{cases}$$

or, by simple combination

$$\text{(62)}\qquad \xi^{\mu\nu}{}_{;\nu} + *\xi^{\mu\nu}\,\partial\alpha/\partial x^\nu = 0\,,$$

$$\text{(63)}\qquad *\xi^{\mu\nu}{}_{;\nu} - \xi^{\mu\nu}\,\partial\alpha/\partial x^\nu = 0\,.$$

We now combine these equations in such a way as to separate the information they give about $\boldsymbol{\xi}$ and about α. Multiply (62) by $\xi_{\alpha\mu}$ and sum over μ. Use the properties (39) of $\boldsymbol{\xi}$ and the identity

$$\text{(64)}\qquad \xi_{\alpha\mu}\,*\xi^{\mu\nu} = 0\,,$$

which, being true in a simple Minkowski frame, and being covariant, is true in any frame. We find the result

$$\text{(65a)}\qquad \xi_{\alpha\mu}\,\xi^{\mu\nu}{}_{;\nu} = 0\,,$$

and, by similar reasoning starting from (63),

$$\text{(65b)}\qquad *\xi_{\alpha\mu}\,*\xi^{\mu\nu}{}_{;\nu} = 0\,.$$

Only four of the eight eq. (65*a*), (65*b*) are independent, as may be seen by going to the simple co-ordinate system where ξ_{01} and $*\xi_{23} = -\xi_{01}$ are the only non-vanishing components of $\boldsymbol{\xi}$. In these co-ordinates we see that the eight eq. (65*a*), (65*b*) are equivalent to the four independent equations

$$\xi_{\alpha\mu}\xi^{\mu\nu}{}_{;\nu} = *\xi_{\alpha\mu}*\xi^{\mu\nu}{}_{;\nu} = 0\,. \tag{66}$$

The identity [22]

$$\begin{aligned}\xi_{\alpha\mu;\nu}\xi^{\mu\nu} &= \tfrac{1}{2}(\xi_{\alpha\mu;\nu} + \xi_{\nu\alpha;\mu} + \xi_{\mu\nu;\alpha})\xi^{\mu\nu} - \tfrac{1}{4}(\xi_{\mu\nu}\xi^{\mu\nu})_{;\alpha}\\ &= *\xi_{\alpha\mu}*\xi^{\mu\nu}{}_{;\nu} - \tfrac{1}{2}(\boldsymbol{\xi}^2)_{;\alpha}\end{aligned}$$

and a similar equation for $*\xi$ in place of $\boldsymbol{\xi}$ puts eq. (66) in the form

$$\tfrac{1}{2}(\xi_{\alpha\mu}\xi^{\mu\nu} + *\xi_{\alpha\mu}*\xi^{\mu\nu})_{;\nu} = 0\,. \tag{67}$$

The quantity in parentheses is the Maxwell stress tensor. This quantity is to be identified with the Ricci curvature, whose trace, R, is zero so that (67) can be written in the form

$$[R_\mu{}^\nu - \tfrac{1}{2}\delta_\mu{}^\nu R]_{;\nu} = 0\,. \tag{68}$$

However, this condition is no requirement at all. BIANCHI proved that the Ricci tensor calculated from an *arbitrary* metric tensor will satisfy (68) *identically*. It has long been known that half of Maxwell's equations are given by these Bianchi identities. Now what have the other half of Mawxell's equations to say about the curvature of space?

2·4.4. Maxwell's other four equations demand that a certain vector combination of the curvature and its first derivative shall have zero curl. – Multiply (62) by $*\xi_{\beta\mu}$ and (63) by $\xi_{\beta\mu}$, sum over μ use (15), and find the result

$$*\xi_{\beta\mu}\xi^{\mu\nu}{}_{;\nu} + \xi_{\beta\mu}*\xi^{\mu\nu}{}_{;\nu} + \delta_\beta{}^\nu\boldsymbol{\xi}^2\,\partial\alpha/\partial x^\nu = 0$$

or

$$\partial\alpha/\partial x^\beta = \alpha_\beta\,, \tag{69}$$

---

[22] The second line of this identity is a special case of the identity

$$\tfrac{1}{2}A^{\alpha\beta}(B_{\mu\alpha;\beta} + B_{\alpha\beta;\mu} + B_{\beta\mu;\alpha}) = *A_{\mu\alpha}*B^{\alpha\beta}{}_{;\beta}\,,$$

which is valid for any two antisymmetrical tensors in 4-space.

where we make the *definition*

(70)
$$\alpha_\beta = -(*\xi_{\beta\mu}\xi^{\mu\nu}{}_{;\nu} + \xi_{\beta\mu}*\xi^{\mu\nu}{}_{;\nu})/\boldsymbol{\xi}^2 .$$

This vector expresses itself in terms of the Ricci curvature in the form

(71)
$$\alpha_\beta = (-g)^{\frac{1}{2}}[\beta\alpha\mu\nu]R^{\lambda\gamma;\mu}R_\gamma{}^\nu/R_{\sigma\tau}R^{\sigma\tau} .$$

For proof of (71), recall the expression (41) for the Ricci part (35) of the Riemann curvature tensor in terms of the external field, ξ; and form the first contracted covariant derivative of this tensor:

(72)
$$E^{\gamma\delta\beta\tau}{}_{;\tau} = -\xi^{\gamma\delta}\xi^{\beta\tau}{}_{;\tau} - *\xi^{\gamma\delta}*\xi^{\beta\tau}{}_{;\tau} - \xi^{\gamma\delta}{}_{;\tau}\xi^{\beta\tau} - *\xi^{\gamma\delta}{}_{;\tau}*\xi^{\beta\tau} =$$
$$= \tfrac{1}{2}(-g^{\gamma\beta}R^{\delta\tau} + g^{\gamma\tau}R^{\delta\beta} - g^{\delta\tau}R^{\gamma\beta} + g^{\delta\beta}R^{\gamma\tau})_{;\tau} = \tfrac{1}{2}(R^{\delta\beta;\gamma} - R^{\gamma\beta;\delta}) .$$

Here we use the fact that every component of the covariant derivative of $g^{\gamma\beta}$ vanishes, and employ the Bianchi identities, $R^{\delta\tau}{}_{;\tau} = 0$, to annul all but two terms among the eight that arise from the differentiation. Define

(73)
$$F_{\alpha\beta\gamma\delta} = \tfrac{1}{2}(-g)^{\frac{1}{2}}[\gamma\delta\mu\nu]E_{\alpha\beta}{}^{\mu\nu} =$$
$$= \tfrac{1}{2}(-g)^{\frac{1}{2}}[\gamma\delta\mu\nu](-\xi_{\alpha\beta}\xi^{\mu\nu} - *\xi_{\alpha\beta}*\xi^{\mu\nu}) = -\xi_{\alpha\beta}*\xi_{\gamma\delta} + *\xi_{\alpha\beta}\xi_{\gamma\delta} =$$
$$= \tfrac{1}{2}(-g)^{\frac{1}{2}}[\gamma\delta\mu\nu]\tfrac{1}{2}(-\delta_\alpha{}^\mu R_\beta{}^\nu + \delta_\alpha{}^\nu R_\beta{}^\mu - \delta_\beta{}^\nu R_\alpha{}^\mu + \delta_\beta{}^\mu R_\alpha{}^\nu) =$$
$$= \tfrac{1}{2}(-g)^{\frac{1}{2}}[\gamma\delta\mu\nu](\delta_\alpha{}^\nu R_\beta{}^\mu - \delta_\beta{}^\nu R_\alpha{}^\mu) .$$

Finally, form the product

(74)
$$F_{\alpha\beta\gamma\delta}E^{\gamma\delta\beta\tau}{}_{;\tau} = -2\boldsymbol{\xi}^2(*\xi_{\alpha\beta}\xi^{\beta\tau}{}_{;\tau} + \xi_{\alpha\beta}*\xi^{\beta\tau}{}_{;\tau}) =$$
$$= \tfrac{1}{2}(-g)^{\frac{1}{2}}[\gamma\delta\mu\nu](\delta_\alpha{}^\nu R_\beta{}^\mu - \delta_\beta{}^\nu R_\alpha{}^\mu)R^{\delta\beta;\gamma} = \tfrac{1}{2}(-g)^{\frac{1}{2}}[\alpha\delta\gamma\mu]R^{\delta\beta;\gamma}R_\beta{}^\mu .$$

The equation

$$\xi_{\gamma\delta}\times\xi^{\gamma\delta}{}_{;\tau} \equiv \tfrac{1}{2}(\xi_{\gamma\delta}*\xi^{\gamma\delta})_{;\tau} = 0 ,$$

which follows from $\boldsymbol{\xi}\times\boldsymbol{\xi} = 0$ by differentiation, as well as the identity (64), were used in computing (74) from (72) and (73). Now divide (74) by $2(\boldsymbol{\xi}^2)^2 = \frac{1}{2}R_{\sigma\tau}R^{\sigma\tau}$ to obtain (71), as was to be proven.

The vector α_β of (71) has a well defined existence in *any* Riemannian space where the Ricci curvature tensor $R_{\mu\nu}$ is non-null and differentiable. From such general Riemannian spaces the geometry of the Einstein-Maxwell theory is distinguished by the circumstance that *this vector*—as shown by RAINICH—is not arbitrary, but *is the gradient of the complexion*, α, *of the electromagnetic field*. Consequently it follows that the curl of α: must vanish:

$$\alpha_{\beta;\gamma} - \alpha_{\gamma;\beta} = \alpha_{\beta,\gamma} - \alpha_{\gamma,\beta} = 0 \, . \tag{75}$$

Conversely, when the curl (75) vanishes, then the line integral of the vector α_β of (71) from some selected point 0 to any arbitrary point x^μ *defines* a scalar complexion

$$\alpha = \int_0^x \alpha_\beta \, \mathrm{d}x^\beta + \alpha_0 \, , \tag{76}$$

up to an additive constant, α_0, provided that the region of space under consideration is simply connected, and provided that the line of integration does not include any point where $R_{\sigma\tau}R^{\sigma\tau}$ vanishes. For a multiply-connected space it is necessary to replace (75) by the demand that the line integral of α_β around any closed path shall be an integral multiple of 2π,

$$\oint \alpha_\beta \, \mathrm{d}x^\beta = 2\pi n \, , \tag{77}$$

provided the line of integration does not touch any null points. This condition, plus the algebraic requirements of Rainich

$$R_\alpha^{\ \alpha} = 0 \, ; \qquad R_{00} \geqslant 0 \, ; \qquad R_\alpha^{\ \mu} R_\mu^{\ \beta} = \delta_\alpha^{\ \beta} (\tfrac{1}{4} R_{\sigma\tau} R^{\sigma\tau}) \, , \tag{78}$$

gives the *necessary and sufficient* conditions that a Riemannian geometry shall reproduce the physics of Einstein and Maxwell, provided that the curvature $R_{\mu\nu}$ is non-null. It may well be that trivial changes in the statement of the theorem will cover the case of null fields, but this point remains to be investigated.

2·5. *Why Rainich-Riemannian geometry?* – We shall give the name Rainich-Riemannian geometry to any 4-space with signature $-+++$ which satisfies (77) and (78). The question poses itself insistently to find a point of view which will make Rainich-Riemannian geometry seem a particularly natural kind of geometry to consider. Presumably a variational principle based on an appropriate scalar Lagrange density will prove the most natural starting point to discuss this question. Whatever the deeper simplicities may be, it is extraordinarily beautiful that the Rainich-Riemannian geometry (77), (78) of empty curved space reproduces all the standard machinery of Maxwell stresses, electromagnetic waves, and generation of gravitational forces by field energy.

3. – Charge as flux in multiply-connected space: electromagnetism within the arena of a prescribed metric; plan of this section; topology; differential geometry; Maxwell's equations and charge.

3·1. *Electromagnetism within the arena of a prescribed metric.* – « Already unified field theory » or geometrodynamics appears to consist entirely of differential equations and algebraic relations on the curvature (eq. (75) and (78))—in other words, appears to have an exclusively local character—so long as space is assumed to be simply connected. As soon as the possibility is admitted of two or more topologically distinct routes to pass from one point to another (Fig. 3), then in addition one has to impose a *periodicity condition*

$$\oint_{C_i} \alpha_\beta \, \mathrm{d}x^\beta = 2\pi n_i \,, \tag{79}$$

for each topologically distinct closed circuit C_i that is free of null points. Only when this condition is satisfied will the electromagnetic field, $\boldsymbol{f} = e^{*\alpha}\boldsymbol{\xi}$, be a single valued function of position. The condition (79) has a non-local character. This circumstance forces us to ask, what *additional* features of a non-local character appear when Einstein-Maxwell physics goes on in a multiply-connected space?

To *recognize charge as a non-local manifestation of charge free electrodynamics in a multiply-connected space*, we will find it helpful to revert from the ideas of the more familiar geometrodynamics to language of Maxwell theory in a pre-existing space time continuum. In keeping close to the most easily visualized terminology, we will not deny that electrodynamics is intrinsically non-linear. A field has an energy density that curves space. This curvature affects the propagation of the field. A field of twice the strength therefore propagates differently from the original field. This non-linearity will remain hidden behind the scenes in the following analysis. Attention will be limited to Maxwell's equations and their consequences. However, these consequences will remain valid when Maxwell's equations for the field are supplemented by Einstein's equations for the metric.

The concept of multiple connectedness is topological in character and logically precedes any idea of metric. Section **3**·2 therefore summarizes the necessary topological preliminaries, including the concepts of continuity, manifold, boundary, homology class, Betti number, differentiable manifold, and co-ordinate patches. No space topologically inequivalent to an open subset of Euclidean space can be covered without singularity by a single non-singular co-ordinate system. This circumstance makes the analysis of vectors, tensors, and other quantities by way of components—in the traditional spirit of tensor analysis—less appropriate than an *intrinsic* type of calculus, such as is familiar from vector analysis in 3-space. Section **3**·3 uses this intrinsic notation of

Cartan side by side with the familiar notation to define the needed concepts of differential geometry in a space not yet endowed with any metric: vectors, alternating tensors, cross product, curl, Stokes theorem, the metric-free half of Maxwell's equations, conservation of flux, charge, vector potential, de Rham's theorem, and the issue of electric *vs.* magnetic charges. The rest of Section **3**·3 traces some of the more important additional consequences that flow from existence of a metric: duality, divergence, differential operators, and relations and integral formulas involving these operators. Section **3**·4 analyzes electric and magnetic fields on one or two space like surfaces as initial-value data for Maxwell's equations; the new feature of charge brought in by multiple connectedness; and the description of charge by way of the theory of harmonic vector fields.

3·2. *Topology*.

3·2.1. Topology and point sets. – Topology ([23]) is the study of a non-quantitative idea of « nearby ». This idea itself is not ordinarily axiomatized; instead, topology axiomatically defines what is meant by a neighborhood, an open set, or a closed subset of space. The relationship of these ideas to « nearby » may be suggested as follows: 1) A neighborhood of a point is a subset containing all points sufficiently near x. 2) An open subset is one which contains all points sufficiently near any of its points. 3) A closed subset C is one which contains every point that is arbitrarily close to C.

Let two sets X_1, X_2 be equivalent as sets, so that they also contain the same number of points. Then the two sets are equivalent as topological spaces, that is *homeomorphic*, if there is a 1-1 transformation h of X_1 onto X_2, called a *homeomorphism*, under which the open sets of X_1 are in 1-1 correspondence with the open sets of X_2. The open sets define the notion of « nearby ». Therefore we may say that a *homeomorphism* h is a 1-1 onto correspondence of X_1 and X_2 which always makes nearby points in one space correspond to nearby points in the other, *i.e.*, it is continuous, and so is its inverse.

We have found ourselves forced to consider spaces that are topologically more general than those usually treated in physics. Nevertheless, we shall restrict ourselves to a very special class of spaces, called manifolds: *An* n-manifold ([24]) *is a topological space which* 1) *is locally Euclidean of dimensions* n.

([23]) A standard text on point set topology is one by J. L. KELLEY: *General Topology* (New York, 1955). For a brief development of the theory see a book by L. PONTRJAGIN: *Topological Groups*, chap. II (Princeton, 1946). Statements of definitions and theorems from point set topology which are most pertinent for a study of manifolds can be found in a book by P. S. ALEKSANDROV: *Combinatorial Topology*, vol. **1**, chap. I (Rochester, 1956).

([24]) G. DE RHAM: *Variétés différentiables* (Paris, 1955), p. 1.

2) *is Hausdorff, and* 3) *has a countable basis.* 1) *A space is locally Euclidean of dimension* n if each point has a neighborhood homeomorphic to Euclidean n-space. 2) A space is *Hausdorff* if every two distinct points have disjoint neighborhoods. Effectively Hausdorff means that no two distinct points are arbitrarily close to each other, but this intuitive notion may also be made precise in other ways. 3) A space has a *countable basis* if there is a countable collection of open sets such that every open set is a union of open sets in this collection. This condition is imposed so that a manifold will not be uncomfortably large.

3·2.2. Examples of manifolds. – The prime examples of manifolds are the Euclidean spaces. Euclidean n-space, R^n, is the space of all n-tuples of real numbers, $\boldsymbol{x} = (x^1, x^2, \dots x^n)$, with the topology customary in analysis. The open subset of R^n defined by

$$\boldsymbol{x}\cdot\boldsymbol{x} = \sum (x^i)^2 < 1 \tag{80}$$

is called the n-ball. It is also an n-manifold, and is in fact homeomorphic to R^n by the transformation $\boldsymbol{x} \to \boldsymbol{x}(1-\boldsymbol{x}\cdot\boldsymbol{x})^{-1}$. Another familiar example of a manifold is the n-sphere S^n which is a subspace of R^{n+1} consisting of all points $\boldsymbol{x}$ satisfying the condition.

$$\boldsymbol{x}\cdot\boldsymbol{x} = \sum_{x=1}^{n+1} (x^i)^2 = 1\,. \tag{81}$$

From S^n we may obtain projective n-space P^n by identifying antipodal points on S^n; *i.e.*, a point x of P^n is an unordered pair $(\boldsymbol{x}, -\boldsymbol{x})$ of points $\boldsymbol{x}$ of R^{n+1} satisfying $\boldsymbol{x}\cdot\boldsymbol{x} = 1$. In general relativity, S^3 and P^3 have been used in cosmological models ([25]). Another manifold, the 3-torus T^3, is encountered in theoretical physics in the frequent instances where one imposes periodic boundary conditions. The n-torus T^n is a space whose points are families of points in R^n, $x = \{\boldsymbol{x} + 2\pi\boldsymbol{m}\}_m$ where $\boldsymbol{m}$ ranges over all n-tuples of integers $\boldsymbol{m} = (m_1, m_2, \dots, m_n)$. As a final example we construct a space W_m which illustrates in a simple way some of the topological possibilities which we are interested in investigating in relation to the idea of charge. Starting from the 3-sphere S^3, we consider only those points $\boldsymbol{x} = (x^1, x^2, x^3, x^4)$ which satisfy both $\boldsymbol{x}\cdot\boldsymbol{x} = 1$ and $|x^4| \leqslant 1-\varepsilon$. We then identify each point $(x^1, x^2, x^3, 1-\varepsilon)$ with $(x^1, x^2, x^3, -1+\varepsilon)$. This may be called the pierced sphere, or W_1. By

([25]) C. MØLLER: *The Theory of Relativity* (London and New York, 1952), p. 361; L. LANDAU and E. LIFSHITZ: *The Classical Theory of Fields* (Cambridge, Mass., 1951), p. 336.

cutting out k pairs of antipodal balls (such as $x^4 > 1 - \varepsilon$ and $x^4 < 1 + \varepsilon$ above) around k pairs of points of S^3 (such as $\boldsymbol{x} = (0, 0, 0, \pm 1)$ above) and making similar identifications of the boundaries, we construct the k-pierced sphere W_k. (See Fig. 4).

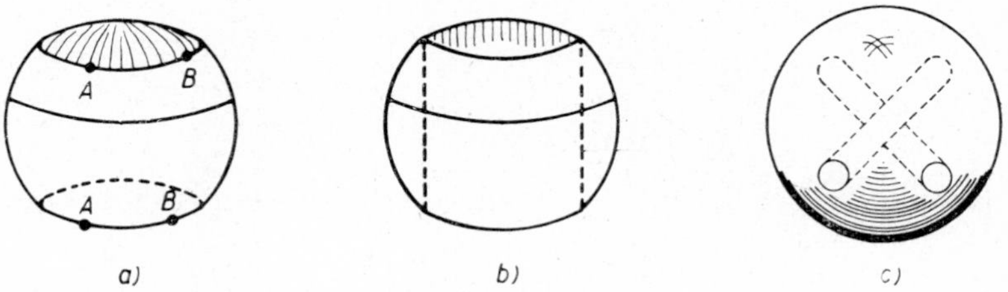

Fig. 4. – The pierced spheres. When the polar caps are excluded from a sphere and the resulting boundaries identified as indicated by the corresponding points A, B, in (a), there results a space which may be called a pierced sphere, W_1. The identification may be visualized by pulling the edges together through the center of the sphere as in (b), so that the resulting manifold is the surface of a ball with a hole drilled through the center. Drilling k such holes in a sphere, in such a way that the drill holes never intersect, gives the k-pierced sphere W_k. In (c) a view of W_2 is shown. The figures show two-dimensional manifolds, while the W_k in the text are 3-manifolds.

3·2.3. Product manifolds. – When $\mathscr{M}^p$ is a p-manifold and $\mathscr{M}^q$ a q-manifold, then we can construct from them a $(p+q)$-manifold $\mathscr{M}^p \times \mathscr{M}^q$ whose points are pairs (x, y) where x is any point of $\mathscr{M}^p$ and y any point of $\mathscr{M}^q$. Euclidean 2-space R^2 is, for example, the product $R^1 \times R^1$, and similarly $R^n = R^1 \times R^1 \times \ldots \times R^1$ (n factors). We note that S^1 and T^1 are homeomorphic.

$$\{x + 2n\pi\}_n \to (x^1, x^2) \quad \text{with} \quad x^1 + ix^2 = e^{ix} . \tag{82}$$

(We write $T^1 = S^1$ since we usually do not need to distinguish homeomorphic manifolds, unless the names of the points, *i.e.*, $\{x + 2\pi n\}_n \in T$ *vs.* $(x^1, x^2) \in S^1$, are needed in a construction.) Then T^n is a product of n circles, $T^n = S^1 \times S^1 \times \times \ldots \times S^1$. It may also be seen that $W_1 = S^2 \times S^1$.

In the examples above we have not defined the topology, or in other words, we have not made the choice of open sets, since the appropriate choice is fairly obvious.

3·2.4. Differentiable manifolds. – To discuss differential geometry we need both a manifold, and a concept of *differentiable function* on this manifold. Let a criterion be supplied which decides which functions defined on a manifold $\mathscr{M}$ are to be called differentiable. Then this criterion is called a *differentiable structure* on $\mathscr{M}$, and $\mathscr{M}$ is called a *differentiable manifold.* The class of differentiable functions is however subject to certain axioms ([24]):

For every point x of $\mathscr{M}$ there exists an open neighborhood U of x, and n real-valued functions $x_1(x), x_2(x), \ldots, x_n(x)$ defined on U such that:

a) The transformation $x \to (x_1(x), x_2(x), \ldots, x_n(x))$ of U into R^n is a homeomorphism of U onto an open set of R^n, so that every function f defined in U can be expressed in terms of the x_i,

$$f(x) = f(x_1, x_2, \ldots, x_n) .$$

b) A function $f(x)$ is differentiable at a point of U if and only if it is defined in an open neighborhood W of that point, with W contained in U, and $f(x_1, x_2, \ldots, x_n)$ has continuous derivatives of all orders with respect to the x_i for values of the x_i corresponding to points in W.

The neighborhood U with the functions x_i is called a *co-ordinate patch*, and the set of functions $x_1(x), x_2(x), \ldots, x_n(x)$ is called a system of *local co-ordinates* in U. It follows from the definition that a co-ordinate $x_i(x)$ is a differentiable function.

We apply the definition of differentiable function by way of illustration to some of the manifolds already mentioned. On the n-sphere we may define $x_i(\boldsymbol{x})$, where $\boldsymbol{x} = (x_1, x_2, \ldots, x_{n+1})$ to be a differentiable function of the points x in S^n. Then some n of these $n+1$ functions will serve as co-ordinates about any point in part *a*) of the axioms, while the remaining differentiable functions are given by *b*). For the projective n-space P^n whose points x are pairs of points, $(\boldsymbol{x}, -\boldsymbol{x})$, of S^n, we say $f(x)$ is a differentiable function on P^n if $f((\boldsymbol{x}, -\boldsymbol{x}))$ is a differentiable function of $\boldsymbol{x} \in S^n$. For the space W_1, the pierced sphere, we consider x_1, x_2 and x_3 as differentiable functions, as they were on the sphere. The quantity x^4 is to be differentiable only in the region $|x^4| < 1 - \varepsilon$. This function is not defined at the rims that have been identified with each other. We need another function which is defined and which can be called differentiable across this region of identification. For this purpose we define $f(x)$ by

$$\text{(84)} \qquad \begin{cases} f(x) = 1 - \varepsilon - x^4(x) & \text{for} \quad 0 < x^4 \leqslant 1 - \varepsilon , \\ f(x) = -1 + \varepsilon - x^4(x) & \text{for} \quad -1 + \varepsilon \leqslant x^4 < 0 , \end{cases}$$

and insist that $f(x)$ is differentiable for $x^4 \neq 0$. From among the functions x_1, x_2, x_3, x_4, and f we can choose local co-ordinates about any point.

Although a topological manifold may be given more than one differentiable structure ([26]), we shall abbreviate differentiable manifold to manifold in what follows, and the word *topology* will include differentiable structure as well as topology.

([26]) J. MILNOR: *Ann. Math.*, **64**, 399 (1956).

3·3. *Differential geometry and the formulation of Maxwell's equations.*

3·3.1. Differentiable functions and fields. – To state physical laws in quantitative form, we are compelled to deal with vectors and tensors in a curved space. These quantities are not most conveniently described in the familiar language of tensor analysis when the space is multiply connected. A new or *intrinsic* formulation is required.

Tensor analysis is not adequate. It demands a non-singular co-ordinate system with respect to which one can give the components of vectors and tensors. However, according to the definition of a differentiable manifold, a single non-singular co-ordinate system is not enough to cover a manifold that is topologically inequivalent to an open set in Euclidean space. It is essential for our physical applications that we be able to distinguish singular tensor fields from non-singular ones. A singularity in a field will ordinarily imply a localized *source term* in the differential equations. Such a source term will represent a non-geometric charge or mass, which has not been eliminated from the theory, but merely idealized to a point charge or a point mass. To investigate the content of pure geometrodynamics we therefore *exclude all singularities in the fields.* Consider for example the two dimensional surface of the unit sphere. The polar angles, θ, φ, are ordinarily called co-ordinates, but they do not cover the surface without singularity: 1) The metric,

$$ds^2 = d\theta^2 + \sin^2\theta \, d\varphi^2, \tag{85}$$

has a component, $g^{\varphi\varphi} = \sin^{-2}\theta$, which goes to infinity at the two poles, $\theta = 0$ and $\theta = \pi$. 2) A vector field with apparently non-singular components, $v_\theta = 1$, $v_\varphi = 0$, is not well defined with respect to direction at either pole. This singularity in the vector $\boldsymbol{v} = \operatorname{grad}\theta$ raises a question about calling θ a co-ordinate. 3) Along the Greenwich meridian the angle φ suffers a discontinuous change from 0 to 2π in this region, making this quantity also inappropriate for a co-ordinate. 4) Only in the region $0 < \theta < \pi$, $0 < \varphi < 2\pi$ do the polar angles supply a well defined « co-ordinate patch ».

Another « co-ordinate patch » is needed. Let a small circular ink pad be centered at the north pole and let the pad be moved down the Greenwich meridian to the south pole. We ask for a new co-ordinate system that is regular everywhere in the blackened region. Of course the new co-ordinate system may be regular over a wider region. For example, consider the point $\theta = \pi/2$, $\varphi = \pi/2$. Let this be north pole of a new set of polar angles, θ', φ', in terms of which 1) the previous north pole is $\theta' = \pi/2$, $\varphi' = \pi/2$, 2) the previous Greenwich meridian runs from $\theta' = \pi/2$, $\varphi' = \pi/2$ to $\theta' = \pi/2$, $\varphi' = 3\pi/2$, 3) the previous south pole lies at $\theta' = \pi/2$, $\varphi' = 3\pi/2$. There is evidently a wide region where the old and new co-ordinate patches overlap. Moreover, at any fixed point on the sphere at least *one* non-singular pair of co-ordinates θ, φ or θ', φ', is well behaved. If we do not know what non-singular co-ordinates are, then we have not yet defined the differentiable structure of the manifold. However, as soon as we have said what we mean by a differentiable function, then the idea of a *differentiable tensor field* is well defined: A tensor is differentiable at a point x if its components with respect to a (non-singular) co-ordinate system around x are differentiable functions at x.

3·3.2. Intrinsic representation of tensors. – In the general differentiable manifold it will be impossible to describe a field, such as the Maxwell field, by giving its components $F_{\alpha\beta}$ with respect to a single set of co-ordinates. If components are to be used at all, they have to be given with respect to the co-ordinates of the several distinct co-ordinate patches. In each patch there is great freedom of choice about the co-ordinate system. Consequently the components, $F_{\alpha\beta}$, of the Maxwell field in the several co-ordinate systems are not individually so important as the concept that can be abstracted from them: the intrinsic value, $\boldsymbol{F}$, of the Maxwell field. This procedure of abstraction is familiar from the analysis of Cartesian vectors. To say that the velocity vector $\boldsymbol{v}$ is known is to say that on demand one can give the components of $\boldsymbol{v}$ in any non-singular co-ordinate system. We propose to generalize this abstract formalism to the case of curved space and tensors of order higher than the first.

In vector analysis it is convenient to express the connection between a vector $\boldsymbol{v}$ and its components by the formula

$$\boldsymbol{v} = v^m \boldsymbol{e}_m \,, \tag{86}$$

where the components v^m depend upon the choice of base vectors $\boldsymbol{e}_m$. « Intrinsic differential geometry » expresses the same type of relation more explicitly in the form

$$\boldsymbol{v} = v_\alpha \operatorname{grad} x^\alpha \,, \tag{87}$$

and more briefly in the notation,

$$\boldsymbol{v} = v_\alpha \mathbf{d} x^\alpha \,, \tag{88}$$

where the letter **d** stands for gradient. Modern text books on differential geometry [27] even replace the boldface **d** by lightface d—as we also shall do

---

(27) E. Cartan: *Leçons sur la géométrie des espaces de Riemann* (Paris, 1946); C. Chevalley: *Theory of Lie Groups I*, chap. 3 (Princeton, 1946); W. V. D. Hodge: *The Theory and Application of Harmonic Integrals* (London and New York, 1952); A. Lichnerowicz: *Algèbre et analyse linéaires*, 2nd ed., part 2, chap. 1 (Paris, 1956); G. de Rham: *Variétés différentiables* (Paris, 1955).

later—but for the time being we keep the boldface notation to emphasize the vectorial character of the gradient operation .

The gradient operation, applied to any function of position, $f = f(P)$, expresses itself in intrinsic notation in the familiar form

$$\text{grad}\, f = (\partial f/\partial x^\alpha)\, \text{grad}\, x^\alpha$$

or

$$\mathbf{d}f = (\partial f/\partial x^\alpha)\, \mathbf{d}x^\alpha \, . \tag{89}$$

Covariant vectors, such as grad f, or $\mathbf{d}f$, and $\boldsymbol{v}$ are linear combinations of the gradients of the co-ordinates and are called differential forms of the first order, or 1-forms.

Instead of using the gradients of a particular set of co-ordinates as base vectors in a certain co-ordinate patch, one can use there alternatively as base vectors any other set of n linearly independent vectors, $\boldsymbol{\omega}^\alpha$. Here the superscript α tells which vector, not which component of one vector. Relative to this set of basic vectors the components of the vector v are again read out of the expansion

$$\boldsymbol{v} = v_\alpha \boldsymbol{\omega}^\alpha \, . \tag{90}$$

The components of grad f or $\mathbf{d}f$ in such a frame are called its Pfaffian derivatives $f_{,\alpha}$ with respect to the $\boldsymbol{\omega}^\alpha$:

$$\text{grad}\, f = \mathbf{d}f = f_{,\alpha} \boldsymbol{\omega}^\alpha \tag{91}$$

3.3.3 Exterior differential forms. – To describe the Maxwell field requires one to deal with a higher order tensor, or 2-form. The simplest 2-form, $\boldsymbol{\alpha}$, is the cross product of two 1-forms, $\boldsymbol{u}$ and $\boldsymbol{v}$, thus,

$$\boldsymbol{\alpha} = \boldsymbol{u} \wedge \boldsymbol{v}$$

in intrinsic notation; or

$$\alpha_{\mu\nu} = u_\mu v_\nu - v_\mu u_\nu \tag{92}$$

in the familiar language of tensor analysis, or

$$\boldsymbol{\alpha} = \tfrac{1}{2}\alpha_{\mu\nu}\, \mathbf{d}x^\mu \wedge \mathbf{d}x^\nu = \tfrac{1}{2}\alpha_{\mu\nu} (\text{grad}\, x^\mu) \times (\text{grad}\, x^\nu)$$

in a formulation that connects the intrinsic form with the component representation.

The *exterior product* operation $\wedge$ (« hook ») generalizes the cross product into a mean for multiplying vectors and alternating tensors in such a way as to obtain tensors that are also alternating. This operation does not apply to symmetric tensors. The $\wedge$ multiplication is defined by the requirements 1) it is associative 2) it is distributive 3) exterior multiplication of two vectors is anticommutative; that is, we ask

$$\boldsymbol{u} \wedge \boldsymbol{v} = -\boldsymbol{v} \wedge \boldsymbol{u} \tag{93}$$

for any two 1-forms or vectors $\boldsymbol{u}$, $\boldsymbol{v}$. In particular, $\boldsymbol{u} \wedge \boldsymbol{u} = 0$.

The exterior product of p vectors, or a linear combination of such vectors, gives a *p-form*. Let each vector be expressed in terms of base vectors $\boldsymbol{\omega}^{\alpha}$. The product of the p vectors, or the linear combination of such products, can be expressed in the form

$$a = \sum_{\alpha_1 < \alpha_2 \ldots < \alpha_p} a_{\alpha_1 \alpha_2 \ldots \alpha_p} \boldsymbol{\omega}^{\alpha_1} \wedge \boldsymbol{\omega}^{\alpha_2} \wedge \ldots \wedge \boldsymbol{\omega}^{\alpha_p} = (p!)^{-1} a_{\alpha_1 \alpha_2 \ldots \alpha_p} \boldsymbol{\omega}^{\alpha_1} \wedge \boldsymbol{\omega}^{\alpha_2} \wedge \ldots \wedge \boldsymbol{\omega}^{\alpha_p}. \tag{94}$$

Here the coefficients or *tensor components* in the first sum are well defined. In terms of these components those that appear in the second sum are *defined* by the requirement that they be alternating functions of the indices.

The exterior product $\mathbf{d}x^1 \wedge \mathbf{d}x^2 = (\text{grad}\, x^1) \times (\text{grad}\, x^2)$ signifies geometrically an area spanned by base vectors along the x^1 and x^2 co-ordinate axes. Similarly the product $\mathbf{d}x^1 \wedge \mathbf{d}x^2 \wedge \mathbf{d}x^3$ represents the parallelepipedal volume spanned by three base vectors.

The commutation rule for a p-form $\boldsymbol{a}$ and a q-form $\boldsymbol{b}$ is easily found:

$$\boldsymbol{a} \wedge \boldsymbol{b} = (-1)^{pq} \boldsymbol{b} \wedge \boldsymbol{a}\,. \tag{95}$$

Functions and vectors are included in this scheme of exterior differential forms as 0-forms and 1-forms, respectively.

3·3.4. Exterior differentiation. – The operator $\mathbf{d}$ which produced the 1-form $\mathbf{d}f = \text{grad}\, f$ from the 0-form f can be extended to a form of higher degree,

$$\boldsymbol{a} = (p!)^{-1} a_{\alpha_1 \ldots \alpha_p} \mathbf{d}x^{\alpha_1} \wedge \ldots \wedge \mathbf{d}x^{\alpha_p}\,, \tag{96}$$

by way of the definition

$$\mathbf{d}\boldsymbol{a} = (p!)^{-1}\, \mathbf{d}a_{\alpha_1 \ldots \alpha_p} \wedge \mathbf{d}x^{\alpha_1} \wedge \ldots \wedge \mathbf{d}x^{\alpha_p}\,. \tag{97}$$

In the language of tensor analysis this equation takes the form

$$(\mathbf{d}\boldsymbol{a})_{\alpha_1 \ldots \alpha_{p+1}} = \sum (-1)^P\, \partial a_{\beta_2 \ldots \beta_{p+1}} / \partial x^{\beta_1}\,, \tag{98}$$

where $P = 0$ or $+1$ according as the indices $\beta_1 \ldots \beta_{p+1}$ form an even or an odd permutation of the indices $\alpha_1 \ldots \alpha_{p+1}$. The operation $\mathbf{d}$, the *exterior derivative*, is an alternating differentiation which generalizes the familiar operations of gradient and curl. It is linear:

$$\mathbf{d}(\boldsymbol{a}_1 + \boldsymbol{a}_2) = \mathbf{d}\boldsymbol{a}_1 + \mathbf{d}\boldsymbol{a}_2 \,. \tag{99}$$

Applied to a product where the first factor is a p-form, it gives the result

$$\mathbf{d}(\boldsymbol{a}\wedge\boldsymbol{b}) = (\mathbf{d}\boldsymbol{a})\wedge\boldsymbol{b} + (-1)^p\,\boldsymbol{a}\wedge\mathbf{d}\boldsymbol{b} \,. \tag{100}$$

Applied twice it gives zero

$$\mathbf{d}(\mathbf{d}\boldsymbol{a}) = 0 \,. \tag{101}$$

This circumstance was employed in passing from expression (96) for an exterior differential form $\boldsymbol{a}$ to expression (97) for its exterior derivative, $\mathbf{d}\boldsymbol{a}$: the base vectors $\mathbf{d}x^\alpha = \text{grad}\, x^\alpha$ give no contribution when the operation of exterior differentiation is applied to them:

$$\mathbf{d}\mathbf{d}x^\alpha = \text{curl grad}\, x^\alpha = 0 \,. \tag{102}$$

No such simplicity results in the case where the same exterior form $\boldsymbol{a}$ is expressed in terms of a more general system of base vectors $\boldsymbol{\omega}^\alpha$; thus $\mathbf{d}\boldsymbol{\omega}^\alpha = \text{curl}\,\boldsymbol{\omega}^\alpha$ will not ordinarily vanish.

Maxwell's equations deal with two antisymmetrical tensors, $f_{\alpha\beta}$ and $*f_{\alpha\beta}$; or in invariant terminology, with two 2-forms,

$$\boldsymbol{f} = \tfrac{1}{2} f_{\alpha\beta}\, \mathbf{d}x^\alpha\wedge\mathbf{d}x^\beta$$

and

$$*\boldsymbol{f} = \tfrac{1}{2} *f_{\alpha\beta}\, \mathbf{d}x^\alpha\wedge\mathbf{d}x^\beta \,. \tag{103}$$

Consider the exterior derivative of $\boldsymbol{f}$; that is, the 3-form

$$\mathbf{d}\boldsymbol{f} = \tfrac{1}{2}(\partial f_{\alpha\beta}/\partial x^\gamma)\, \mathbf{d}x^\gamma\wedge\mathbf{d}x^\alpha\wedge\mathbf{d}x^\beta \,. \tag{104}$$

Here the coefficient of a typical basic 3-form, such as $\mathbf{d}x^\lambda\wedge\mathbf{d}x^\mu\wedge\mathbf{d}x^\nu$, with $\lambda < \mu < \nu$, has the value

$$\partial f_{\mu\nu}/\partial x^\lambda + \partial f_{\lambda\mu}/\partial x^\nu + \partial f_{\nu\lambda}/\partial x^\mu \,, \tag{105}$$

or in a locally Minkowskian frame,

(106)
$$\begin{cases} \operatorname{div} \boldsymbol{h} & (\lambda, \mu, \nu = 1, 2, 3), \\ \operatorname{curl} \boldsymbol{e} + \partial \boldsymbol{h}/\partial T & (\lambda = 0;\ \mu, \nu = \text{space}). \end{cases}$$

These expressions vanish, according to Maxwell, so one half of his equations take the form

(107)
$$\mathbf{d}\boldsymbol{f} = 0 .$$

Similarly, in charge free space the other half of Maxwell's equations take the form

(108)
$$\mathbf{d}{*}\boldsymbol{f} = 0 .$$

To satisfy Maxwell's first set of equations it is *sufficient* to express the field $\boldsymbol{f}$ as the curl of a four-potential

$$\boldsymbol{f} = \mathbf{d}\boldsymbol{a} ;$$

or

$$\tfrac{1}{2} f_{\alpha\beta}\, \mathbf{d}x^\alpha \wedge \mathbf{d}x^\beta = (a_\gamma\, \mathbf{d}x^\gamma) = \mathbf{d}a_\gamma \wedge \mathbf{d}x^\gamma =$$
$$= (\partial a_\gamma/\partial x^\delta)\, \mathbf{d}x^\delta \wedge \mathbf{d}x^\gamma = \tfrac{1}{2}(\partial a_\beta/\partial x^\alpha - \partial a_\alpha/\partial x^\beta)\, \mathbf{d}x^\alpha \wedge \mathbf{d}x^\beta$$

or

(109)
$$f_{\alpha\beta} = \partial a_\beta/\partial x^\alpha - \partial a_\alpha/\partial x^\beta .$$

Then the exterior derivative of $\boldsymbol{f}$ vanishes automatically:

(110)
$$\mathbf{d}\boldsymbol{f} = \mathbf{dd}\boldsymbol{a} \equiv 0 .$$

3·3.5. Integration: motivation and method. – From the differential properties of the 2-form $\boldsymbol{f}$ what integral properties can be deduced? How do these consequences differ 1) when we know merely that $\mathbf{d}\boldsymbol{f} = 0$ and 2) when we know in addition $\boldsymbol{f} = \mathbf{d}\boldsymbol{a}$? More generally, how does one define integrals of forms?

A p-form can be integrated over a p-dimensional surface to give a scalar or co-ordinate-independent quantity. To combine a local q-form ($q \neq p$) with a local p-dimensional surface element would give a result with local directional properties; but there is no invariant way to add together vectors or other directed quantities at different points in curved space to obtain a well-defined total. Therefore integrals of p-forms on p-dimensional surfaces alone need be considered.

The surface of integration will require for its coverage one or more p-dimensional co-ordinate patches. Break the surface up into curvilinear p-dimensional parallelepipeds at least equal in number to the number of required co-ordinate patches. Consider the *standard unit p-dimensional* cube, I^p, with co-ordinates λ^α:

$$0 \leqslant \lambda^\alpha \leqslant 1 \qquad (\alpha = 1, 2, \ldots, p). \tag{111}$$

Map the points of I^p into $\mathscr{M}$,

$$C: I^p \to \mathscr{M}\,. \tag{112}$$

This map C may be thought of as a curvilinear parallelepiped in $\mathscr{M}$, but we shall call it a *cube in* $\mathscr{M}$ because we have no metric with which to distinguish « curved » from « straight ». In terms of co-ordinates the cube takes the form

$$x^\alpha = C^\alpha(\lambda^1, \lambda^2, \ldots \lambda^p)\,, \tag{113}$$

where the C^α are differentiable functions. A great number of different cubes cover the same set of points in $\mathscr{M}$. For instance

$$x^\alpha = C^\alpha(1 - \lambda^1, \lambda^2, \ldots \lambda^p) \tag{114a}$$

and

$$x^\alpha = C(\lambda^2, \lambda^1, \ldots \lambda^p) \tag{114b}$$

are cubes in $\mathscr{M}$ different from C, and with the opposite *orientation* to C, while

$$x^\alpha = C^\alpha(1 - \lambda^1,\ 1 - \lambda^2, \lambda^3, \ldots \lambda^p) \tag{115}$$

is a cube in $\mathscr{M}$ different from C, but with the same orientation. The orientation of the cube governs the sign of the integral we are evaluating, but other differences in cubes that cover the same points of $\mathscr{M}$ will not influence the value of the integral. If $f: I^p \to I^p$ is an orientation preserving homeomorphism of I^p onto itself, if in other words it has a positive Jacobian, we will not distinguish the cube $x = C(\lambda^1, \lambda^2, \ldots \lambda^n)$ from the cube $x = C\big(f(\lambda^1, \lambda^2, \ldots \lambda^n)\big)$. We should therefore speak of an « *oriented cube in* $\mathscr{M}$ ». Substitute the parametric description (113) of the surface into the expression (96) for a p-form, $\boldsymbol{a}$, to get the mapping

$$C: \boldsymbol{a} \to \boldsymbol{a}^0 \tag{116}$$

of the form $\boldsymbol{a}$ on $\mathcal{M}$ into the form $\boldsymbol{a}^C$ on I^p:

$$\text{(117)} \qquad \boldsymbol{a}^C = (p!)^{-1} a_{\alpha_1 \ldots \alpha_p} \mathbf{d}x^{\alpha_1}(\lambda) \wedge \ldots \wedge \mathbf{d}x^{\alpha_p}(\lambda) =$$

$$= (p!)^{-1} a_{\alpha_1 \ldots \alpha_p} (\partial x^{\alpha_1}/\partial \lambda^{\beta_1}) \mathbf{d}\lambda^{\beta_1} \wedge \ldots \wedge (\partial x^{\alpha_p}/\partial \lambda^{\beta_p}) \mathbf{d}\lambda^{\beta_p} =$$

$$= \sum_{\alpha_1 < \ldots < \alpha_p} a_{\alpha_1 \ldots \alpha_p} \frac{\partial(x^{\alpha_1}, \ldots, x^{\alpha_p})}{\partial(\lambda^1, \ldots, \lambda^p)} \mathbf{d}\lambda^1 \wedge \ldots \wedge \mathbf{d}\lambda^p .$$

Replace the volume element $\mathbf{d}\lambda^1 \wedge \ldots \wedge \mathbf{d}\lambda^p$ by the volume element of the stan·dard unit cube, $\mathrm{d}\lambda^1 \mathrm{d}\lambda^2 \ldots \mathrm{d}\lambda^p$ ane *define* the integral of $\boldsymbol{a}$ over the oriented cube C as the quantity

$$\text{(118)} \qquad \int_C \boldsymbol{a} = \int_{I^p} \boldsymbol{a}^C = \int \sum_{\alpha_1 < \ldots < \alpha_p} a_{\alpha_1 \ldots \alpha_p} \frac{\partial(x^{\alpha_1}, \ldots, x^{\alpha_p})}{\partial(\lambda^1, \ldots, \lambda^p)} \mathrm{d}\lambda^1 \ldots \mathrm{d}\lambda^p .$$

The appearance of the Jacobian in the integral gives assurance what the value of the integral is independent of *a*) the choice of co-ordinates x^α in $\mathcal{M}$ and *b*) the choice of the map $I^p \to \mathcal{M}$ used to represent the oriented cube in $\mathcal{M}$.

Having defined an integral over one oriented curvilinear p-cube, we have now to piece together the entire p-dimensional surface in $\mathcal{M}$ as the sum of a finite number of such oriented p-cubes,

$$\text{(119)} \qquad c = C_1 + C_2 + \ldots + C_N .$$

Instead of concentrating our attention on such surfaces, it turns out to be more convenient and more significant (see Homology Theory, below) to include as well a slightly more general object, a *p-chain*, *c*, which is simply a formal linear combination of a *finite* number of oriented p-cubes:

$$\text{(120)} \qquad C = \sum_{i=1}^{N} s^i C_i .$$

It might appear that the only algebraic structure necessary is $\pm$ signs, so that if C is the oriented cube defined by the map (113), we may write $-C$ for the oriented cube defined by (114). However it may happen that the same cube C appears several times on the boundary of a surface and we therefore wish to write nC, where n is a positive or negative integer or zero. If the coefficients s^i in eq. (120) were required to be integers, we would call c an integral chain. In connection with integration, it is more appropriate to let the coefficients s^i be any real numbers, so that we have in eq. (120) a *real p-chain*. The integral of a p-form $\boldsymbol{a}$ over the p-dimensional surface, or p-chain, c, then is defined as the sum of elementary contributions of the form (118):

$$\int_c \boldsymbol{a} = \sum_{1=i}^{N} s^i \int_{C_i} \boldsymbol{a} = \sum_{i=1}^{N} s^i \int_{I^p} \boldsymbol{a}^{C_i} . \tag{121}$$

3·3.6. Surfaces or p-chains, and their boundaries: homology theory. – Particularly interesting is the relation between a p-chain or surface c and its *boundary*, ∂c. This relation is very simple in the case of a cube, C. Use the symbol C^{j+} to stand for the j-th upper face of C; that is, for the $(p-1)$-dimensional cube

$$x^\alpha = C^\alpha(\lambda^1, \dots \lambda^{j-1}, 1, \lambda^{j+1}, \dots \lambda^p) . \tag{122}$$

Likewise let C^{j-} stand for the lower face,

$$x^\alpha = C^\alpha(\lambda 1, \dots \lambda^{j-1}, 0, \lambda^{j+1}, .. \lambda^p) \tag{123}$$

Then define the boundary of the oriented cube, C as the chain

$$\partial C = \sum_{j=1}^{p} (-1)^{j-1}(C^{j+} - C^{j-}) . \tag{124}$$

The p-dimensional cube has a $(p-1)$-dimensional boundary. It might be thought that this $(p-1)$-dimensional surface has in turn a $(p-2)$-dimensional boundary. However, being closed, the surface evidently has no boundary at all. One comes to the same conclusion by applying eq. (124) twice in succession. The result derived in this way for cubes applies to volumes and surfaces and more generally to any p-chain built up out of cubes.

Let a p-chain be expressed in the form

$$c = \sum_i s^i C_i . \tag{125}$$

Then we *define* the boundary of the p-chain in terms of the boundaries of the constituent cubes, C_i, in $\mathscr{M}$, through the equation

$$\partial c = \sum_i s^i \partial C_i . \tag{126}$$

When the boundary of the p-chain vanishes,

$$\partial c = 0 , \tag{127}$$

then c is called a *cycle* or *closed p-chain*. For example, a closed orientable surface which is broken up into cubes and represented by a chain c will be repre sented by a closed chain. Whether the chain is closed or not, whether ∂c vanishes or not, it follows from the formula $\partial\partial C_i = 0$ and from the Definition (125) that the boundary of any chain is a closed chain; *i.e.*, has *no* boundary:

(128) $$\partial\partial c = 0\,.$$

Table V gives a few illustrations.

The notion of boundary as now defined is adequate for deriving the theorem of Stokes in a general form, and from this as a special case the theorem of Gauss with its electromagnetic applications. A fuller analysis of boundaries and their relationships is given by that branch of algebraic topology which is known as homology theory ([28]). Some of the ideas of this theory are needed

TABLE V. – *Examples of p-chains, both closed (=cycles) and open* ([a]).

Dimensionality, p	Description of p-chain, c	Is it a closed chain (=cycle)?	Its boundary, ∂c
1	open line	no	2 end points
1	closed line in a Euclidean space	yes	0
1	closed line about minor circumference of a torus	yes	0
1	closed line about major circumference	yes	0
2	upper face of a disc	no	circle
2	surface of a sphere in flat 3-space	yes ([b])	0
2	surface of a sphere inscribed about mouth of one wormhole	yes ([c])	0
2	surface of a torus	yes	0
3	volume of a sphere in flat 3-space	no	sphere
3	3-dimensional closed space	yes	0

(*a*) There is no need to include in the table a last column to say that the $(p-1)$ dimensional boundary, ∂c, of the p-cycle, c has itself in every case no boundary: $\partial(\partial c) = 0$.

(*b*) Yes; and it also *bounds* a certain volume interior to the sphere.

(*c*) Yes; but there is no limited volume interior to the sphere which the surface can be said to bound.

([28]) Basic theory in extenso is given by S. EILENBERG and N. STEENROD: *Foundations of Algebraic Topology*, vol. 1 (Princeton, 1952); vol. II considers practical methods of computation. Presentation of the theory in a less extensive form, with applications, is made by H. SEIFERT and W. THRELFALL: *Variationsrechnung im Großen*, especially pp. 16-21. Repr. (New York, 1951). For details and additional intuitive insight see S. LEFSCHETZ: *Introduction to Topology* (Princeton, 1949) and H. SEIFERT and W. THRELFALL: *Lehrbuch der Topologie* Repr. (New York, 1947). Rigorous treatment of *cubical* singular homology theory is given by J. P. SERRE: *Ann. Math.*, **54**, 439-441 (1951).

to analyse charge-free electrodynamics in a multiply-connected space. Consider by way of example a sphere drawn in 3-space around one mouth of a wormhole—or, in the lower dimensional illustration of Fig. 3, consider a circle drawn on the indicated 2-space around one mouth of the handle. As a consequence of the existence of the wormhole, there is *no well-defined interior* to the sphere or the circle. An imaginary being supposedly locked up on the inside can enter the wormhole, pass freely through it, emerge from the other mouth, and come around outside and look at the exterior of his prison. The same topological information can be stated in another form by thinking of the spherical boundary as a bubble. Let the bubble be shrunk but not be allowed to break. It contracts into the interior of the wormhole. Let it be pushed through the tunnel and out the other side and expanded about the other wormhole mouth. Let the positive sides of the original sphere and of the new sphere be defined by the direction of a line of force that goes through the tunnel and crosses both spheres. Let the two *oriented* surfaces or -2chains so defined be called c_1 and c_2, or more explicitly, $c_1^{(2)}$ and $c_2^{(2)}$ to indicate the dimensionality, $p=2$, of the chains. Then c_1 and c_2 are said to be *homologous* to each other. More generally, when two p-chains, c_1^p and c_2^p together form the boundary of a finite $(p+1)$-dimensional chain, in the sense

$$\partial c_a^{p+1} = c_1^p - c_2^p \,, \tag{129}$$

then we say that the *two p-chains are homologous.* In the example of Fig. 3, the two 1-chains or circles about the two mouths together completely bound the two-dimensional region of the tunnel, or 2-chain, c_a^2. In contrast, a circle, c_g^1, drawn in the 2-space of Fig. 3 in a place where it does *not* enclose the mouth of a wormhole *will* by itself completely bound the 2-space, or 2-chain, c_b^2, interior to it:

$$\partial c_b^2 = c_g^1 \,. \tag{130}$$

If in this case the bounding line c_g^1 is considered subject to pressure from one side, and considered to deform accordingly, it will not have any wormhole to pass through nor any chance to re-expand into a new circle. Instead, it will collapse to nothingness. More generally, when a p-cycle c^p all by itself is a boundary,

$$c^p = \partial c^{p+1} \,, \tag{131}$$

it is said to be *homologous zero.*

Two surfaces—or more generally, two p-chains—that are homologous to each other are said to belong to the same homology class. A homology class is defined to consist of all the closed p-chains or p-cycles that are homologous to each other. We denote the homology class containing a p-cycle c_i^p by $\{c_i^p\}$. In space that is topologically Euclidean all the p-cycles are shrinkable to nothingness; are therefore all homologous zero; and therefore all belong to the zero homology class, $\{c_0^p\} = \{0\}$. In a multiply connected space the p-cycles are not in general all homologous to each other. The number of *linearly independent* homology classes of order p,

$$(132) \qquad \{c_1^p\}, \{c_2^p\}, \ldots, \{c_{R_p}{}^p\}$$

is called the p-th *Betti number* R_p of the space (Table VI). The number

$$(133) \qquad \chi = \sum_{p=0}^{n} (-1)^p R_p$$

is called the Euler characteristic of the space.

Consider two surfaces of the same homology class, one of which is identical with the other except for having a wart or incipient bubble on its surface. Combine the two surfaces with opposite signs. Then they cancel out except at the bubble. The resultant surface, like a small sphere, is homologous zero. These considerations generalize readily from surfaces to p-cycles of any order. In counting distinct homology classes, we therefore always omit the class of cycles which are homologous zero. Normally there exist infinitely many homology classes. None is more fundamental than another. The situation is reminiscent of the displacements of a crystal lattice—say a simple cubic lattice—which carry it from one position to an equivalent position. One can have a displacement a in the x-direction; or a displacement a in the y-direction; or a knight's move of a in the x-direction simultaneously with $2a$ in the y-direction; etc. The general allowed move can be represented as a linear combination of three basic or linearly independent moves. However, there is no unique choice of these basic moves. Similarly, by number of distinct homology classes we mean the number of linearly independent homology classes in the following sense: A set of homology classes $\{c_i^p\}$ is *linearly independent* if and only if every relation of the form

$$\sum_i s^i \{c_i^p\} = \{\sum_i s^i c_i^p\} = \{0\},$$

with real coefficients s^i, implies that all the s^i are zero; that is, if and only if no linear combination of the cycles c_i^p is a boundary. When the homology classes $\{c_i^p\}$ are linearly independent we shall say that the cycles c_i^p representing these homology classes are *independent cycles*.

The basic relationships between chains, cycles and boundaries which we

TABLE VI. – *Homology classes $\{c_1^p\}$, $\{c_2^p\}$, ... $\{c_{R_p}^p\}$ and Betti numbers, R_p, for two sample spaces. A p-cycle is a p-dimensional region, or p-chain, with the special property that it has no boundary.*

Space: the two-dimensional surface of a torus imbedded in Euclidean 3-space; more briefly, a 2-torus, T^2. Its Betti numbers: $R_0=1$; $R_1=2$; $R_2=1$. Euler characteristic $\chi=0$.

Homology classes	Description of typical p-cycle in this homology class
$\{c^0\}$	A point; all points are homologous
$\{c_1^1\}$	A closed curve that goes around minor circumference ([a])
$\{c_2^1\}$	A closed curve around major circumference ([a])
$\{c^2\}$	The 2-torus itself

Space: start with a 3-dimensional closed space — visualizable as the 3-surface of a sphere imbedded in Euclidean 4-space — and modify this space topologically to the extent needed to install one wormhole with mouths M_1 and M_2. This is the pierced sphere $W_1=S^2\times S^1$. Its Betti numbers: $R_0=1$; $R_1=1$; $R_2=1$; $R_3=1$. Euler characteristic $\chi=0$.

Homology classes	Description of typical p-cycle in this homology class
$\{c^0\}$	A point; all points are homologous
$\{c^1\}$	Closed line of force that goes once through the wormhole ([b])
$\{c^2\}$	Closed surface about the mouth M_1 ([c])
$\{c^3\}$	The 3-space itself.

(*a*) A closed curve that can be shrunk to zero can be constructed as the combination of two such lines drawn in opposite senses about the torus.

(*b*) A closed curve that can be shrunk to zero is the linear combination with opposite senses — that is, the difference — of two such lines. A closed curve that goes around the mouth, M_1, of the wormhole can be moved away from this location and shrunk to zero. Three dimensions give freedom to conduct this operation. It is impossible on the lower dimensional space of Fig. 3.

(*c*) A closed surface that can be shrunk to zero is the linear combination of two such surfaces with opposite sign.

have been discussing may be summarized in a purely algebraic form. Since we can add chains together, the set of chains in a manifold $\mathscr{M}$ forms a group. We may also multiply a p-chain by a real number. Consequently the p-chains form an infinite-dimensional vector space, $C_p(\mathscr{M}, R)$, called the *group of real p-chains*. The chains c^p satisfying $\partial c^p = 0$ form a subspace $Z_p(\mathscr{M}, R)$ called the group of p-cycles. Every chain c^p which is a boundary, $c^p = \partial c^{p+1}$, is a cycle. Consequently the set of all bounding p-cycles $B_p(\mathscr{M}, R)$ is a vector space which is a subspace of $Z_p(\mathscr{M}, R)$. The quotient space

$$H_p(\mathscr{M}, R) = Z_p(\mathscr{M}, R)/B_p(\mathscr{M}, R) \tag{134}$$

is called the p-dimensional *homology group* of $\mathscr{M}$ with real coefficients. The Betti number R_p is the dimension of the vector space $H_p(\mathscr{M}, R)$ and is finite for any compact manifold.

It may happen that in a closed (compact) n-manifold, every n-chain has a boundary so that $R_n = 0$. In this case the manifold is called non-orientable; in the opposite case $R_n = 1$ and the manifold is orientable. This distinction points up a difference between the idea of boundary expressed by ∂ and the idea of a boundary as consisting of points on the « edge » of a set. In a manifold every point has a neighborhood homeomorphic to Euclidean space, so no point can be considered as being on an « edge » or « boundary » of the manifold. When, however, we break the manifold up into cubes,

$$\mathscr{M} = c^n = \sum_{i=1}^{N} C_i^n , \tag{135}$$

we may not be able to choose the orientation of the cubes in such a way that the faces of all the cubes cancel out in pairs when we calculate ∂c. This is the situation in a non-orientable manifold. An example is given in Fig. 5 where we compute the Betti numbers of the projective plane P^2.

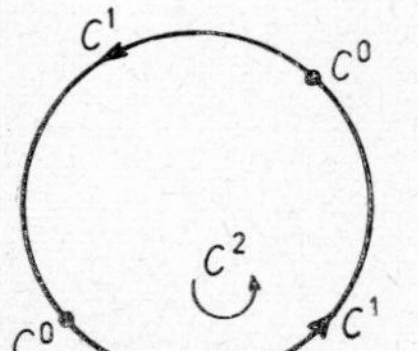

Fig. 5. – The projective plane P^2 as an example of a non-orientable manifold. The points of the projective plane are pairs of antipodal points on the 2-sphere S^2. In the figure we show the upper hemisphere c^2 of S^2, and its equator. Two points on the equator of S^2, such as those marked c^0 in the figure, correspond to exactly *one* point c^0 in P^2. Similarly a single line c^1 in P^2 appears twice as shown in the figure on the equator of S^2. Regarding c^0, c^1, c^2, as chains, *i.e.*, as being broken up into a large finite number of small « cubes », we see that $\partial c^2 = 2c^1$ when c^2 and c^1 are oriented as indicated by the arrows in the figure. Since c^2 has a boundary $2c^1$ in the ∂ sense of boundary, the Betti number $R_2(P^2)$ is zero. The curve c^1 has no boundary: $\partial c^1 = c^0 - c^0 = 0$. However c^1 is the boundary of the 2-chain $\frac{1}{2}c^2$, so every 1-cycle bounds and $R_1(P^2) = 0$. The point c^0 has no boundary of course, and it is not the boundary of any 1-chain, so there is one class of 0-cycles, $\{c^0\}$, different from zero, and $R_0(P^2) = 1$.

3.3.7. Stokes theorem. – We are now in a position to state Stokes theorem concerning the integral of a p-form $\boldsymbol{a}$ over the p-dimensional boundary ∂c^{p+1} of a $(p+1)$-chain c^{p+1}:

$$\int_{c^{p+1}} \mathbf{d}\boldsymbol{a} = \int_{\partial c^{p+1}} \boldsymbol{a} . \tag{136}$$

The integral of a form over a chain is defined in terms of the integral in eq. (118) over the standard unit cube. Therefore the proof of Stokes theorem reduces to integration by parts on this cube, I^{p+1}. The simplest case of Stokes theorem is that of a 0-form or function, f, whose gradient is integrated over a curve c^1 with end points x_1 and x_0;

$$\int_{c^1} \mathbf{d}f = \int_{\partial c^1 = x_1 - x_0} f \equiv f(x_1) - f(x_0) . \tag{137}$$

Here we make the convention that the integral of a function over a 0-cube, or point, is the value of the function at that point. For a 1-form, such as the magnetic field $\boldsymbol{h} = h_i\,\mathbf{d}x^i$ in 3-space, Stokes theorem reads

$$\int_{c^2} \mathbf{d}\boldsymbol{h} \equiv \frac{1}{2}\int_{c^2}\left(\frac{\partial h_j}{\partial x^i} - \frac{\partial h_i}{\partial x^j}\right)\mathbf{d}x^i \wedge \mathbf{d}x^j = \int_{\partial c^2} h_i\,\mathbf{d}x^i . \tag{138}$$

This is the formula which usually carries Stokes' name. Gauss' theorem is also included in formula (136) as we may see by considering a 2-form

$$*\boldsymbol{e} = \frac{1}{2!}\, *e_{ij}\,\mathbf{d}x^i \wedge \mathbf{d}x^j . \tag{139}$$

We have in this case, for a volume c^3 in 3-space,

$$\int_{c^3} \mathbf{d}*\boldsymbol{e} \equiv \frac{1}{3!}\int_{c^3}\left(\frac{\partial * e_{jk}}{\partial x^i} + \frac{\partial * e_{ki}}{\partial x^j} + \frac{\partial * e_{ij}}{\partial x^k}\right)\mathbf{d}x^i \wedge \mathbf{d}x^j \wedge \mathbf{d}x^k = \tag{140}$$

$$= \int_{c^3}\left(\frac{\partial * e_{23}}{\partial x^1} + \frac{\partial * e_{31}}{\partial x^2} + \frac{\partial * e_{12}}{\partial x^3}\right)\mathbf{d}x^1 \wedge \mathbf{d}x^2 \wedge \mathbf{d}x^3 = \frac{1}{2}\int_{\partial c^3} *e_{ij}\,\mathbf{d}x^i \wedge \mathbf{d}x^j \equiv \int_{\partial c^3} *\boldsymbol{e} .$$

This equation takes the usual form of Gauss' theorem in flat space when we write e_1 for $*e_{23}$, etc.

3·3.8. Applications of Stokes theorem: electric charge, magnetic charge, and the vector potential. – Two particular cases of Stokes theorem are of principal interest:

1) If c^{p+1} is a *closed chain*, *i.e.*, a cycle, and $\boldsymbol{a} = \boldsymbol{a}^p$ is a p-form, then eq. (136) reads:

$$\int_{c^{p+1}} \mathbf{d}\boldsymbol{a}^p = 0 \qquad \text{if} \qquad \partial c^{p+1} = 0 . \tag{141}$$

2) If $\mathbf{d}\boldsymbol{a}^p = 0$ we call $\boldsymbol{a}^p$ a *closed form*. In this case Stokes theorem gives:

$$\int_{\partial c^{p+1}} \boldsymbol{a}^p = 0 \qquad \text{if} \qquad \mathbf{d}\boldsymbol{a}^p = 0\,. \tag{142}$$

This second case may be put in the form of a *conservation law*: Let c_a and c_b be homologous p-cycles, so $c_b - c_a = \partial c^{p+1}$. Then eq. (142) becomes

$$\int_{\partial c^{p+1}} \boldsymbol{a}^p = \int_{c_b} \boldsymbol{a}^p - \int_{c_a} \boldsymbol{a}^p = 0\,. \tag{143}$$

In other words, *the integral of a closed form over a closed surface depends only upon the homology class of the surface.* The value of this integral is called the *period* of $\boldsymbol{a}$ on $\{c_a\}$, the common homology class of c_a and c_b. According to Maxwell's equations, (104) and (108), both $\boldsymbol{f}$ and $*\boldsymbol{f}$ are closed forms. To the periods of these tensors we give names ([29]), to be justified in the next paragraph:

$$\int_{c^2} \boldsymbol{f} = 4\pi p^* = 4\pi \text{ (magnetic charge of } \{c^2\})\,, \tag{144a}$$

$$\int_{c^2} *\boldsymbol{f} = 4\pi q^* = 4\pi \text{ (electric charge of } \{c^2\})\,. \tag{144b}$$

When the electromagnetic field is derived from a vector potential $\boldsymbol{a} = a_\mu\, \mathbf{d}x^\mu$, then there is zero net flux through every surface c^2 that is closed ($\partial c^2 = 0$):

$$\int_{c^2} \boldsymbol{f} = \int_{c^2} \mathbf{d}\boldsymbol{a} = \int_{\partial c^2} \boldsymbol{a} = 0\,. \tag{145}$$

In other words, *the existence of a vector potential implies that there is no magnetic charge.*

In reasonable examples the homology class of the surface c^2 includes *a*) similar appearing surfaces of larger or smaller size at the same time, that

---

([29]) The superscript * indicates that we are measuring both kinds of charge in the purely geometrical units of length. As we pass from the geometrical measure of field strength, $\boldsymbol{f}$ (cm^{-1}) to the conventional measure of field, $\boldsymbol{F}$ (gauss or g$^{\frac{1}{2}}$/cm$^{\frac{1}{2}}$ s) by multiplication with the factor $c^2/G^{\frac{1}{2}}$ (g$^{\frac{1}{2}}$ cm$^{\frac{1}{2}}$/s), so the same factor translates from the geometrical measure of charge, q^* (cm), to the conventional measure of charge in electrostatic units (g$^{\frac{1}{2}}$ cm$^{\frac{3}{2}}$/s):

$$q\ (\text{esu}) = (c^2/G^{\frac{1}{2}})\,q^*\ (\text{cm})\,.$$

is, in the same spacelike surface and *b*) surfaces like these at earlier and later times. Both f and $*f$ are closed. Then eq. (143) says that the flux through all of these surfaces is the same—independent of the size of the surface (Gauss' law) and independent of time (law of conservation of charge). Therefore charge as defined in eq. (144) has the properties that one is accustomed to demand. The four-dimensional character of the analysis has combined into a single law two laws normally regarded as separate. In brief, we have shown from Maxwell's equations that charge—regarded as lines of force trapped in the topology—stays constant with time regardless of changes in the details of the electromagnetic field, and regardless of changes in space. No mention of the metric even entered the proof of the conservation theorem.

To see in a little more detail the reasonableness of the identification (144) consider flat space with the usual time and space co-ordinates. Then the forms f and $*f$ are related to electric and magnetic fields in the following way:

$$f = -\,\mathbf{d}t\wedge(e_i\,\mathbf{d}x^i) + (*h)_{ij}\,\mathbf{d}x^i\wedge\mathbf{d}x^j\,, \tag{146a}$$

$$*f = \mathbf{d}t\wedge(h_i\,\mathbf{d}x^i) + (*e)_{ij}\,\mathbf{d}x^i\wedge\mathbf{d}x^j\,. \tag{146b}$$

Here e_i and h_i are the components of the usual electric and magnetic fields, and $(*h)_{xy}=h_z$, $(*e)_{yz}=e_x$, etc. When c^2 is a closed surface, say a sphere, in the $T=$ const. hyperplane, and when f is the electromagnetic field produced by a particle inside this sphere, then the magnetic pole strength p^* and the electric charge q^* of this particle are given by

$$4\pi p^* = \int_{c^2} (*\boldsymbol{h})_{ij}\,\mathbf{d}x^i\wedge\mathbf{d}x^j = \int_{c^2} f\,, \tag{147a}$$

$$4\pi q^* = \int_{c^2} (*\boldsymbol{e})_{ij}\,\mathbf{d}x^i\wedge\mathbf{d}x^j = \int_{c^2} *f\,, \tag{147b}$$

The first equalities in these equations are familiar expressions of Gauss' law in flat space; the second equalities hold because the $\mathbf{d}T$ terms in eq. (146) contribute nothing to an integral over a surface such as c^2 on which T is constant. In other words, the vector $\mathbf{d}T = \operatorname{grad} T$ is orthogonal to any surface on which T is constant, and therefore the projection of $\mathbf{d}T$ on that surface is zero. In this way we see that eq. (144) are direct generalizations of familiar equations to a curved space-time.

3'3.9. Examples of spaces permitting charge. – To fill the gap between the very general language of the conservation laws in the last section and the simple intuitive picture of charge in Fig. 3 as lines of force trapped in the topology, it is appropriate to present here two examples of spaces permitting charge; that is, spaces endowed with one or more wormholes: $R_2 \geqslant 1$. These examples are the manifolds $R \times W_k$ and $R \times T^3$ which were defined earlier in Section **3**˙2.2 (Examples of manifold, Product of manifolds). To define the differentiable structure of W_k (see Differentiable manifolds) we introduce on W_1 a functions $f(x)$; in W_k we use k such functions $f_i(x)$, $i = 1, 2, \ldots, k$. Let $c_i^2(r)$ be the sphere in W_k defined by $f_i(x) = r$. In the two dimensional analog of W_k shown in Fig. 4, the sphere is doubly pierced ($k = 2$). The typical surface $c_1(r)$ is a circle that runs around the mouth of one of the tubes that connects opposite faces of the sphere. The typical surface $c_2(r)$ runs around the mouth of the other tube. In the product manifold $R \times W_k$, of a real line, $-\infty < T < \infty$, with W_k, there is on each hypersurface $T =$ const. a copy of $c_i^2(r)$ which we will call $t_i^2(r, T)$. Moreover, the p-th Betti number $R_p(R \times W_k)$ of the product manifold is the same as the p-th Betti number $R_p(W_k)$ of W_k itself. Now consider on $R \times W_k$ a 2-form $\boldsymbol{f}$, or $*\boldsymbol{f}$. Then the flux

(148a) $$4\pi p_i{}^*(r, T) = \int_{c_i^2(r,T)} \boldsymbol{f},$$

or

(148b) $$4\pi q_i{}^*(r, T) = \int_{c_i^2(r,T)} *\boldsymbol{f},$$

apparently depends on r and T. To see that $p_i^*(r, T)$ or $q_i^*(r, T)$ in fact depends only on i we need a) to require that $\mathbf{d}\boldsymbol{f} = 0$ or $\mathbf{d}*\boldsymbol{f} = 0$ and b) to see that all the surfaces $c_i^2(r, T)$ for fixed i belong to the same homology class. The surface $c_i^2(0, 0)$ is a 2-sphere. As we let r increase this sphere sweeps out a 3-surface $c_i^3(R)$ $0 \leqslant r \leqslant R$ which is topologically identical to the volume $1 \leqslant x^2 + y^2 + z^2 \leqslant 2$ in Euclidean 3-space. From this mental image of the 3-space $c_i^3(R)$ in the familiar Euclidean 3-space R^3, we see the boundary of $c_i^3(R)$:

(149) $$\partial c_i^3(R) = c_i^2(R, 0) - c_i^2(0, 0)\,.$$

We conclude that $c_i^2(r, 0)$ is homologous to $c_i^2(0, 0)$. No metric notions have entered yet. Therefore we can let $c_i^2(0, T)$ sweep out of a 3-surface $c_i^3(T)$ just as we did above for r, and find

(150) $$\partial c_i^3(T) = c_i^2(0, T) - c_i^2(0, 0)\,,$$

so that $c_i^2(0, T)$ and $c_i^2(0, 0)$ are homologous. A similar construction shows that $c_i^2(r, T)$ is homologous to $c_i^2(r, 0)$. More generally, we conclude that all the surface $c_i^2(r, T)$ for the same i are homologous. Moreover, the equations $\mathbf{d}\boldsymbol{f}=0$ and $\mathbf{d}{*}\boldsymbol{f}=0$ say that no flux gets lost between homologous surfaces. Therefore the charges $p_i^*(r, T)$ and $q_i^*(r, T)$ are independent of r and T.

The preceding discussion made no use of any metric on $R\times W_k$, and is therefore valid no matter what metric we introduce. For example, at one value of T the space-like hypersurface $T=\text{const}$ may have the appearance of the doubly-pierced sphere of Fig. 4(*c*). At a later T the two ends of one of the wormholes may move together preparatory to annihilation as in Fig. 3. But as long as the topology does not actually change, the lines of force remain trapped and the flux $4\pi q_i^*$ through the closed surface $c_i^2(r, T)$ is unaltered by disturbances of the metric.

In this analysis of the wormhole space-time $R\times W_k$, we *assumed* the existence of a closed form ${*}\boldsymbol{f}$ or $\boldsymbol{f}$ for which the charges and pole strengths in eq. (148) do not all vanish. In the following section on de Rham's theorem we shall see that many such forms do exist. In a simpler example, $R\times T^3$, we can display them explicitly.

On the torus, T^3, functions x^i $(i=1, 2, 3)$ cannot be defined continuously everywhere except to within an additive multiple of 2π. However, the *gradients* $\mathbf{d}x^i$ are differentiable vector fields. In the simpler case of a 2-torus one of these gradients may be a field of unit vectors (red!) that circle about the minor circumference of the torus. The other field of unit vectors (green!) may be taken to be parallel to the major circumference. Similarly vector fields are definable in the space $R\times T^3$. From them one can construct a form,

$$ {*}\boldsymbol{f} = \mathbf{d}x^2\wedge \mathbf{d}x^3 \,, $$

which is obviously closed $({\mathbf{d}}{*}\boldsymbol{f}=0)$. It represents a uniform electric field in the x^1 direction (see eq. (146*b*)). Integrating this 2-form over the surface $x_1^2(x^1, T)$ defined by $T=\text{const}$, $x^1=\text{const}$, we get the value

$$ (151) \qquad 4\pi q_1{}^* = \int_{c_1^2(x^1, T)} \mathbf{d}x^2\wedge\mathbf{d}x^3 = (2\pi)^2 \,. $$

Thus we verify directly that in this case q_1^* is independent of x^1 and T. We might hesitate to call q_1^* a charge since we cannot imagine any metric that makes all the lines of force appear to originate in a *small* region of space. However q_1^* clearly measures the total flux of the electric field around the 3-torus through the closed surface c_1^2. Similarly, there are two other independent directions on the 3-torus, in each of which the flux can be given what value one pleases. There this space is endowed with three arbitrary constants of charge.

3.3.10. De Rham's theorem proves the existence of 2-forms endowed with charge. – To have given an example of a charge-like solution is far from having proven that such solutions are always possible in a four-space endowed with wormholes; that is, in a space with Betti number $R_2 \geqslant 1$. The existence of such solutions is established by the *first theorem of de Rahm* [30]: If c_i^p are R_p independent p-cycles of a manifold $\mathscr{M}$, and Q_i any R_p real numbers, there exists a p-form $\boldsymbol{a}^p$ which is closed ($\mathbf{d}\boldsymbol{a}^p = 0$) and differentiable throughout $\mathscr{M}$ and which satisfies

$$\int_{c_i^p} \boldsymbol{a}^p = Q_i \,. \qquad (i = 1, 2, \ldots, R). \tag{152}$$

To translate into physical terms, we note that $\boldsymbol{a} = \boldsymbol{f}^2$ or $*\boldsymbol{f}^2$ is the form that represents the electromagnetic field or its dual. The Betti number R_2 is the number of wormholes, and $Q_i = 4\pi p_i^*$ or $4\pi q_i^*$ is the magnetic or electric flux through the i-th wormhole. More precisely, Q_i is the flux through surfaces of the i-th independent homology class, or in mathematical terms the so-called *period* on this class. We have to recall again the arbitrariness in the choice of the R_2 independent or basic homology classes of order 2, linear combinations of which give all homology classes of order 2. There are situations where it is reasonably clear that two wormholes are well separated from each other, so that it might be particularly appropriate for Q_1 to designate the flux through one, and Q_2 the flux through the other. However, it is also possible to give instances where one wormhole is imbedded inside the other and where $Q_1' = Q_1 + Q_2$ and $Q_2' = Q_1 - Q_2$, or some other combinations, are just as natural as Q_1 and Q_2 as measures of charge. Thus de Rham's theorem says that there exists a solution $\boldsymbol{f}$ of the Maxwell equation, $\mathbf{d}\boldsymbol{f} = 0$ *or* a solution, $*\boldsymbol{f}$, of the Maxwell equations, $\mathbf{d}*\boldsymbol{f} = 0$, which has arbitrarily assignable real magnetic or electric charges.

Now demand that the magnetic charge of every wormhole vanish; in other words, demand that the period of $\boldsymbol{f}$ on every homology class $\{c^2\}$ shall be zero:

$$\int \boldsymbol{f} = 0 \,. \qquad \text{for all } c^2. \tag{153}$$

Then the *second theorem of de Rahm* guarantees the existence of a vector potential, $\boldsymbol{a}$:

When $\boldsymbol{f}^p$ is a p-form on $\mathscr{M}$ which is closed ($\mathbf{d}\boldsymbol{f}^p = 0$) and all of whose periods are zero, then $\boldsymbol{f}^p$ is derived from a differentiable $(p-1)$-form:

$$\boldsymbol{f}^p = \mathbf{d}\boldsymbol{a}^{p-1} \,. \tag{154}$$

---

(30) W. V. D. HODGE: *The Theory and Applications of Harmonic Integrals* (London and New York, 1952), pp. 88 and 100; G. DE RHAM: *Variétés différentiables: formes, courants, formes harmoniques*, chap. 4 (Paris, 1955).

In a case such as this, where there exists a potential, so that the one form, $\boldsymbol{f}$, can be written as the curl of another form, $\boldsymbol{a}$, then the form $\boldsymbol{f}$ is said to be *exact*. To be exact is a more demanding requirement on a form than merely to be closed (Table VII).

TABLE VII. – *Similarities between the concepts of cycles or closed chains (such as closed surfaces) and closed forms* ([a]).

Surfaces	
c	General p-chain; a surface for $p=2$.
$\partial c=0$	Means that p-chain is closed; c is then called a p-cycle; signifies for $p=2$ a closed surface.
$c^p=\partial c^{p+1}$	Means that c^p is the boundary of c^{p+1}; it then follows that $\partial c^p=0$, in other words, $\partial^2=0$. However, from $\partial c^p=0$ it does not necessarily follow that there exists any c^{p+1} of which c^p is the boundary.
Stokes' theorem:	Given *one* chain c^p that is a boundary: $c^p=\partial c^{p+1}$ (whence $\partial c^p=0$ and $c^p=$ a cycle); then on this cycle the period $\int_{c^p}\boldsymbol{f}$ vanishes for *every* p-form $\boldsymbol{f}$ that is closed ($\mathbf{d}\boldsymbol{f}=0$).
de Rham's theorem:	Given *one* chain c^p which is closed ($c^p=$a cycle; $\partial c^p=0$); and given that the period $\int_{c^p}\boldsymbol{f}$ vanishes for *every* p-form $\boldsymbol{f}$ that is closed; then c^p is itself a boundary: $c^p=\partial c^{p+1}$.
Forms	
$\boldsymbol{f}$	General p-form; a vector for $p=1$; alternating tensor for $p=2$.
$\mathbf{d}\boldsymbol{f}=0$	Then $\boldsymbol{f}$ is called a closed form. The Maxwell field tensor is described by a closed form.
$\boldsymbol{f}=\mathbf{d}\boldsymbol{a}$	Then $\boldsymbol{f}$ is said to be an *exact* form, or $\boldsymbol{f}$ is said to *bound* $\boldsymbol{a}$ (the four-potential, for example). It then follows from the relation $\mathbf{d}^2=0$ that $\boldsymbol{f}$ is automatically closed. However, from the closure of a form $\boldsymbol{f}$ it does not necessarily follow that there exists any $(p-1)$-form $\boldsymbol{a}$ of which $\boldsymbol{f}$ is the curl or boundary.
Stokes' theorem:	Given *one* p-form $\boldsymbol{f}$ that is exact: $\boldsymbol{f}=\mathbf{d}\boldsymbol{a}^{p-1}$ (whence $\mathbf{d}\boldsymbol{f}=0$); then the period $\int_{c^p}\boldsymbol{f}$ vanishes on *every* p-cycle ($\partial c^p=0$).
de Rham's theorem:	Given one p-form $\boldsymbol{f}$ that is closed ($\mathbf{d}\boldsymbol{f}=0$) and given that the period $\int_{c^p}\boldsymbol{f}$ vanishes on every p-cycle ($\partial c^p=0$), then $\boldsymbol{f}$ is exact: $\boldsymbol{f}=\mathbf{d}\boldsymbol{a}^{p-1}$.

([a]) The concept of chain as defined earlier and used here means a linear combination of a finite number of cubes — a form of definition important for open or non-compact manifolds.

3.3.11. Concepts based on the metric: duality and divergence: completion of Maxwell's equations. – We have just derived Gauss' theorem and the law of conservation of charge from Maxwell's eight equations, $\mathbf{d}\boldsymbol{f}=0$ and $\mathbf{d}{*}\boldsymbol{f}=0$, without making any appeal whatsoever to the notions of metric or length. The burden of the proof lay on topology. We avoided any appeal to Riemannian geometry by treating the Maxwell field

(155a) $$\boldsymbol{f}=\tfrac{1}{2}f_{\mu\nu}\,\mathbf{d}x^{\mu}\wedge\mathbf{d}x^{\nu}$$

and its dual

(155b) $$*\boldsymbol{f}=\tfrac{1}{2}{*}f_{\mu\nu}\,\mathbf{d}x^{\mu}\wedge\mathbf{d}x^{\nu}$$

as two completely independent objects. We extract extra content from Maxwell's equations, and impose additional restrictions on the field $\boldsymbol{f}$, when we note the one-to-one relation between one field and the other that is established by the metric. We shall therefore now define duality and divergence, and formulate the remaining content of Maxwell's equations.

The connection (11) between the electromagnetic tensor $\boldsymbol{f}$ and its dual $*\boldsymbol{f}$ is generalizable to a connection between any p-form

(156) $$\boldsymbol{a}=(p!)^{-1}a_{\alpha_1\ldots\alpha_p}\,\mathbf{d}x^{\alpha_1}\wedge\ldots\wedge\mathbf{d}x^{\alpha_p}$$

and its dual, the $(n-p)$-form

(157) $$*\boldsymbol{a}=\sum_{\substack{\alpha_1<\ldots<\alpha_p\\ \beta_1<\ldots<\beta_{n-p}}}(|g|)^{\frac{1}{2}}a^{\alpha_1\ldots\alpha_p}[\alpha_1\ldots\alpha_p\beta_1\ldots\beta_{n-p}]\,\mathbf{d}x^{\beta_1}\wedge\ldots\wedge\mathbf{d}x^{\beta_{n-p}}\,.$$

Here n is the dimensionality of the manifold and p and $(n-p)$ the orders of the two forms, g is the determinant of the metric tensor $g_{\alpha\beta}$, and the quantities with upper indices are the contravariant components of the original tensor:

(158) $$a^{\alpha_1\ldots\alpha_p}=g^{\alpha_1\mu_1}\ldots g^{\alpha_p\mu_p}a_{\mu_1\ldots\mu_p}\,.$$

Applied to a special 0-form, the constant function 1, the duality gives the *volume element*

(159) $$*1=|g|^{\frac{1}{2}}\,\mathbf{d}x^1\wedge\ldots\wedge\mathbf{d}x^n\,.$$

The following general formulas are most readily proven by applying the definition of the duality operation in an orthonormal reference system:

(160) $$**\boldsymbol{a}^p=(-1)^{np+p+s}\boldsymbol{a}^p$$

(double duality)

(161) $$\boldsymbol{a}^p \wedge *\boldsymbol{b}^p = \boldsymbol{b} \wedge *\boldsymbol{a} = (p!)^{-1} a^{\alpha_1 \ldots \alpha_p} b_{\alpha_1 \ldots \alpha_p} *1$$

(relation between exterior product and scalar product)

(162) $$(*\boldsymbol{a}) \wedge *(*\boldsymbol{b}) = (-1)^s \boldsymbol{a} \wedge *\boldsymbol{b}$$

(scalar product of dual forms expressed in terms of scalar product of forms themselves). In these equations s stands for the signature of the metric: $s = 0$ on spacelike hypersurfaces, where the metric is of the form $+++$; $s = 1$ in four-space with the metric $-+++$; and more generally, s is the maximum number of orthogonal vectors with negative norm.

The p-form and its dual are distinguished in the following way, that the integral

(163) $$\int_{c_p} \boldsymbol{a},$$

may be said to be the integral of the tangential component of $\boldsymbol{a}$ over a surface or p-chain c^p, whereas the quantity

(164) $$\int_{c^{n-p}} *\boldsymbol{a},$$

represents the integral of the normal component of $\boldsymbol{a}$ over an $(n-p)$-chain c^{n-p}.

Take the electric field $\boldsymbol{e}$, a 1-form in 3-space; form its dual, a 2-form; take its exterior derivative and secure a 3-form; and finally take its dual and obtain a 0-form or scalar. This scalar represents the divergence of the electric field, as seen most quickly by writing out the indicated sequence of operations in flat space:

(165) $$\begin{cases} \boldsymbol{e} = e_k \, \mathbf{d}x^k \, ; \\ *\boldsymbol{e} = e_1 \, \mathbf{d}x^2 \wedge \mathbf{d}x^3 + \text{two similar terms} \, ; \\ \mathbf{d}*\boldsymbol{e} = (\partial e_1/\partial x^1) \, \mathbf{d}x^1 \wedge \mathbf{d}x^1 \wedge \mathbf{d}x^3 + \text{two similar terms} \\ \quad = (\operatorname{div} \boldsymbol{e}) \, \mathbf{d}x^1 \wedge \mathbf{d}x^2 \wedge \mathbf{d}x^3 ; \\ *\mathbf{d}*\boldsymbol{e} = \operatorname{div} \boldsymbol{e} \, . \end{cases}$$

Generalizing to a curved space and a p-form of any order, the theory of forms defines a general *divergence* or *co-differential* operation $\boldsymbol{\delta}$ which takes a p-form $\boldsymbol{a}$ into a $(p-1)$ form,

(166) $$\boldsymbol{b}^{p-1} = \boldsymbol{\delta} \boldsymbol{a}^p \equiv (-1)^{np+n+s+1} *\mathbf{d}*\boldsymbol{a}^p \, ,$$

where the $\pm$ sign is introduced to simplify the statement of Green's theorem. For a $(p-1)$ form $\boldsymbol{a}$ and a p-form $\boldsymbol{b}$ this theorem connects the n-fold integral of two scalars over all or part of the manifold $\mathscr{M}$ with the $(n-1)$ fold integral of a normal vector, $\boldsymbol{a}*\boldsymbol{b} \equiv \boldsymbol{a}\wedge *\boldsymbol{b}$, over the boundary of this region:

$$\int_{\partial\mathscr{M}} \boldsymbol{a}*\boldsymbol{b} = \int_{\mathscr{M}} \mathbf{d}(\boldsymbol{a}*\boldsymbol{b}) = \int_{\mathscr{M}} \boldsymbol{b}*\mathbf{d}\boldsymbol{a} - \int_{\mathscr{M}} \boldsymbol{\delta}\boldsymbol{b}*\boldsymbol{a}\,. \tag{167}$$

TABLE VIII. – *Properties of the duality operation* $*$, *the exterior derivative* $\mathbf{d}$, *and the divergence operation* $\boldsymbol{\delta}$ *in space-time and on a spacelike hypersurface. The notation* $\boldsymbol{u}*\boldsymbol{v}$ *stands for the exterior product* $\boldsymbol{u}\wedge *\boldsymbol{v} = \boldsymbol{v}\wedge *\boldsymbol{u}$.

Property	4-manifold	3-manifold
Signature of metric	$-+++$	$+++$
Dual of dual of p-form	$**=(-)^{p+1}$	$**=1$
Divergence of p-form	$\boldsymbol{\delta} = *\mathbf{d}*$	$\boldsymbol{\delta} = *\mathbf{d}*\,(-)^p$
Second order differential operator	«$-\Box$» $= \Delta \equiv \boldsymbol{\delta}\mathbf{d} + \mathbf{d}\boldsymbol{\delta}$	«$-\nabla^2$» $= \Delta \equiv \boldsymbol{\delta}\mathbf{d} + \mathbf{d}\boldsymbol{\delta}$
	General formulas, n-manifold $\mathscr{M}^n$, any metric	
	$*\mathbf{d} = \boldsymbol{\delta}*(-1)^{p+1}$; $\quad *\boldsymbol{\delta} = \mathbf{d}*(-1)^p$	
	$*\Delta = \Delta*$; $\quad \mathbf{d}\Delta = \Delta\mathbf{d}$; $\quad \boldsymbol{\delta}\Delta = \Delta\boldsymbol{\delta}$	
Stokes' theorem	$\int_{\partial c} \boldsymbol{a} = \int_c \mathbf{d}\boldsymbol{a}$	
	Integral formulas for case $\partial\mathscr{M}^n = 0$	
$\boldsymbol{\delta}$ is adjoint of $\boldsymbol{v}$	$\int_{\mathscr{M}} \boldsymbol{b}*\mathbf{d}\boldsymbol{a} = \int_{\mathscr{M}} \boldsymbol{b}*\boldsymbol{a}$	$(\boldsymbol{a} = \boldsymbol{a}^{p-1};\quad \boldsymbol{b} = \boldsymbol{b}^p)$
Δ is self adjoint	$\int_{\mathscr{M}} \boldsymbol{b}*\Delta\boldsymbol{a} = \int_{\mathscr{M}} \Delta\boldsymbol{b}*\boldsymbol{a}$	$(\boldsymbol{a} = \boldsymbol{a}^{p};\quad \boldsymbol{b} = \boldsymbol{b}^p)$
For $n = 4m-1$, $*\mathbf{d}$ is self adjoint on $(2m-1)$ forms	$\int_{\mathscr{M}^{4m-1}} \boldsymbol{b}*(*\mathbf{d}\boldsymbol{a}) = \int_{\mathscr{M}^{4m-1}} (*\mathbf{d}\boldsymbol{b})*\boldsymbol{a}$	$(\boldsymbol{a} = \boldsymbol{a}^{2m-1};\quad \boldsymbol{b} = \boldsymbol{b}^{2m-1})$

The negative d'Almbertian operator

$$\Delta = \boldsymbol{\delta}\mathbf{d} + \mathbf{d}\boldsymbol{\delta} (= -\text{«}\nabla^2\text{» or } -\text{«}\Box\text{» for a scalar}) \tag{168}$$

carries a p-form into a p-form. In particular it carries the scalar, φ, into the scalar

$$\Delta\varphi = \boldsymbol{\delta}\mathbf{d}\varphi = -\operatorname{div}\operatorname{grad}\varphi = -\varphi^{;k}{}_{;k}\,. \tag{169}$$

The properties of the differential operators $\mathbf{d}$, $\boldsymbol{\delta}$, and Δ are summarized in Table VIII.

In terms of the divergence operation $\boldsymbol{\delta}$, the entire content of Maxwell's equations can now be summarized in the form

$$\mathbf{d}f = 0 = \boldsymbol{\delta} f .$$

3·4. *Characterization of solutions of Maxwell's equations by initial value data: charge and wave number.*

3·4.1. Alternative formulations of the initial value problem: summary of analysis. – On a space like surface endowed with a metric it is well known to be enough to specify arbitrary continuous electric and magnetic fields—satisfying $\operatorname{div} \boldsymbol{e} = 0$, $\operatorname{div} \boldsymbol{h} = 0$—in order to be able to continue the fields to the future and the past by way of Maxwell's equations ([31]). This type of initial value data is the natural analogue of the x and $\dot{x}$, or x and p, needed to predict the future of a classical particle. A different choice of data is made in the Lagrange formulation. Applied to a particle, it demands that x be known at the initial and final times, with no information needed about either $\dot{x}$ or p. Applied to the Maxwell field, the Lagrange formulation asks for example for the magnetic field—or the electric field, but not both—on the two spacelike hypersurfaces $T = T_1$ and $T = T_2$. This « two-surface » type of boundary condition is appropriate when one is interested in the classical action of the field integrated over the space-time interval between the two surfaces, or when one wants to know Feynman's quantum propagator: the probability amplitude to pass from configuration C_1 on σ_1 to configuration C_2 on σ_2. When the two cotimes have a finite separation one knows how to analyse this classical boundary value problem in flat space and in some types of curved space (see below) but not in the general type of curved space. However, when the two surfaces in question are so close together that the boundary value data can be considered to define the magnetic field and its first cotime derivative, then the two-surface problem reduces to the one-surface initial-value problem. To it we shall henceforth limit our attention in either form A or form B:

(171A) A: Give $\boldsymbol{h}$ and $\partial \boldsymbol{h}/\partial T$ on σ; and give the R_2 electric charges or wormhole fluxes q_i^* once and for all.

(171B) B: Give $\boldsymbol{h}$ and $\boldsymbol{e}$ on σ.

([31]) This is a familiar application of the standard Cauchy-Kowaleski theory. See E. Goursat: *Cours d'analyse mathématique*, 2nd ed., vol. **2** (Paris, 1911), pp. 632-637. See also M. Riesz: *Acta Math.*, **81**, 1, 223 (1949); G. F. Duff: *Can. Journ. Math.*, **5**, 57 (1953); E. Cartan: *Soc. Math. de France, Bull.*, **59**, 88 (1931).

We shall first analyse the relation between a form in 4-space and its projection or trace on a 3-space; then the connection between the metric on the hypersurface and the metric of 4-space; and then Maxwell's equations expressed in terms of forms on the hypersurface. We show that specifications (171*A*) and (171*B*) are equally appropriate to determine uniquely the future evolution of the system. Finally we treat briefly the specification of the initial value data, not directly in a spacelike form as in (171*A*, *B*), but by way of a natural generalization of Fourier analysis to curved space.

3·4.2. The concept of projection or trace. – A hypersurface σ in the manifold $\mathscr{M}$ can be defined by an equation of the form $\varphi(x) = 0$ where φ is a function with $\mathbf{d}\varphi \neq 0$ at σ. We may, if we wish, choose φ as one of our co-ordinates and call it T or x^0. We now consider an operation which enables us to obtain from any covariant tensor on the 4-manifold $\mathscr{M}$, a corresponding tensor on the 3-manifold σ. In the special case where $\varphi(x)$ is any scalar function on $\mathscr{M}$, its *projection* or *trace* on σ is the function $\varphi^\sigma(x)$ defined for x on σ by the equation:

$$\varphi^\sigma(x) = \varphi(x), \quad x \text{ on } \sigma\,. \tag{172}$$

Representing φ in terms of co-ordinates as $\varphi(T, x^1, x^2, x^3)$, where σ is given by

$$x^0(x) = T(x) = T_0, \quad x \text{ on } \sigma\,, \tag{173}$$

we can rewrite eq. (172) in the particularly simple form

$$\varphi^\sigma(x^1, x^2, x^3) = \varphi(T_0, x^1, x^2, x^3)\,. \tag{174}$$

Similarly, for a p-form

$$\boldsymbol{a} = (p!)^{-1} a_{\mu_1 \ldots \mu_p}(x^0, x^1, x^2, x^3)\, \mathbf{d}x^{\mu_1} \wedge \ldots \wedge \mathbf{d}x^{\mu_p}\,, \tag{175}$$

we obtain the *trace* $\boldsymbol{a}^\sigma$ of $\boldsymbol{a}$ on σ by substituting in eq. (175) the values $x^0 = T_0$, $\mathbf{d}x^0 = 0$. Likewise, the quadratic form

$$\mathbf{ds}^2 = g_{\mu\nu}\, \mathbf{d}x^\mu\, \mathbf{d}x^\nu\,, \qquad (\mu, \nu = 0, 1, 2, 3), \tag{176}$$

on σ reduces to

$$\mathbf{d}\boldsymbol{l}^2 \equiv g_{ij}{}^\sigma\, \mathbf{d}x^i\, \mathbf{d}x^j = (\mathbf{ds}^2) = g_{ij}\, \mathbf{d}x^i\, \mathbf{d}x^j \qquad (i, j = 1, 2, 3) \tag{177}$$

which displays the components $g_{ji}{}^\sigma$ of the metric we use on the 3-manifold σ.

The exterior derivative $\mathbf{d}^\sigma$ on σ involves no differentiations with respect to x^0, but the identity

$$\mathbf{d}^\sigma \boldsymbol{a}^\sigma = (\mathbf{d}\boldsymbol{a})^\sigma \tag{178}$$

assures us that it will cause no confusion to write $\mathbf{d}$ for $\mathbf{d}^\sigma$.

Now we may define, *relative to the spacelike hypersurface* σ, the dual *magnetic* field, $*\boldsymbol{h}$ and the dual *electric* field, $*\boldsymbol{e}$, by the equations

$$*\boldsymbol{h} = \boldsymbol{f}^\sigma , \tag{179a}$$

$$*\boldsymbol{e} = (*\boldsymbol{f})^\sigma . \tag{179b}$$

We have written $*\boldsymbol{h}$ and $*\boldsymbol{e}$ here so that $\boldsymbol{e}$ and $\boldsymbol{h}$ will be vectors or 1-forms of the familiar kind on σ. The duality to be used here is based on the metric $g_{ij}{}^\sigma$ of σ, and so could be written $*_\sigma$. This allows us to define

$$\boldsymbol{h} = *_\sigma \boldsymbol{f}^\sigma , \tag{180a}$$

$$\boldsymbol{e} = *_\sigma (*\boldsymbol{f})^\sigma , \tag{180b}$$

consistent with eq. (179) because of the identity $*_\sigma *_\sigma = 1$. We shall never apply $*_\sigma$ to a form on $\mathscr{M}$, so the meaning will be clear from the context if we drop the subscription on $*_\sigma$ as in eq. (179). From Maxwell's equations on $\mathscr{M}$, $\mathbf{d}\boldsymbol{f} = 0 = \mathbf{d}*\boldsymbol{f}^\sigma$, and the identity (178) we obtain the trace of Maxwell's equations on σ, $\mathbf{d}\boldsymbol{f}^\sigma = 0 = \mathbf{d}(*\boldsymbol{f})^\sigma$. In terms of the definitions of (180) and of Table VIII, *the trace of Maxwell's equations on a spacelike surface* takes the form

$$\boldsymbol{\delta}_\sigma \boldsymbol{h} = 0 = \boldsymbol{\delta}_\sigma \boldsymbol{e} . \tag{181}$$

We will normally omit the subscript σ on $\boldsymbol{\delta}$ because it will be clear from the context that we are dealing with a space like surface. We use subscripts on $\boldsymbol{\delta}_\sigma$ and $*_\sigma$ because they are not simply the traces on σ of the corresponding operations on $\mathscr{M}$; in other words, no identity holds for $\boldsymbol{\delta}$ or $*$ like (178) for $\mathbf{d}$; for instance, $*_\sigma \boldsymbol{f}^\sigma$ is a 1-form, whereas $(*\boldsymbol{f})^\sigma$ is a 2-form.

3·4.3. Maxwell's equation in 3-dimensional form. – To reconstruct the electromagnetic field $\boldsymbol{f}$ from the 3-dimensional fields $\boldsymbol{e}$ and $\boldsymbol{h}$ it simplifies the analysis to make a more careful choice of a cotime co-ordinate T than the one that was demanded in the previous section. Let T be the cotime measured along a geodesic which starts out normal to a spacelike hypersurface σ_0. Then σ_0 is given by $T(x) = 0$ and each σ_T, defined by $T(x) = \text{const}$, is again a spacelike hypersurface. The quadratic form $\mathbf{ds}^2$ can be written

$$\mathbf{ds}^2 = -(\mathbf{d}T)^2 + \mathbf{d}\boldsymbol{l}^2 , \tag{182}$$

where $\mathbf{d}\boldsymbol{l}^2$ is the positive definite quadratic form defined by the metric on σ_T. Our construction of geodesically parallel surfaces σ_T may carry us into 4-space for only a small interval of T ([32]), but in the 3-spaces σ_T we nevertheless have a well-defined global topology. We know from the definitions of $\boldsymbol{e}$ and $\boldsymbol{h}$ that at σ, $\boldsymbol{f}$ and $*\boldsymbol{f}$ must have the form

$$\boldsymbol{f} = *_\sigma \boldsymbol{h} - \mathbf{d}T \wedge \boldsymbol{\epsilon} \,, \tag{183a}$$

$$*\boldsymbol{f} = *_\sigma \boldsymbol{e} + \mathbf{d}T \wedge \boldsymbol{\varkappa} \,, \tag{183b}$$

where $\boldsymbol{\epsilon}$ and $\boldsymbol{\varkappa}$ are 1-forms which remain to be determined. When we use T, and any co-ordinates x^i $(i = 1, 2, 3)$ on σ_0, as co-ordinates x^μ in 4-space $(\mu = 0, 1, 2, 3)$ with $x^0 = T$, the metric components have the property $g_{00} = -1$, $g_{0i} = 0$. Then from eq. (157) and (183) we compute $*\boldsymbol{f}$ and $*(*\boldsymbol{f}) = -\boldsymbol{f}$. In this way we discover that $\boldsymbol{\epsilon} = \boldsymbol{e}$ and $\boldsymbol{\varkappa} = \boldsymbol{h}$, that is

$$\boldsymbol{f} = *_\sigma \boldsymbol{h} - \mathbf{d}T \wedge \boldsymbol{e} \,, \tag{184a}$$

$$*\boldsymbol{f} = *_\sigma \boldsymbol{e} + \mathbf{d}T \wedge \boldsymbol{h} \,. \tag{184b}$$

Since $\mathbf{d}$ and $\mathbf{d}^\sigma$ are related by the formula

$$\mathbf{d} = \mathbf{d}^\sigma + \mathbf{d}T \wedge \frac{\partial}{\partial T} \,, \tag{185}$$

we can use this expression in Maxwell's equations, $\mathbf{d}\boldsymbol{f} = 0 = \mathbf{d}*\boldsymbol{f}$, together with eq. (184) and (100) to find

$$\mathbf{d}^\sigma(*_\sigma \boldsymbol{h}) + \mathbf{d}T \wedge \left(\frac{\partial}{\partial T} *_\sigma \boldsymbol{h} + \mathbf{d}^\sigma \boldsymbol{e} \right) = 0 \,, \tag{186a}$$

$$\mathbf{d}^\sigma(*_\sigma \boldsymbol{e}) + \mathbf{d}T \wedge \left(\frac{\partial}{\partial T} *_\sigma \boldsymbol{e} - \mathbf{d}^\sigma \boldsymbol{h} \right) = 0 \,. \tag{186b}$$

Here $\partial/\partial T$ is the derivative along the geodesic normal to σ. The terms in $\mathbf{d}T$ in eq. (186) must vanish independently of the other terms, so we may rewrite eq. (186) as 3-dimensional equations (Table IX), treating T as a parameter and omitting the σ's:

$$\boldsymbol{\delta h} = 0 \,, \qquad \partial(*\boldsymbol{h})/\partial T = -\,\mathbf{d}\boldsymbol{e} \,, \tag{187a}$$

$$\boldsymbol{\delta e} = 0 \,, \qquad \partial(*\boldsymbol{e})/\partial T = \mathbf{d}\boldsymbol{h} \,. \tag{187b}$$

Here we have written $\boldsymbol{\delta h} = 0$ in place of the $\mathbf{d}*\boldsymbol{h} = 0$ of eq. (186*a*) to agree with the customary three-dimensional forms of Maxwell's equations.

([32]) A. Raychaudhuri: *Phys. Rev.*, **104**, 544 (1956); **106**, 172 (1957); A. Komar: *Phys. Rev.*, **104**, 544 (1956).

TABLE IX. – *The trace of Maxwell's equations on a spacelike surface.*

	« Electric equations »		« Magnetic equations »	
	Intrinsic notation	3-vector notation on flat space	Intrinsic notation	3-vector notation on flat space
Equations in 4-space	$\boldsymbol{\delta f} = 0$ or $\mathbf{d}{*}\boldsymbol{f} = 0$	$\operatorname{div} \boldsymbol{e} = 0$ and $\partial \boldsymbol{e}/\partial T = \operatorname{curl} \boldsymbol{h}$	$\mathbf{d}\boldsymbol{f} = 0$ (or $\boldsymbol{\delta}{*}\boldsymbol{f} = 0$)	$\operatorname{div} \boldsymbol{h} = 0$ and $\partial \boldsymbol{h}/\partial T = -\operatorname{curl} \boldsymbol{e}$
Trace on σ	$\mathbf{d}({*}\boldsymbol{f})^\sigma = 0$ Define $\boldsymbol{e} = {*}_\sigma({*}\boldsymbol{f})^\sigma$ Then $\mathbf{d}({*}_\sigma \boldsymbol{e}) = 0$ or $\boldsymbol{\delta}_\sigma \boldsymbol{e} = 0$	$\operatorname{div} \boldsymbol{e} = 0$	$\mathbf{d}(\boldsymbol{f}^\sigma) = 0$ Define $\boldsymbol{h} = {*}_\sigma(\boldsymbol{f}^\sigma)$ Then $\mathbf{d}({*}_\sigma \boldsymbol{h}) = 0$ or $\boldsymbol{\delta}_\sigma \boldsymbol{h} = 0$	$\operatorname{div} \boldsymbol{h} = 0$

3·4.4. Formulation *B* of the initial-value problem. – Eq. (187) are now in the form to which the Cauchy-Kowalewski theorem applies. More explicitly, the equations

(188*a*) $$\partial({*}\boldsymbol{h})/\partial T = -\,\mathbf{d}{*}({*}\boldsymbol{e})\,,$$

(188*b*) $$\partial({*}\boldsymbol{e})/\partial T = \mathbf{d}{*}({*}\boldsymbol{h})\,,$$

are six equations, solved for the time derivatives, for six unknown functions, the components of ${*}\boldsymbol{e}$ and ${*}\boldsymbol{h}$. They determine ${*}\boldsymbol{e}$ and ${*}\boldsymbol{h}$ uniquely when the initial values of ${*}\boldsymbol{e}$ and ${*}\boldsymbol{h}$ on the hypersurface σ_0 are given. When in addition these initial values satisfy

(189) $$\mathbf{d}{*}\boldsymbol{h} = 0 = \mathbf{d}{*}\boldsymbol{e}$$

on σ_0, then these same requirements of zero divergence will also be satisfied on σ_T as a consequence of eq. (188):

(190) $$\partial(\mathbf{d}{*}\boldsymbol{h})/\partial T = 0 = \partial(\mathbf{d}{*}\boldsymbol{e})/\partial T\,.$$

The proof depends on the facts that $\mathbf{d} = \mathbf{d}^\sigma$ commutes with $\partial/\partial T$, and that $\mathbf{d}^2 = 0$. De Rahm's theorem assures us that we can find initial values ${*}\boldsymbol{h}$ and ${*}\boldsymbol{e}$ on σ_0 which 1) satisfy the divergence requirements (189) and 2) have any desired values for the magnetic and electric charges

(191*a*) $$4\pi p_i^* = \int_{c_i^2} {*}\boldsymbol{h}\,,$$

and

$$4\pi p_i{}^* = \int_{c_i^2} *\boldsymbol{e} \tag{191b}$$

on R_2 independent wormholes in σ_0. Granted such initial value data, we are assured ([33]) of the existence for some finite time beyond σ_0 of a unique solution of the source-free Maxwell equations that displays constantly the specified charges.

3·4.5. Formulation *A* of the initial-value problem. – So much for the case where $\boldsymbol{e}$ and $\boldsymbol{h}$ are specified on σ; now for the alternative case where 1) we know the electric charges q_i^* once and for all, and where in addition 2) we know on σ the quantities $*\boldsymbol{h}$ and $\partial *\boldsymbol{h}/\partial T$, as the limit of information about the magnetic field on two infinitesimally close spacelike surfaces—information of the kind suited to the Lagrangian formulation of quantum mechanics.

The initial-value data must satisfy the divergence conditions,

$$\mathbf{d}*\boldsymbol{h} = 0 \tag{192}$$

and

$$\mathbf{d}(\partial *\boldsymbol{h}/\partial T) = 0 \tag{193}$$

and the requirement that the magnetic fluxes—if any—through all wormholes shall stay constant in time:

$$\int_{c_i^2} (\partial *\boldsymbol{h}/\partial T) = 0\,. \tag{194}$$

This granted, we find the electric field $\boldsymbol{e}$ on the spacelike surface uniquely from the three pieces of information

$$\boldsymbol{\delta e} = 0\,, \tag{195}$$

$$\mathbf{d}\boldsymbol{e} = -\,\partial *\boldsymbol{h}/\partial T\,, \tag{196}$$

$$\int_{c_i^2} \boldsymbol{e} = 4\pi q_i{}^*\,, \tag{197}$$

([33]) The Cauchy-Kowalewski theorem requires analyticity, while the de Rham theorem supplies only differentiable initial values $\boldsymbol{e}$ and $\boldsymbol{h}$. To remedy this fault in the demonstration one may employ the existence theorem of Y. Fourès-Bruhat: *Acta Math.*, **88**, 141 (1952); see also Duff: ref. ([31]).

TABLE X. – *Classification of real non-singular vector fields in a compact 3-space endowed with positive definite metric; the transverse waves are said to have right- or left-handed polarization according as the scalar wave number, k, is positive or negative.*

Type of vector field	Longitudinal	Transverse	Coulomb (harmonic)
Symbol	$\boldsymbol{L}$	$\boldsymbol{X}$	$\boldsymbol{C}$
Definition	$\Delta \boldsymbol{L} = \varkappa^2 \boldsymbol{L}$ $\mathbf{d}\boldsymbol{L} = 0$	$* \mathbf{d}\boldsymbol{X} = k\boldsymbol{X}$ $\boldsymbol{\delta}\boldsymbol{X} = 0$ $\lvert k \rvert > 0$	$\mathbf{d}\boldsymbol{C} = 0 = \boldsymbol{\delta}\boldsymbol{C}$
Association with eigenvalues or surfaces	$\boldsymbol{L}_1 \boldsymbol{L}_2 \ldots$ $\varkappa_1^2 \varkappa_2^2 \ldots$	$\boldsymbol{X}_1 \boldsymbol{X}_2 \ldots$ $k_1 k_2 \ldots$	$\boldsymbol{C}_a \boldsymbol{C}_b \ldots \boldsymbol{C}_{R_2}$ $S_a S_b \ldots S_{R_2}$
Consequence	$\Delta(\mathrm{d}\boldsymbol{L}) = \varkappa^2(\boldsymbol{\delta}\boldsymbol{L})$	$\Delta \boldsymbol{X} = k^2 \boldsymbol{X}$	$\Delta \boldsymbol{C} = 0$
Potential	scalar φ	2-form $\boldsymbol{Y}$	none
Potential from field	$\varphi = \varkappa^{-1} \boldsymbol{\delta}\boldsymbol{L}$	$\boldsymbol{Y} = * \boldsymbol{X} = k^{-1} \mathbf{d}\boldsymbol{X}$	—
Field from potential	$\boldsymbol{L} = \varkappa^{-1} \mathrm{d}\varphi$	$\boldsymbol{X} = k^{-1} \boldsymbol{\delta}\boldsymbol{Y} = * \boldsymbol{Y}$	—
Potential equations	$\Delta\varphi = k^2 \varphi$	$* \mathrm{d}\boldsymbol{Y} = k\boldsymbol{Y}$ $\mathbf{d}\boldsymbol{Y} = 0$	— —
Potential simplifies analysis?	Yes	No	—
Standardization	$\int \boldsymbol{L} * \boldsymbol{L} = 1$	$\int \boldsymbol{X} * \boldsymbol{X} = 1$	$\int_{S_a} * \boldsymbol{C}_b = 4\pi\delta_{ab}$
Scalar product with $\boldsymbol{L}$	$\int \boldsymbol{L}_m * \boldsymbol{L}_n = \delta_{mn}$	$\int \boldsymbol{L}_m * \boldsymbol{X}_n = 0$	$\int \boldsymbol{L}_m * \boldsymbol{C}_b = 0$
Scalar product with $\boldsymbol{X}$	$\int \boldsymbol{X}_m * \boldsymbol{L}_n = 0$	$\int \boldsymbol{X}_m * \boldsymbol{X}_n = \delta_{mn}$	$\int \boldsymbol{X}_m * \boldsymbol{C}_b = 0$
Scalar product with $\boldsymbol{C}$	$\int \boldsymbol{C}_a * \boldsymbol{L}_n = 0$	$\int \boldsymbol{C}_a * \boldsymbol{X}_n = 0$	$\int \boldsymbol{C}_a * \boldsymbol{C}_a \doteqdot 8\pi / R_{a\,\mathrm{min}}$ $\int \boldsymbol{C}_a * \boldsymbol{C}_b \doteqdot 4\pi \cdot \sum_{\substack{(\pm)_a \\ (\pm)_b}} (\pm 1)_a (\pm 1)_b / r_{(a\pm)(b\pm)}$

—for example, by the methods of Fourier analysis described in the following section (Table X). Knowing both $\boldsymbol{e}$ and $\boldsymbol{h}$, we are back at an initial value problem that has already presented itself, and that possesses a unique solution for some finite time beyond σ_0.

3·4.6. Generalization of Fourier Analysis to curved space. – When one is dealing with electrodynamics in curved space it is most natural to specify initial value data as a function of *position* on σ, as in (171A, B). An ordinary Fourier analysis is completely out of the question. However, one can give a generalization of Fourier analysis to curved and even multiply-connected space which is of use in considering special situations where the metric is constant, or nearly constant, with respect to a suitably chosen cotime co-ordinate, T. It permits the initial-value data to be specified in terms of Fourier coefficients.

On the spacelike hypersurface σ consider initial-value data such as the electric field $\boldsymbol{e}$, the magnetic field $\boldsymbol{h}$, or more generally any vector field or 1-form, $\boldsymbol{v}$. According to the analysis of HODGE ([27]), we can decompose $\boldsymbol{v}$ uniquely into the sum of three parts, characterized as in Table X, by the names *longitudinal*, *transverse*, and *harmonic*—or, as we may say, *Coulomb*. We will be limiting attention to 3-space. Therefore it will be permissible as in Table X to omit the superscripts σ that evidences the space-like character of the operations of curl, $\mathbf{d}^\sigma$, and divergence, $\boldsymbol{\delta}^\sigma$. For simplicity of analysis we shall assume that the space is closed.

A longitudinal field has zero curl, but a non-conserved flux because it has a non-zero divergence. Electric or magnetic fields of this type would correspond to distribution of «real» charge or magnetic poles. Therefore we exclude such fields from attention.

A transverse field has zero divergence and zero flux through any wormhole, but its curl is non-zero. Such a field can be decomposed into *proper modes* $\boldsymbol{X}_m$, each endowed with a characteristic *scalar* wave number $k_m (\neq 0)$ of its own:

$$*\mathbf{d}\boldsymbol{X}_m (= \operatorname{curl} \boldsymbol{X}_m) = k\boldsymbol{X}_m \,. \tag{198}$$

Modes with positive k we describe as right-handedly polarized; conversely for modes with negative k.

A harmonic or Coulomb field has zero divergence and zero curl, but a non-vanishing flux through at least one wormhole. Such a vector field can be decomposed uniquely into a linear combination of *characteristic harmonic vector fields* $\boldsymbol{C}_a$ $(a = 1, 2, \dots, R_2)$, such that $\boldsymbol{C}_a$ attributes a unit charge to the a-th wormhole, and contributes no flux at all to any other wormholes—that is, to any other of R_2 basic linearly independent homology classes.

The general vector field in curved multiply-connected 3-space can be Fourier-analysed in the form

$$\boldsymbol{v} = \sum_m \lambda_m \boldsymbol{L}_m + \sum_m \xi_m \boldsymbol{X}_m + \sum_{a=1}^{R_2} Q_a \boldsymbol{C}_a \,. \tag{199}$$

The orthogonality relations and the normalization conventions summarized in Table X permit one to find all the coefficients in this expansion by relations of which the following is typical:

$$\xi_m = \int \boldsymbol{X}_m *\boldsymbol{v} \,. \tag{200}$$

Without attempting to derive here the general expansion (199), we can note some of the underlying principles. 1) The inner product of two vector fields,

$$\langle \boldsymbol{a}, \boldsymbol{b} \rangle = \int_\sigma \boldsymbol{a} *\boldsymbol{b} \,, \tag{201}$$

is positive definite, so that

$$\langle \boldsymbol{a}, \boldsymbol{a} \rangle > 0 \tag{202}$$

unless $\boldsymbol{a} = 0$. 2) It follows that the set of all vector fields or 1-forms of finite norm generate a Hilbert space. 3) The operators Δ and $*\mathbf{d}$ are self adjoint when applied to vectors in 3-space (Table IX) and therefore have eigenvalues and complete sets of eigenfunctions. 4) From the property

$$(\boldsymbol{v}, \Delta \boldsymbol{v}) = (\boldsymbol{\delta v}, \boldsymbol{\delta v}) + (\mathbf{d}\boldsymbol{v}, \mathbf{d}\boldsymbol{v}) \geqslant 0 \tag{203}$$

it follows that the eigenvalues of Δ are non-negative numbers, k^2. 5) Given any non-zero solution of the equation

$$\Delta \boldsymbol{v} = k^2 \boldsymbol{v} \tag{204}$$

with $k > 0$, one can decompose it into two parts,

$$\begin{cases} \boldsymbol{v} = \boldsymbol{a} + \boldsymbol{b}\,, \\ \boldsymbol{a} = k^{-2}\,\mathbf{d}\boldsymbol{\delta v}\,, \\ \boldsymbol{b} = k^{-2}\,\boldsymbol{\delta}\mathbf{d}\boldsymbol{v}\,, \end{cases} \tag{205}$$

both of which satisfy the same space-like version (204) of the wave equation, and one of which is longitudinal; the other, transverse:

$$\mathbf{d}\boldsymbol{a} = 0\,, \tag{206}$$

$$\boldsymbol{\delta b} = 0\,. \tag{207}$$

6) For those eigenvalues Δ for which there exists a non-zero transverse field $\boldsymbol{b}$, there can be constructed out of this field a curl,

$$\boldsymbol{c} = k^{-1} * \mathbf{d}\boldsymbol{b} (= k^{-1}\,\mathrm{curl}\,\boldsymbol{b})\,, \tag{208}$$

such that

$$k^{-1} * \mathbf{d}\boldsymbol{c} (= k^{-1}\,\mathrm{curl}\,\boldsymbol{c}) = k^{-2}\,\Delta \boldsymbol{b} = \boldsymbol{b}\,. \tag{209}$$

From $\boldsymbol{b}$ and $\boldsymbol{c}$ we can build right-handedly and left-handedly polarized fields

$$\begin{cases} \boldsymbol{X}_+ = \boldsymbol{b} + \boldsymbol{c}\,, \\ k^{-1} * \mathbf{d}\boldsymbol{X}_+ (= k^{-1}\,\mathrm{curl}\,\boldsymbol{X}_+) = \boldsymbol{X}_+\,, \end{cases} \tag{210}$$

and

$$(211)\qquad \begin{cases} \mathbf{X}_- = \boldsymbol{b} - \boldsymbol{c} \\ -k^{-1}*\mathbf{d}\mathbf{X}_-(=-k^{-1}\,\mathrm{curl}\,\mathbf{X}_-) = \mathbf{X}_-\,, \end{cases}$$

not both of which can vanish. As example, consider in flat space the transverse field or 1-form,

$$\boldsymbol{b} = \mathbf{d}x^2 \sin kx^1\,,$$

$$\boldsymbol{c} = k^{-1}\,\mathrm{curl}\,\boldsymbol{b} = k^{-1}*\mathbf{d}\boldsymbol{b} = \mathbf{d}x^3 \cos kx^1\,,$$

from which we build the circularly polarized fields

$$(212)\qquad \mathbf{X}_\pm = \mathbf{d}x^2 \sin kx^1 \pm \mathbf{d}x^3 \cos kx^1\,.$$

3·4.7. Relation of harmonic field to familiar pattern of electric lines of force. – The harmonic or Coulomb fields are unique to multiply-connected space, with Betti number $R_2 \geqslant 1$. A typical one of these fields has a pattern of lines of force like that shown in Fig. 3. Consider the case where the space has an enormous radius of curvature, so that it is nearly flat, except in the immediate vicinity of the + and — mouths of typical wormholes, a, b, with exceedingly small radii R_a, R_b, ... Let the length « underground » of the connection between matching wormhole mouths be very short, and also of the order R_a, R_b, ... Let the fluxes $4\pi q^*_a$, $4\pi q^*_b$, ... go through the respective wormholes. In this very special model the field almost everywhere looks like that of R_2 pairs of equal and opposite charges:

$$(213)\qquad \begin{cases} \boldsymbol{e} = q^*_a \boldsymbol{C}_a + q^*_b \boldsymbol{C}_b + \dots \\ \sim q^*_a(\boldsymbol{r}_{a^+}/r^3_{a^+} - \boldsymbol{r}_{a^-}/r^3_{a^-}) + q^*_b(\dots) + \dots\,. \end{cases}$$

The electrostatic energy of the fields,

$$(214)\qquad \int \boldsymbol{e} *\boldsymbol{e}/8\pi\,,$$

consists of 1) self energy terms of the order

$$(215)\qquad q^{*2}_a/R_a + q^{*2}_b/R_b + \dots$$

and 2) interaction terms of the form

$$(216)\qquad q^*_a Q^*_b(r^{-1}_{a^+b^+} - r^{-1}_{a^+b^-} - r^{-1}_{a^-b^+} + r^{-1}_{a^-b^-}) + \dots\,.$$

From this circumstance one can immediately deduce the integrated value of the products of individual harmonic forms,

$$\int C_a * C_b \, , \tag{217}$$

as indicated in Table X. One sees that these harmonic forms give one all the machinery needed to describe *classical* charge in a completely consistent and divergence-free manner.

3·4.8. Fourier coefficients as initial-value data; dynamic equations for their rate of change. – To specify the initial values of $\boldsymbol{e}$ and $\boldsymbol{h}$ on a spacelike surface σ it is enough, we conclude, to know the Fourier coefficients in the following expansions:

$$\begin{cases} \boldsymbol{e} = \sum_m^\infty e_m \boldsymbol{X}_m + \sum_{a=1}^{R_2} q_a^* \boldsymbol{C}_a \, , \\ \boldsymbol{h} = \sum_m^\infty h_m \boldsymbol{X}_m \, . \end{cases} \tag{218}$$

We have omitted magnetic pole terms from the second expression as without interest.

The evolution of the electromagnetic field with time proceeds most simply when the metric does not change with increase of the geodesically normal cotime co-ordinate T. Then the dynamical eq. (108) reduce to an immediately integrable form,

$$\begin{cases} \mathrm{d}q_i^*/\mathrm{d}T = 0 \, ; \qquad q_i^* = \text{const} \\ \mathrm{d}e_m/\mathrm{d}T = k_m h_m \, ; \\ \mathrm{d}h_m/\mathrm{d}T = - k_m e_m \, ; \end{cases} \tag{219}$$

$$\begin{cases} e_m = (\tfrac{1}{2})(e_m + ih_m)_0 \exp[-ik_m T) + \text{c.c.} \, ; \\ h_m = (\tfrac{1}{2})(e_m + ih_m)_0 \exp[-ik_m T] + \text{c.c.} \end{cases} \tag{220}$$

Here the generalizations of the familiar normal mode decomposition of the field are simple and obvious.

No such simplicity reigns when the metric changes with time in a complicated way. Then the normal modes themselves alter. Consequently the dynamical equations (219) acquire new terms,

$$\begin{cases} \mathrm{d}e_m/\mathrm{d}T = k_m h_m + \sum K_{mn} e_n + \sum_a L_{ma} q_a^* \, , \\ \mathrm{d}h_m/\mathrm{d}T = - k_m e_m + \sum K_{mn} h_n \, , \end{cases} \tag{221}$$

which might loosely be considered to represent 1) the emission of energy into the transverse field, or absorption of energy from the transverse field, by the Coulomb fields due to the motion of the charges or other changes in the metric 2) the pumping or scattering of energy into one transverse mode out of another mode or out of the metric itself, as a result of changes in the metric. It is true that one can define the local density of eletromagnetic field energy in an unambiguous way. However, the same is not true of the integrated field energy ([34]). There is no common set of space and time co-ordinates with respect to which one could even hope to refer the components of a total energy-momentum four-vector. Moreover, the local conservation laws, integrated over a closed space such as we are considering here, produce nothing of interest, only the trivial identity $0=0$. Consequently it is necessary to use with caution the idea of energy transfer from one mode to another. This caution in no way depreciates either the dynamical eq. (221) or what they have to say about the most interesting coupling between modes of the field and modifications of the metric.

4. – Charge and mass as aspects of geometry.

We have just finished examining the response *of* an electromagnetic field to curvature and multiple connectedness in the metric without asking—or having to ask—about the influence of this field *on* the metric. However, an adequate analysis of classical charge and mass (in the sense of Table I) demands that both sides of the interaction be examined. For this reason 1) we consider a spacelike surface σ and ask what initial-value data have to be given on this surface—and what conditions these data must satisfy—to specify uniquely the future evolution of *both* the electromagnetic field and the metric 2) we examine the properties of the Schwarzschild and Reissner-Nordström solutions as solutions of these equations that manifest mass, and mass together with charge 3) we note an exact solution of the initial-value condition that generalizes the Reissner-Nordström solution to a space endowed with many charges and masses, all momentarily at rest at the moment of observation and 4) we remark that such wormhole solutions, together with geons, furnish two techniques of building disturbances in empty space, out of which one can make rich combinations.

4·1. *The initial-value conditions and the existence of solutions to the Maxwell-Einstein equations.* – Consider a space-like surface σ. On it let the trace of the

---

([34]) L. Landau and E. Lifshitz: *The Classical Theory of Fields*, translated by M. Hamermesh (Cambridge, Mass., 1951), p. 320.

metric *tensor* $\mathbf{d}l^2$, take on prescribed values as a function of position,

(222) $$\mathbf{d}l^2 = g_{ik}^{\ \sigma}\, \mathbf{d}x^i\, \mathbf{d}x^k .$$

Also let $\boldsymbol{e}$ and $\boldsymbol{h}$ have prescribed values on σ. Then there will in general exist no acceptable solution either of the Maxwell equations or of the Einstein equations. The equations of Maxwell will have a well defined solution if and only if the initial value conditions (189) are satisfied:

(223) $$\boldsymbol{\delta}_\sigma \boldsymbol{e} = 0 = \boldsymbol{\delta}_\sigma \boldsymbol{h} .$$

Similarly, the field equations of Einstein will have a well-defined solution if and only if certain initial value requirements are satisfied (eq. (224) and (225) below). *Granted* that these conditions as well as eq. (223) are fulfilled, then a solution of the combined Einstein-Maxwell equations with the prescribed initial values will exist for some finite time.

The initial value problem for general relativity has been studied extensively by LICHNEROWICZ ([35]), and an existence theorem which does not require analyticity has been given by FOURÈS ([36]). In general relativity, the four of Einstein's equations involving $R^0_\mu - \frac{1}{2}\delta^0_\mu R$ *provide the initial value requirements analogous to eq.* (223) *in electromagnetic theory*—requirements which connect the time rate of change of curvature on σ with the Poynting flux and Maxwell energy density:

(224) $$(P_i^{\ j} - \delta_i^{\ j} P)_{ij} = -2(g^{(3)})^{\frac{1}{2}}[ijk)\, e^j h^k = -2[*(\boldsymbol{e}\wedge\boldsymbol{h})]_i ,$$

(225) $$P^2 - P^{ij}P_{ij} + R^{(3)} = 2(e_i e^i + h_i h^i) = 2*(\boldsymbol{e}*\boldsymbol{e} + \boldsymbol{h}*\boldsymbol{h}) .$$

Here we follow the notation of Mme. FOURÈS ([37]), who has demonstrated the existence of solutions of eq. (224) and (225) in the case where there is no electromagnetic field. We let the surface σ be given by $x^0 = T = 0$, and write $g_{00} = -V^2$, $g_{0i} = V\eta_i$ $(i = 1, 2, 3)$. Then $g_{ij} = g^{(3)}_{ij}$ provides the metric $\mathbf{d}l^2$ on σ which is used to raise indices and define covariant derivatives in eq. (224) through (228). With $\eta^2 = \eta_i \eta^i$, we define

(226a) $$h^i = \tfrac{1}{2}(g^{(3)})^{\frac{1}{2}}[ijk]\, f_{jk} .$$

(226) $$e_i = (1+\eta^2)^{-\frac{1}{2}}(V^{-1} f_{i0} - f_{ij}\eta^j) ,$$

(227) $$P_{ij} = \tfrac{1}{2}(1+\eta^2)^{-\frac{1}{2}}[V^{-1}\, \partial g_{ij}/\partial x^0 - (\eta_i\, \partial/\partial x^j + \eta_j\, \partial/\partial x^i)V - (\eta_{i;j} + \eta_{j;i})] ,$$

([35]) A. LICHNEROWICZ: *Problèmes globaux en méchanique relativiste* (Paris, 1939); *Journ. Math. Pure Appl.*, (9) **23**, 37 (1944); *Helv. Phys. Acta*, Suppl. IV, 176 (1956); also E. CARTAN, ref. ([31]).

([36]) Y. FOURÈS-BRUHAT: *Acta Math.*, **88**, 141 (1952).

([37]) Y. FOURÈS-BRUHAT: *Journ. Rational Mech. Anal.*, **4**, 951 (1956).

and

$$P = P_i^{\ i}\,. \tag{228}$$

Thus $P_i^{\ i}$ is essentially the time derivative of the metric, while $R^{(3)}$ is the scalar curvature of the metric $g_{ij}^{(3)}$ on σ. The formulas (226) translate eq. (180) into components relative to the co-ordinates chosen here.

4·2. *The Schwarzschild and Reissner-Nordström solutions.* – The Schwarzschild metric furnishes the most familiar example of a solution of the field equations and therefore a solution of the initial value requirements (224) and (225). In this example the electric and magnetic fields vanish,

$$\boldsymbol{e} = 0 = \boldsymbol{h}\,. \tag{229}$$

The metric

$$\mathrm{d}s^2 = -(1 - 2m^*/r)\,\mathrm{d}T^2 + (1 - 2m^*/r)^{-1}\,\mathrm{d}r^2 + r^2(\mathrm{d}\theta^2 + \sin^2\theta\,\mathrm{d}\varphi^2) \tag{230}$$

satisfies the field equations $R_{\mu\nu} = 0$. In contrast, the Ricci curvature tensor for the metric on the space like surface $T = \text{const}$ has the non-zero value

$$R_i^{(3)k} = \begin{pmatrix} -2m^*/r^3 & & \\ & m^*/r^3 & \\ & & m^*/r^3 \end{pmatrix}, \tag{231}$$

but still a zero trace,

$$R^{(3)} = 0\,. \tag{232}$$

Also the quantities P_{ik} vanish in virtue of the constancy of the metric. Thus the initial value requirements (224) and (225) are fully satisfied by the Schwarzschild solution.

The Schwarzschild metric appears at first sight to have a singularity at the point $r = 2m^*$. However the Ricci curvature tensor (231) is perfectly well behaved at this point, as is also the full Riemann curvature tensor in the appropriate mixed covariant-contravariant representation. To bring part of this regularity into evidence, we make a co-ordinate transformation of a type suggested before by more than one writer ([38,39]),

$$(233) \qquad r = [1 + (m^*/2\varrho)]^2 \varrho \,.$$

Then the metric takes the form:

$$(234) \qquad ds^2 = -\left(\frac{1 - m^*/2\varrho}{1 + m^*/2\varrho}\right)^2 dT^2 + (1 + m^*/2\varrho)^4 (d\varrho^2 + \varrho^2\, d\Omega^2)\,.$$

Here

$$(235) \qquad d\Omega^2 = d\theta^2 + \sin^2\theta\, d\varphi^2$$

is the metric of a unit sphere. This result can be interpreted as follows: In making the transformation (233) we have redefined the differentiable structure of the manifold we are considering, so that *now* ϱ, *rather than* r, *is to be called a differentiable function*. As a result, the metric dl^2 on the space-like surface $T = 0$ is now non-singular at the Schwarzschild radius. The *space-time* metric ds^2 remains singular, however, since g_{TT} vanishes at the Schwarzschild radius, *i.e.*, $g^{TT} \to \infty$. We do not know how to eliminate this singularity explicitly for all time, but according to the initial-value theory of Lichnerowicz and Fourès, we can remove it for some undetermined, but non-zero, length of time. This we see by noting that the initial-value conditions (224) and (225) leave $g_{TT} = -V^2$ completely arbitrary on the initial surface. We take as initial con-

---

([38]) G. Lemaitre: *Ann. Soc. Sci. Bruxelles*, A **53**, 51 (1933); A. Einstein and N. Rosen: *Phys. Rev.*, **48**, 73 (1935); J. L. Synge: *Proc. Roy. Irish Acad.*, A **53**, 83 (1950); L. Landau and E. Lifschitz: *The Classical Theory of Fields* (Cambridge, Mass., 1951), p. 310.

([39]) The regularization in all of these cases removes only the singularity in the space part of the metric, not that in the time part, and therefore falls short in every instance of the regularization described in the text. Einstein and Rosen, supposing that they would not be able to eliminate the singularity in the space part of the metric by a co-ordinate transformation alone, also changed the sign of the constant of gravitation. Of course this step gives a negative value for the electromagnetic contribution to the mass, and for the energy of electromagnetic fields in general, in contradiction with experience. Einstein and Rosen pictured their regularizing transformation in terms of a space nearly flat except near particles, and a mirror space, close to and parallel to the first space, with a bridge across at the Schwarzschild singularity. On this picture the charge or charges in the primary space need not add up to zero. In contrast, the analysis in terms of harmonic forms 1) imposes no such mirror property on space; 2) treats all points of space as on the same footing; 3) brings in the idea of a real continuation of electric lines of force through a wormhole; 4) normally contemplates a closed space, with no excess unbalanced lines of force that have to end at infinity.

ditions therefore, the following:

$$ds^2 = -V^2\,dT^2 + dl^2\,, \tag{236}$$

$$dl^2 = (1 + m^*/2\varrho)^4\,(d\varrho^2 + \varrho^2\,d\Omega^2)\,, \tag{237}$$

$$\partial g_{\mu\nu}/\partial T = 0\,. \tag{238}$$

We may, for instance, choose $V = 1$. Since V need only be differentiable, not analytic, we may also choose $V = V_{\text{Schwarzschild}}$ as in (234) when ϱ is a small distance ε away from the singular surface $\varrho = m^*/2$, but fill in over the previously singular surface with differentiable, non-zero, values of V. With g_{TT} specified on the initial surface $T = 0$ in a manner such as this, the solution that results from integrating the Einstein equations is at least asymptotically stable. It will exist; and coincide ([40]) with the Schwarzschild solution for a cotime T which is arbitrarily large as $\varrho \to \infty$. Furthermore, for any fixed $\varrho_0 > m^*/2$ a solution of this type may be found which exists for all $\varrho > \varrho_0$ for at least any prescribed length of time, say 100^{100} years.

These same arguments apply equally well when the center of attraction is endowed with charge in addition to mass. We start with the Reissner-Nordström ([41]) solution for this problem. It differs from the Schwarzschild solution (230) only in the replacement of the factor $(1 - 2m^*/r)$ everywhere by

$$(1 - 2m^*/r + q^{*2}/r^2)\,.$$

The dual of the electric field in this case is

$$*e = q^*\,\sin\theta\,d\theta \wedge d\varphi\,. \tag{239}$$

Then we write

$$r = \varrho[(1 + m^*/2\varrho)^2 - q^{*2}/4\varrho^2] \tag{240}$$

and find for the metric

$$ds^2 = -V_{\text{RN}}^2\,dT^2 + dl^2\,, \tag{241}$$

where

$$V_{\text{RN}}^2 = \left(1 - \frac{m^{*2} - q^{*2}}{4\varrho^2}\right)^2 \Big/ \left[\left(1 + \frac{m^{*2}}{2\varrho}\right)^2 - \left(\frac{q^*}{2\varrho}\right)^2\right]^2 \tag{242}$$

and

$$dl^2 = [(1 + m^*/2\varrho)^2 - (q^*/2\varrho)^2](d\varrho^2 + \varrho^2\,d\Omega^2)\,. \tag{243}$$

([40]) K. Stellmacher: *Math. Ann.*, **115**, 136, 740 (1938).

([41]) K. Reissner: *Ann. Phys.*, (4) **50**, 106 (1916); L. Nordström: *Proc. Amsterdam Acad.*, **20**, 1238 (1918).

The singularity of the *space-time* metric due to the vanishing of V_{NR} when $2\varrho = (m^{*2} - q^{*2})^{\frac{1}{2}}$, may again be removed by modifying $g_{TT} = -V^2$ on an initial surface near this critical value of ϱ. To make possible this regularization we must demand that the mass exceed the minimum limit that is associated by general relativity with the charge in question:

$$m^* \text{ (cm)} > q^* \text{ (cm)}$$

or

(244) $$m(g) > G^{-\frac{1}{2}} q = (3.88 \cdot 10^3 g/\text{esu})\, q(\text{esu}) .$$

This condition is quite incompatible with the properties of the « dressed » particles studied by experiment. This circumstance stresses again that we are dealing here exclusively with a description of *classical* charge and mass that has nothing whatsoever directly to do with the particles found in nature.

Thus far we have shown how the singular surface in the Schwarzschild metric may be removed, but there apparently remains in eq. (237) and (243) a singularity as $\varrho \to 0$. We shall now see that we cannot call this a singularity unless we are willing to say that the metric is also singular as $\varrho \to +\infty$. The transformation

(245) $$\frac{2\varrho}{(m^{*2} - q^{*2})^{\frac{1}{2}}} \xrightarrow{J} \frac{(m^{*2} - q^{*2})^{\frac{1}{2}}}{2\varrho} ,$$

maps the entire manifold, $\varrho > 0$, onto itself in a differentiable, 1-1, *metric preserving* way. Therefore the vicinity of $\varrho = 0$ is in every meaningful way equivalent to the vicinity of $\varrho = \infty$. The initial surface $T = 0$ is a *complete* Riemannian manifold, that is, every geodesic can be continued to infinite length. One might nevertheless wish a stronger property to specify the global meaning of « non-singular ». One might insist that the manifold be either closed or that there be only one region (*either* $\varrho \to \infty$ *or* $\varrho \to 0$) where the space is asymptotically flat. An example of this type may be constructed from the charge-free Schwarzschild solution (237). We complete the definition of the mapping J of eq. (246) by defining

(246) $$T \xrightarrow{J} T ,$$

(247) $$\theta \xrightarrow{J} \pi - \theta ,$$

(248) $$\varphi \xrightarrow{J} \varphi + \pi .$$

The mapping J then has no fixed points, and we may identify the point x with the point Jx to obtain a new manifold with only one region, $\varrho \to +\infty$, which is asymptotically flat. The surface $T=0$ in this manifold is topologically equivalent to projective 3-space P^3 (see Section **3˙2**) with one point removed, « the point at ∞ ». This procedure cannot be applied to the Reissner-Nordström solution, for although the metric is invariant under J, the electromagnetic field changes sign and is therefore not consistent with the identifications. The time dependence of this non-singular modification of the charge-free Schwarzschild solution has been investigated by DUBMAN ([42]) to first order in T^2. He finds that the area of the critical sphere begins to decrease.

4˙3. *Many charges and masses.* – The Reissner-Nordström initial conditions (239) and (241)-(243) can be generalized to the case of N wormhole mouths endowed with charge and mass in the following way: Set

$$ds^2 = -V^2\,dT^2 + (\chi^2 - \varphi^2)^2(dx^2 + dy^2 + dz^2)\,, \tag{249}$$

$$*e = [ijk]\left(\varphi\frac{\partial\chi}{\partial x^i} - \chi\frac{\partial\varphi}{\partial x^i}\right)dx^j\wedge dx^k\,, \tag{250}$$

$$\partial g_{\mu\nu}/\partial T = 0 \tag{251}$$

at $T=0$, let V be any non-singular, positive definite function, and let each χ, φ, satisfy the flat space Laplace equation

$$(\partial^2/\partial x^2 + \partial^2/\partial y^2 + \partial^2/\partial z^2)f = 0\,. \tag{252}$$

These initial values make the initial surface a complete Riemannian manifold when we choose

$$\chi = 1 + \sum_a \alpha_a/r_a\,, \qquad \varphi = \sum_a \beta_a/r_a\,, \tag{253}$$

with $r_a = |\boldsymbol{r} - \boldsymbol{r}_a|$ and $\alpha_a \geqslant |\beta_a|$, $a = 1, 2, \ldots N$. The points $\boldsymbol{r}_0 = (x_a, y_a, z_a)$ are of course excluded from the manifold. The restriction $\alpha_a \geqslant |\beta_a|$ arises from the fact that the metric would be singular if $(\chi^2 - \varphi^2) = 0$ at any point. The completeness requirement also *excludes negative masses* as well as multipole terms in either χ or φ. The α's and β's are related to mass and charge respectively, but do not give the masses and charges directly ([43]). In the special

([42]) M. R. DUBMAN, senior thesis submitted to Princeton University in partial fulfillment of the requirements for the A.B. degree, 1957 (unpublished).

([43]) See R. W. LINDQUIST and J. A. WHEELER: *Rev. Mod. Phys.*, **29**, 432 (1957) for the relationship between m_a^* and the α_a, and for a study of the time dependence of some solutions of this type.

case where there is no charge, $\varphi = 0$, one obtains a class of problems which has been studied by LICHNEROWICZ ([44]). As long as only instantaneously static solutions of the initial value conditions aıe desired, a similar $(\chi^2-\varphi^2)^2$ factor may be used to modify any three dimensional metric in place of the $dx^2+dy^2+dz^2$ of eq. (249). The initial value conditions then reduce to the form

$$\bar{\Delta}\chi + \tfrac{1}{8}\bar{R}\chi = 0 \tag{254}$$

plus a similar equation for φ that replaces eq. (252). Here $-\bar{\Delta}$ and $\bar{R}$ are the Laplacian and scalar curvature of the unmodified metric.

4·4. *Relation to geons.* – Electromagnetic geons ([45]) are objects built out of electromagnetic radiation and held together by mutual gravitational attraction. The metric is greatly altered in the region occupied by the geon but the topology of space is still isomorphic to the normal Euclidean topology. Short wave-length radiation sent directly at the geon comes out again whether it experiences in the encounter a small or a large alteration in direction. In contrast, short wave-length radiation directed at one mouth of a wormhole will come out the other mouth. Despite this difference in properties, the two objects curve space in the same way and are indistinguishable, mass for mass, as regards their $1/r^2$ gravitational attraction.

These two techniques for constructing masslike solutions of the equations of geometrodynamics need not be employed separately. One can envisage an object endowed both with circulating radiation and with wormhole mouths, drawn together and moving about in a limited region of space as a consequence of mutual gravitational attraction. In addition, a sufficient number of wormhole mouths of the same sign moving on nearly identical orbits will simulate a current. They can create magnetic fields strong enough to have a substantial or even a dominating effect on the structure. It follows that the variety of objects that can be built out of curved empty space is exceedingly rich and very far from having been explored or even surveyed.

4·5. *Equations of motion.* – Masses and charges are not objects distinct from the fields in the theory we are presenting here—not even to the extent of being singularities in the fields. It is therefore obvious that the field equations determine the motions of the masses and charges. We must, however, insist that these motions correspond in the appropriate limit to the Newtonian and Lorentz force laws, for these laws express most basic and well tested properties

([44]) A. LICHNEROWICZ: *Journ. Math. Pure Appl.*, (9) **23**, 37 (1944).

([45]) J. A. WHEELER: *Phys. Rev.*, **97**, 511 (1955); E. POWER and J. A. WHEELER: *Rev. Mod. Phys.*, **29**, 480 (1957).

of idealized classical point particles. In geometrodynamics, mass and charge are not idealized as properties of *point* particles, they are rather aspects of the geometrical structure of space. To discuss equations of motion it will be necessary to view space-time with less resolving power than heretofore, and collapse the entire structure of a mass or charge down to a point whose motion we may then compare with the laws of Newton and Lorentz. For instance, an entire region about one mouth of a wormhole, as in Fig. 3, may be *called* one point x_1, and a similar region about the other mouth may be called x_2. The tube connecting these two regions we simply leave out altogether. A similar idealization may be made for a geon, and likewise for an object that is built out of radiation and wormholes. In this way the manifold of Fig. 3 is mapped in a *singular* way onto a topologically Euclidean space, and the metric which is carried over will have two singularities, at x_1 and x_2. Similarly for many masses and charges: by collapsing each to a point we ignore all details of inner structure and pass to a limit where it becomes appropriate to compare motions with those predicted by the force laws of Newton and Lorentz. The problem so defined is the problem so carefully studied by EINSTEIN, INFELD, and HOFFMANN. Those and other investigators *derive* the mechanical equations of motion of singularities ([46]) from the field equations. Consequently we can conclude that the objects discussed here—charges and masses built out of curved empty space and nothing more—satisfy in the appropriate limit the equations of Newton and Lorentz.

4·6. *No units but length in purely classical physics.* – The purely geometrical character of classical physics shows itself in the circumstance that space curvatures are measured in cm^{-2}, electromagnetic fields in cm^{-1}, charges in cm, and masses in cm. There is no place for any units other than length. A parable may be pardoned, of a kingdom where distances to the north were sacred and measured in miles, while those to the east and west and up and down were measured in feet. A special education was needed to calculate diagonal distances from co-ordinate readings until the discovery was made that a single constant of nature sufficed for the theory of the calculation. Thereafter much attention was devoted to « explaining » how nature happened to be endowed with a natural « slope » of 5 280 feet per mile. The parable perhaps makes one charitable towards similar attempts to « explain » why the speed

---

([46]) A. EINSTEIN, L. INFELD and B. HOFFMAN: *Ann. Math.*, **39**, 65 (1938) deal with uncharged singularities of finite mass in slow motion; L. INFELD and A. SCHILD: *Rev. Mod. Phys.*, **21**, 408 (1949) treat uncharged singularities of infinitesimal mass moving at arbitrary velocities; and D. M. CHASE: *Phys. Rev.*, **95**, 243 (1954) (See also L. INFELD: *Rev. Mod. Phys.*, **29**, 398 (1957)) analyses charged singularities of infinitesimal mass moving at arbitrary velocities.

of light should be $3 \cdot 10^{10}$ cm/s. That Boltzmann's constant k is only a conversion factor between two chance units of energy is of course a familiar idea. It is less familiar that grams and centimeters are two equivalent units for length: that the Schwarzschild radius of an object, $r_{\text{Schw}} = Gm/c^2 \equiv m^*$ (cm), is a purely geometrical way to characterize its inertia. We have seen that *classical* electromagnetism likewise requires nothing but units of length for its simplest expression. The field is only a manifestation of curved empty space. Classical physics in the sense of Table I reduces to pure geometry.

5. – Problems and prospects of geometrodynamics.

Certain gaps remain to be filled in the logical structure of geometrodynamics and almost everything remains to be done to exploit the richness of this subject.

5'1. *Case of null fields.* – The algebraic relations (4), (5) of already unified field theory were developed quite generally but the differential eq. (7), (8) were derived only on the assumption that the Ricci curvature tensor is non-null. For this simplifying assumption to fail, for the tensors $R_{\mu\nu}$ (and $F_{\mu\nu}$) to be null, it is necessary that the two electromagnetic field invariants should simultaneously vanish:

$$\boldsymbol{e}\cdot\boldsymbol{h} = 0\,; \qquad \boldsymbol{h}^2 - \boldsymbol{e}^2 = 0\,. \tag{256}$$

At a given moment of time this condition will ordinarily be fulfilled only on certain isolated lines in space. As time advances these lines will trace out surfaces in space time,

$$x^\beta = x^\beta(\xi, \eta)\,. \tag{257}$$

On such surfaces eq. (7) gives no well defined value for the vector α_β, the gradient of the complexion of the electromagnetic field. Is α itself well defined? Can the equations of already unified theory be formulated in such a way as to hold right across such a surface? Does the presence of such surfaces impose any additional topological or periodicity requirements on the Ricci curvature tensor? Do any special problems arise when the invariants (256) vanish, not merely on surfaces in space time, but throughout regions of greater dimensionality? These questions all obviously hang together.

5'2. *Why only one kind of charge?* – A second group of questions concerns charge. The interpretation of charge in terms of lines of force trapped in the topology allows all charges to be as well purely magnetic as purely electric.

However, the difference between the two possibilities is well known to be only one of names. The duality transformation

$$\boldsymbol{f}' = {}^*\boldsymbol{f}\,; \qquad {}^*\boldsymbol{f}' = {}^*{}^*\boldsymbol{f} = -\boldsymbol{f}$$

or

$$\boldsymbol{h}' = \boldsymbol{e}\,; \qquad \boldsymbol{e}' = -\boldsymbol{h} \tag{258}$$

renames magnetic charges so that they are all electric, in conformity with the usual convention. The charges associated with all wormholes—or homology classes in dimension two—can again be renamed as purely electric when in the original frame of reference each is a *mixture* of an electric charge e_i and a magnetic pole p_i, provided that the ratio of the two has for each wormhole the same value

$$e_i/p_i = \cos\beta/\sin\beta\,. \tag{259}$$

Then the duality rotation

$$\boldsymbol{f}' = e^{*\beta}\boldsymbol{f} \tag{260}$$

accomplishes the renaming in accordance with tradition. However, this renaming of all charges as electric is only possible when the *ratio* (259) of the two kinds of charges is identical for all the homology classes or wormholes in the original duality reference system. Can this ratio condition be restated in other terms?

When the regions over which space is appreciably curved are small compared to the distances between different wormhole mouths, then there is an approximate localizability of the typical charge. We are invited to look at it in a local Lorentz frame where it appears momentarily to be at rest. In this frame the field close to the charge is practically purely electric. Consequently there will be a surface, either around the mouth of the wormhole, or deep down in its throat, where the complexion, α, is either everywhere zero or equal to some integral multiple of 2π. Moreover, we expect the surface $\alpha = 2\pi n$ to remain tied to the neck of the wormhole in the same way as time advances; similarly for other wormholes, i. Insofar as the characteristic complexion, $\alpha_{\text{char}} = \alpha^{(i)}$, for each is well defined, the condition that all charges be electric therefore says

$$\alpha^{(i)} - \alpha^{(j)} = 2\pi\cdot\begin{pmatrix}\text{positive or negative}\\ \text{integer or zero}\end{pmatrix}. \tag{261}$$

This condition reminds one of the periodicity requirement,

$$\oint \alpha_\mu \, dx^\mu = 2\pi \cdot \text{integer} \tag{262}$$

(eq. (77)) imposed by already unified field theory upon the Ricci curvature tensor. Nevertheless, we have seen no way to derive (261) from (262). There fore we are not clear whether the requirement that all charges be electric is a part of the theory as it exists, or whether it has to be added to the theory.

For all magnetic poles to be zero ([47]) it is enough, according to eq. (145), that the field should be derivable from a 4-vector potential:

$$\boldsymbol{f} = \mathbf{d}\boldsymbol{a} \tag{263}$$

or

$$f_{\mu\nu} = \partial a_\nu / \partial x^\mu - \partial a_\mu / \partial a\nu \, . \tag{264}$$

This is an assumption that goes beyond Maxwell's equations, for in Section **3·4** we saw that there exist solutions of Maxwell's equations which display electric *and* magnetic charge side by side. There, however, electromagnetism was considered within the arena of a *prescribed* metric. Only in this framework of ideas is it clear that the exclusion of magnetic poles—or the existence of a 4-potential—is a demand independent of, and supplemental to, the Maxwell equations themselves.

When we turn to the full coupled Einstein-Maxwell equations, and note that the Ricci curvature $R_{\mu\nu}$ is completely determined by the field, then it is *not* clear that the nullity of magnetic poles, or the existence of a 4-potential, has to be added as a supplementary condition. Moreover, no example is known of a solution of the coupled Einstein-Maxwell equations in which the magnetic poles cannot all be eliminated by a duality rotation. It is obviously an important issue of principle to decide whether the existence of a 4-potential really has to be *added* to eqs. (4), (5), (7), and (8) of already unified field theory. Can it be *derived* from those equations? (1961 note: Counter examples have been given by L. WITTEN, *Phys. Rev.* **120**, 635 (1960) and by R. PENROSE (unpublished; cited by WITTEN).

Another issue presents itself. Can eq. (4), (5), (7), and (8) of geometrodynamics, with or without a possible supplementary condition about a 4-potential, all be derived from a single variational principle? Some work has been done that is relevant to this issue ([48]) but the problem itself appears

([47]) See W. V. R. MALKUS (*Phys. Rev.*, **81**, 315 (1951)) for the convincing experimental evidence against the existence of free magnetic poles.

([48]) W. PAULI: *Phys. Zeits.*, **20**, 457 (1919); H. WEYL: *Math.-Zeits.*, **2**, 384 (1918); *Ann. Phys.*, (4) **59**, 101 (1919); *Phys. Zeits.*, **22**, 473 (1921); R. BACH: *Math. Zeits.*, **9**, 110 (1921); C. LANCZOS: *Phys. Rev.*, **39**, 716 (1932) and **61**, 713 (1942); *Ann. Math.*, **39**, 842 (1938); *Rev. Mod. Phys.*, **21**, 497 (1949).

never even to have been formulated in the literature. (1961 note: See however D. SHARP, *Phys. Rev. Lett.* **3**, 108 (1959)).

Now we turn from the question of the best formulation of the field equations to the problem how best to deal with the initial value requirements. For the case of pure electromagnetism one has long ago learned to satisfy automatically the requirement div $\boldsymbol{h} = -\boldsymbol{\delta h} = 0$ on the initial hypersurface by introducing as primary data, not $\boldsymbol{h}$ itself, but a 3-potential $\boldsymbol{a}$ that generates an acceptable $\boldsymbol{h}$. In the case of the coupled equations of geometrodynamics, we meet non-linear initial value requirements (224) and (225) on the measure, P_{ij}, of the time derivative of the metric. Does there exist any kind of freely choosable superpotential, analogous to $\boldsymbol{a}$, which will generate a tensor P_{ij} which in turn will automatically satisfy (224) and (225)? If so, the properties of such a superpotential should reveal much about the truly independent variables of geometrodynamics. To clarify this point is essential for the understanding of already unified theory, for its most efficient application, and for illumination on what it means to quantize it.

Still another question of principle raises itself. In electromagnetism we can make a linear combination of two solutions to obtain a third. Geometrodynamics is of course non-linear. Does there nevertheless exist a method to combine two solutions to obtain a third? To search for such a combinatorial scheme would seem to demand an investigation of the continuously infinite dimensional space of field histories. On raising this issue, we were kindly advised by our colleague, Professor V. BARGMANN, that the methods of Lie ([49]) should suffice to obtain a definitive answer to our question.

To the questions of principle that we have raised, about null fields, about the existence of a 4-potential, about a possible superpotential, and about the combinatorial properties of the infinite dimensional space of field histories, there should be added many issues about the consequences of the classical theory, on which we shall only touch ([50]). (1) How wide a variety of wormholes and multiple connectedness is topologically conceivable. 2) When the deterministic evolution of the metric with time leads at a certain moment to fission or coalescence of wormhole mouths or to any other change in topology, what new phenomena occur? 3) What can one do to construct closed mathematical expressions for the metrics of spaces that show as much as possible of the richness of geometrodynamics-gravitational waves, wormholes, shocks, trapped radiation, and combinations of all these features?

([49]) S. LIE and F. ENGEL: *Theorie der Transformationsgruppen*, 3 vols. (Leipzig, 1888-1893); S. LIE: *Vorlesungen über continuierliche Gruppen mit geometrischen und anderen Anwendungen* (G. SCHEFFERS, ed.) (Leipzig, 1893).

([50]) See E. POWER and J. A. WHEELER: *Rev. Mod. Phys.*, **29**, 480 (1957) for a table of the analogies between geometrodynamics and hydrodynamics, and the problems that are suggested by this analogy.

One's attentions is inevitably drawn beyond these fascinating questions to the still deeper issue, what is the nature of quantum geometrodynamics [51] and what ideas have to be added to quantum geometrodynamics for the description of nature?

* * *

We wish to express our appreciation to VALENTINE BARGMANN, PETER BERGMANN, HUGH EVERETT, and MARKUS FIERZ for discussions on the physical side, and to PIERRE CONNOR, J. GÉHÉNIAU, J. A. SCHOUTEN, DONALD SPENCER, HALE TROTTER, and many other colleagues for illumination on the mathematics of geometrodynamics. We are grateful to Professor S. R. DE GROOT and the other members of the Lorentz Institute for the hospitality shown us duiing our stay in Leiden.

---

[51] In this connection see papers by H. EVERETT: *Rev. Mod. Phys,*, **29**, 454 (1957); C. MISNER: *Rev. Mod. Phys.* **29**, 497 (1957); J. A. WHEELER: *Rev. Mod. Phys.*, **29**, 463 (1957); *Ann. of Phys.*, **2**, 604 (1957).

Subject Index

Author Index

Tipografia Compositori - Bologna - Italy